The Struggles of Petroleum V. Nasby

The Nasby Letters originally appeared as newspaper articles during the Civil War era, and after the war were collected as a large subscription volume published by I. N. Richardson and Company in 1872 under the title *The Struggles of Petroleum V. Nasby*. This volume contained 189 letters, three platform lectures, a portrait of Locke and 23 illustrations by Thomas Nast. The Beacon edition, taken directly from this text, contains approximately one-third of the letters, one of the lectures and a selection of the Nast illustrations.

DAVID ROSS LOCKE (1833-1888) was an obscure young radical when he published the first of his Nasby Letters in the Findlay, Ohio, *Jeffersonian*, of which he was editor, in March 1861. The letters became immediately famous for their merciless satire of the Copperheads (northern Democrats opposed to Lincoln's war policies). In 1865, Locke became editor of the influential Toledo *Blade* and continued publication of the letters in that paper. After the war, Locke continued to use the Nasby Letters in behalf of the various liberal causes which he championed.

THOMAS NAST (1840-1902) was already famous as an illustrator when he began covering the Civil War for *Harper's Weekly* in 1861. After the war he was immortalized for his creation of several lasting symbols: the Tammany tiger, the Republican elephant and the Democratic donkey.

———◦◆◦———

JOSEPH JONES is professor of English at the University of Texas and author of *The Cradle of Erewhon: Samuel Butler in New Zealand*. He has traveled extensively and has held visiting professorships at the universities of Illinois and Minnesota and at Wellington and Auckland, New Zealand, and Cape Town and Johannesburg, South Africa.

GUNTHER BARTH, a German journalist, who studied at the University of Cologne, came to the United States under State Department auspices. He received his Ph.D. in history from Harvard University in 1961 and is presently on the faculty of the University of California at Berkeley.

The Struggles of

PETROLEUM V. NASBY

BY DAVID ROSS LOCKE

ORIGINAL ILLUSTRATIONS BY
THOMAS NAST

———•—•—•———

Abridged edition. Selected, edited and with an
introduction by Joseph Jones. Notes to the
chapters by Gunther Barth.

———•—•—•———

BEACON PRESS   BOSTON

The Struggles of Petroleum V. Nasby was first published by
I. N. Richardson and Company, Boston, in 1872
Abridged edition first published as a Beacon paperback in
1963
Copyright © 1963 by Beacon Press
Library of Congress catalog card number: 63-8275
Printed in the United States of America

Contents

List of Illustrations

Preface

The Civil War was a bitter time, Reconstruction even more so. However picturesque the era has been made to appear, its realities were grim. But cruel eras have their ways of raising up heroes and calling out prophets. Among those at whose reputation the current Civil War centennials afford a second look is David Ross Locke, a young Jeremiah whose satiric pen cut swaths as broad as Grant's to Vicksburg or Sherman's to Savannah. The literature of the Civil War without the Nasby Letters would be as incomplete as that of the American Revolution without the writings of Thomas Paine. It is hoped that this reintroduction of Nasby may come to the hands not only of those readers and students concerned with the period of the Civil War, but of those whose tastes for humor and satire have led them already into many an odd byway.

Though some of the war-kindled fire has departed inevitably from the Nasby Letters with the passage of time, they still smolder and throw off heat: Petroleum Vesuvius Nasby is still entitled to his middle name. One may realize even from a partial reading how clearly these newspaper buffooneries define the issues and how well they must have served as homely vessels for bringing these same issues home—to where the Copperheads, it may be, lived. They were, said Locke himself, "a convenient vehicle for conveying political truths, backwards." No other humorist of the War and Reconstruction approaches Locke in scope or in the intensity of his comico-satiric vision. Thomas Nast's illustrations serve to show, without need for comment, how sympathetic to Locke's text America's greatest cartoonist must have felt: the pair were a natural combination.

The present selection aims to offer enough of Nasby's plenitude to do justice to the author without immersing readers too deeply in the political intricacies of the whole series. Several groupings show the directions which the comedy and satire took: excursions into religion, education and such vagaries as spiritualism, along with main-line political and social concerns, chief among which were slavery and its succeeding race problems. Locke's masterpiece—the platform lecture "Cussid Be Canaan!"— is printed in full, as is each of the separate letters chosen. For knowledge about Locke himself, and his period, a chronological checklist has been provided.

For numerous courtesies the editor is grateful: to the Library of Congress, the Toledo Public Library, the Toledo *Blade*, the Library and the Visual Instruction Bureau of The University of Texas, and to his daughter, Susan Z. Jones, for assistance with the manuscript.

Austin, Texas   *Joseph Jones*

Introduction: Abe Lincoln's Copperhead

by Joseph Jones

"For the genius to write these things," said Abraham Lincoln, "I would gladly give up my office." Lincoln was speaking—in March 1865, about a month before his assassination—to Senator Charles Sumner, about the Union's prize humorist, Nasby. And to indoctrinate the dignified Senator from Massachusetts, whose acquaintance with Nasby was not in Lincoln's opinion sufficiently thorough, the President read from the Nasby letters for twenty minutes with evident relish.

Late in 1958 the Library of Congress received into its collections Lincoln's personal copy of *The Nasby Papers,* 1864, with pages which (according to the AP dispatch) "he inadvertently singed one night." Perhaps it was from this copy that he read to Sumner. At the end of the war the author received from the White House a special message of thanks; and there were undoubtedly many Americans at the time who were ready to agree with the then Commissioner of Internal Revenue, George S. Boutwell, who declared that the success of the North could be credited to three forces: the Army, the Navy and the Nasby Letters.

If tradition is right, and Lincoln did inadvertently singe the pages of his Nasby Letters in a midnight candle, it was an accident of symbolic retaliation. These same pages had done some singeing of their own, and by no means inadvertently. The Nasby Letters, amazingly good morale builders among the troops in the field as well as at home, had been appearing throughout the entire Civil War. They had in fact created a comic world of their own—a sort of verbal continuous comic strip long before the comic strip in visual form was born. The drawings of Thomas Nast, shortly, were added to assist the image of Nasby as envisioned by Locke.

The pattern was both simple and flexible. In an imaginary community known as "Confedrit X Roads, Kentucky," there was to be found the concentrated essence of white trash, symbolized by Petroleum V. Nasby and his cronies, who rejoiced in names like Guttle, Gamp, Pogram, Podhammer and Sniffles. From this rustic headquarters, Nasby the Copperhead periodically belched forth his judgments and interpreted the course of the conflict. His political philosophy was opportunism, simon-pure, tailored to the lowest possible motives assignable to the Southern cause and invariably associated with the Democratic Party. Nasby's tirades and antics entertained a large national audience, without a doubt, but they served at the same time the deeper purpose of defining and debating the issues for which men were dying every day.

The man who invented Nasby was David Ross Locke (1833-1888), a young newspaperman from Ohio. In the earliest days of the Republican Party—before the election of Lincoln, the Civil War and the postwar years gave the G.O.P. its title to the G. and the O.—the Republican banner was borne largely by fighting editors. Such men were characteristically radicals, in the root sense of the word: they plumbed into the grass roots of current issues with a steady insistence on facing fundamentals. Locke as one of them, beginning obscurely with small-town papers in Ohio and becoming at length editor of the Toledo *Blade,* rose to recognition as the Tom Paine of the Civil War under the grotesque pen name of Petroleum Vesuvius Nasby. It has been said of him that in the early days he composed his letters at the type case, setting them directly into type without manuscript. (Years later, he was one of the first in the country to use the typewriter.) With the *Blade* and other enterprises, Locke became a wealthy man, but his ingrained liberalism never left him. In dozens of letters he flailed the South unmercifully, not overlooking lukewarm politicians in the North (Vallandigham of Ohio was a favorite victim) and the confusions in the border states. The Nasby Letters are the Civil War etched in sulfuric acid. "There was but one Nasby," said one of Locke's old colleagues of the *Blade,* writing from Chicago at the time of his death in 1888, "and the people have not yet posted their books with him and given him credit for the full value of his work."

Lincoln's attachment to the Letters, and his official thanks, have already been mentioned; and there is other evidence of his gratitude which is even more concrete. He invited Locke to visit him in Washington, and Locke made two trips—the first in 1863, the second in 1865, on an errand of mercy to procure pardon (successfully) for a young man who had deserted under uncommonly compelling circumstances. Both Lincoln and Grant offered Locke his choice of a wide range of federal positions, including diplomatic posts abroad, but the only public office he ever sought or would accept was aldermanship in the Third Ward of Toledo, late in life. The artist Carpenter testifies further to Lincoln's enthusiasm (in 1865) for Nasby; and it is on record that Lincoln entertained friends by reading from the Letters just prior to the dinner from which he proceeded to Ford's Theater on the night of his assassination. Thus Nasby remained Abe Lincoln's captivating Copperhead to the last; and the President, in addition to being so warm an admirer, proved himself a more perceptive critic than many of his more "literary" contemporaries. From the practical standpoint, at least, he was undoubtedly in the best position to judge. "These javelins of horseplay journalism Lincoln welcomed," writes Carl Sandburg. "They fought for his cause. It was not strange that he got out of bed and paraded around the White House past midnight to find someone else awake to share his reading of Nasby."

David Ross Locke has received, at the hands of critics and collection-makers of American humor and satire, rather less than his due. It has been too often assumed that he was merely one more imitator of Artemus Ward, an ephemeral newspaper wit whose mission ended at Appomattox. Even a cursory reading of the Nasby Letters will reveal that such a view is far too limited. Lincoln's opinion deserves a second hearing.

When Locke came to create Nasby, he had at hand two skeins with which to do his weaving: the humor of the Old Southwest, which gave him prototypes in plenty for rascally characters, and the work of a later group of more or less professional humorists or funnymen, with their pseudo-dialects, creaky grammar, and shattered orthography. Technically speaking, Nasby emerged as an amalgam of these two schools. However, the prime factor in his birth was not entertainment but politics—the bloodiest politics this country has ever known. Thus, "Petroleum" (the name seems to have been picked hot off the wires after Edwin Laurentine Drake first struck oil near Titusville, Pennsylvania in 1859) in a stylistic sense is the offspring of earlier characters like Simon Suggs, masquerading in the trappings of Artemus Ward and Josh Billings. There the similarity ends; for while there were other humorists who exploited political themes upon occasion (more and more frequently as warlike preparations and then warfare itself progressed), no satirist devoted himself so wholeheartedly to the cause of politics as did Locke. In his political morals he was an old-line puritan, the satiric Cromwell of our literature.

Locke discharged his debt to earlier American humor, however, when he handed over Nasby to Mark Twain as a life-sized model for Pap Finn, the epitome of all white trash in American literature. Everything Pap has to say in his drunken ravings over Negroes and Abolition and the ballot had already been said by an equally sordid predecessor in the Nasby Letters. Pap is a foreshortened recollection of Nasby in the same way that much of *Huckleberry Finn* is a foreshortened recollection of *Life on the Mississippi*. Moreover, he is used quite deliberately for the same purposes as Locke used Nasby; and it might be added that Clemens (who extended his critique of uncivil civil rights into *Pudd'nhead Wilson* and later fulminations such as "The United States of Lyncherdom") was hardly less severe in his judgment than Locke was.*

The difference between this pair is of the order of the difference between Ben Jonson and Shakespeare—the first hard and brutal in his characterizations but logically idealistic and unwilling to compromise a principle, the second more warm and sympathetic, usually more tolerant if capable of occasionally sharp delineation, painting a broader canvas with many richly contrasting figures. There is no question that Locke was a great satirist, just as Jonson was a great dramatist; his name has been obscured by a critical neglect or misunderstanding of his role and his achievement. A harder bitten generation would later have recognized his talents in the same measure as it did during the press of war and reconstruction, but his work could not appeal strongly to the majority in the mushy-minded Gilded Age. As also in G. W. Harris's *Sut Lovingood Yarns*, there is in the Nasby Letters much less softening of vulgarity in deference to public taste than in Mark Twain or Howells. Ironically enough, a few of his public seem to have taken him at face value, just as Ralph Waldo Emerson's step-grandfather Parson Ezra Ripley believed implicitly in the physical reality of Major Jack Downing. As the Nasby Letters continued, Locke began receiving communications addressed to Petroleum V. Nasby, informing him that his correspondents

---

* Not every Northern humorist was an advocate of the Negro, by any means. C. F. Browne ("Artemus Ward"), for example contrasts sharply with Locke in his attitudes. Locke was a crusading satirist; Browne a professional humorist who was not above using Negroes, Mormons, Shakers or any other minority simply as grist for his humor-mill—a tendency which continued throughout the rest of the nineteenth century and on into the twentieth. During his service with the Cleveland *Plain Dealer*, Browne wrote sketches ridiculing Negro preaching and Negro theatricals, and his sketch of Oberlin College shows rather plainly that he was no equalitarian. His later remarks on "The Negro Question" satirize reformers.

agreed wholeheartedly with his ideas but cautioning him against risking himself by speaking so openly at the moment—urging him to wait for better times before being quite so frank!

The evolution of Nasby as a character and the filling-in of a setting for him—or more properly, a series of settings, selected by the fortunes of war and the accidents of politics—are interesting to watch as the letters progress. Apparently Locke intended his first sketches as nothing more than a little something to help pad out the paper, but awoke one morning with a full-blown satiric character on his hands. Shortly he began to develop a backdrop for Nasby and to introduce other characters—Deacon Pogram, Elder Gavitt, Bascom the saloon-keeper, Captain McPelter ("late of the Confederate army," a local distiller), Pennibacker (another distiller), and—as an opposition party—an Illinois store-keeper named Pollock and a disillusioned Southern veteran named Joe Bigler. These were kept ready for use as needed, and others—including many persons of national renown or notoriety —woven in and out from letter to letter.

The style, as has been suggested, owes much to the broad humor of the Old Southwest. Ironically enough, the ante-bellum humorists of the South helped arm their adversary. In language, the letters display a good bit of the bastard-baroque journalese that practically all editors of the day affected, along with a mulligan of the sentimental clichés, oratorical posturings, foreign phrases, literary allusions, pat quotations and general windiness that infested prose and poetry alike. To all this must be added a very special brand of super-piousness in the numerous pages of pseudo-religion. Finally, to his everlasting credit, Locke is unashamedly coarse; intrinsically vulgar. Most satirists and humorists of his time veered timidly away from the calculated vulgarity that properly pugnacious satire—which can have no intention of being fair-minded if it means to pack a really effective wallop— must show. The deliberate low tone, set early, is strictly maintained. The modern reader must remember this; must remind himself, at times, that for all his twentieth century freedom with four-letter words, his own taboos can render Locke (or rather Nasby) offensive to those not careful to maintain satiric perspective in addition to historical perspective on the work. The satirist —be he a Juvenal, Rabelais, Swift or an Aldous Huxley—must be granted room enough to swing his shillelagh. Locke's was a gnarly and knotty one, particularly on the racial issue.

By 1867, the guerrilla warfare of newspaper controversy,

through two violent presidential campaigns, together with the discipline that the long series of Nasby Letters imposed, had prepared Locke for his most sustained and masterly stroke of all, the platform lecture "Cussid Be Canaan!" This he produced some time before the Nasby series ended, but he loaded it with what had been nearest his heart and most consistently dwelt upon. Epitomizing as it does Locke's views, it is worth pausing over to examine at some length what lay in the background, along with what it meant—and continues to mean.

Negro slavery, to Nasby the Copperhead, was of course both natural and right. In the course of his harangues, posing as preacher (Nasby was a little of everything, as circumstances dictated, but yearned continually and pathetically to be postmaster by political appointment), this tongue-in-cheek defender of slavery found it perennially convenient to lean upon passages of Scripture which had been offered by other defenders of the "institoo-shun"—for example:

"By Hager, I proved that slavery was scriptooral.

"By 'cussid be Kanan,' et settry, I shode concloosively that the nigger wuz the identikle indivijjle who wuz to be the sed slave aforesed."

But it was not until after the War that Locke put together his final assault upon the venerable piece of casuistry that deduced perpetual bondage out of the "Curse of Noah."

Locke's personal religious views were ultra-liberal. Nominally a Methodist, he supported, to the extent of some thousands of dollars, the dissident Unitarian minister Francis Ellingwood Abbot in his establishment of an independent "free religion" congregation in Toledo and the publication of a nonconformist, rationalistic weekly called *The Index* during the early 1870s. Such heterodoxy must have rendered all the easier and more enjoyable Locke's making free with Biblical literalism at a time that most others were unable or at least unready to go quite so far.

Possibly there can still be found, somewhere within the ranks of embattled segregationists, an anachronistic survival of the Scriptural defense of slavery. In South Africa, for instance, only within recent years have the more liberal (and more courageous) among the Dutch Reformed Clergy begun to disown it as a bulwark of *apartheid*. But whatever current belief may be, it was only a hundred years ago that the "curse of Canaan" was taken very seriously in many American circles—both South and North, it should be noted, for by no means all the apologists for slavery lived below the Mason-Dixon line. *Mark Twain's Autobiography* describes ante-bellum churches and churchmen as "closing their doors against the hunted slave, beating his handful of humane defenders with Bible texts and billies, and pocketing the insults and licking the shoes of his Southern master."

Any number of contemporary witnesses (as Mark Twain himself was) might be summoned. The year 1836—rather early in the rising controversy—saw Sarah M. Grimké's "Epistle to the Clergy of the Southern States" attacking the Scriptural argument in such a way as to suggest its universal prevalence:

"Again, it is often peremptorily asserted that 'the Africans are a divinely condemned and proscribed race.' If they are, has God constituted the slave holders the ministers of his vengeance? This question can only be answered in the negative, and until it can be otherwise answered, it is vain to appeal to the curse on Canaan, or to Hebrew servitude, in support of American slavery."

Miss Grimké's question and answer was, in fact, an echo of what Samuel Sewall, Chief Justice of Massachusetts, had said as early as 1700 in *The Selling of Joseph,* which drew *A Brief and Candid Answer* . . . from John Saffin in 1701. After citing Genesis 9, Sewall remarks, "Of all Offices, one would not begg this; *viz.* Uncall'd for, to be an Executioner of the Vindictive Wrath of God; the extent and duration of which is to us uncertain." He continues by querying whether "by cursory reading, this Text may have been mistaken," and argues that in any case "for men obstinately to persist in holding their Neighbours and Brethren under the Rigor of perpetual Bondage, seems to be no proper way of gaining Assurance that God has given them Spiritual Freedom. Our Blessed Saviour has altered the Measures of the ancient Love-Song, and set it to a most Excellent New Tune, which all ought to be ambitious of Learning."

From Sewall's observation that "All men, as they are the sons of Adam, are co-heirs, and have equal right unto liberty, and all other outward comforts of life," there is no great ideological distance to the Declaration of Independence; and it is well known that Jefferson's first draft contained a strong anti-slavery passage, omitted to placate discordancies that still bedevil and stultify American politics. Between Sewall and Jefferson lies a long period of quiet but persistent agitation, principally on the part of American Quakers, among whom John Woolman (in *A Plea for The Poor,* 1763, for example) takes first rank. Nor should it be forgotten that the latter eighteenth century saw the rise of a powerful anti-slavery movement in Britain, the success of which not only encouraged its rising American counterpart but furnished, at length, active collaborators. Except for the most compelling of economic reasons, slavery might easily have died as early in America as it did in the British colonies—in 1833, the year David Ross Locke was born. As things turned out, opponents and defenders became increasingly hostile to each other during the 1830s and soon any accommodation of views was impossible. Into the clamor rushed the Biblical controversialists, with little apparent change of opinions since Sewall and Saffin had locked horns at the beginning of the "Age of Reason."

In 1843 there appeared at Albany a full-throated baying of the moon—340 pages of conjectural anthropology, Scriptural commentary and licentious chronicling of alleged bestialities—in Josiah Priest's *"SLAVERY, As It Relates to the NEGRO, OR AFRICAN RACE, Examined in the Light of Circumstances, History and the HOLY SCRIPTURES; with an Account of the ORIGIN OF THE BLACK MAN'S COLOR, Causes of His State. of Servitude and Traces of His Character as well in Ancient as in Modern Times: WITH STRICTURES ON ABOLITIONISM. Embellished with Engravings."* The size of type used for the words "Holy Scriptures" was only the gentlest of hints as to the contents, the curious reader discovers when he looks inside. Page after page, in section after section, is given over to proving how and why the "appalling anathema" of Genesis 9:24-27 is "a curse, a dreadful curse, which not only covered the person and fortunes of Ham, but that of his *whole* posterity also, to the very end of time, for aught that appears to the contrary." This was reprinted not long afterward in Louisville, Kentucky, under the title of *Bible Defence of Slavery,* etc., and went through several editions. There is enough ammunition in Priest alone (one among many who touched the subject) to supply sermons *ad infinitum* (and if very closely followed, *ad nauseam*) to such parsons as the Rev. Petroleum V. Nasby, who makes ample use of the golden text in Genesis. How much this kind of thing had to do with the parting of Northern and Southern church bodies, long before the Civil War, it is difficult to say, but it must have had its share in creating the intolerable tensions that led to schisms. Even Canadians, such as Goldwin Smith (*Does The Bible Sanction American Slavery?,* 1863) joined in the argument.

Herman Melville, in his allegory *Mardi* (1849), could depend upon a widespread knowledge of the "Ham" scripture when he brought his pilgrims to Vivenza (the U.S.) where they read an inscription on an arch: "In this republican land all men are born free and equal," followed by a phrase in much smaller letters, "Except the tribe of Hamo." Along with Melville, the other leaders of the New England Renaissance were anti-slavery and those among the Transcendentalists were more than likely to be active Abolitionists: Alcott, Parker, Emerson, Thoreau, Sanborn.

On the eve of the Civil War we find Samuel M. Wolfe of Virginia, in a reply to Hinton Helper's famous *The Impending Crisis* (1857), harping away on the Biblical proslavery case. Under "Bible Testimony" (Chapter VII), Helper had insisted that the Bible—far from sanctioning slavery—was "the only original and complete anti-slavery text-book." Wolfe, in *Helper's Impending Crisis Dissected* (1860), sums up as follows:

"We know that, in the scale of humanity, the negro holds the lowest place; that no system of jurisprudence, no principle of science, no rule of art, has ever originated from the brain of an African.

"That he has not the capacity for becoming under any circumstances, an enlightened man; that the nearest approach to that state which he has made has not been permanent; and that, deprived of his teacher, he again degenerates into the condition of a barbarian.

"To account for these conditions, some supposition is necessary. The first was, that the decree of Heaven had blasted the parent source of the race, and that the successors of the son of Noah had never been permitted to regain their former capacity, or to rival their brethren in the part which they enacted in the world's history."

On this and other premises, argues Wolfe, slavery is inevitable and right.

What was the answer? It would seem to have been contained clearly enough in the Sermon on the Mount, but to bandy one part of Scripture against another was futile. At length the War gave military and legal sanction to the hated cause of Abolition, but in the confused power-politics of Reconstruction the issues were even more entangled. *Had* slavery in fact really been abolished, or was it being bootlegged back, in wholesale lots? The contention was now between the unreconstructed Rebels and the unreconstructed Abolitionists—each a far smaller band than ever faced each other in the War. As his weapon, David Ross Locke chose again the old cornknife of ridicule—which in fact he had not yet put aside, as President Andrew Johnson for one could testify.

No one who had followed the Nasby Letters could have any doubt where Locke stood on the issues of Abolition and Reconstruction. At a time of hesitation his voice remained that of the radical; he wished slavery abolished in deed as well as in name, demanding a Reconstruction that would truthfully reconstruct. Unless one went directly and thoroughly to the root, Locke feared, much of the agony of the War might be in vain. A sensitive man of honor, he challenged the nation to live up to its promises; and as he read his lecture to large audiences season after season, the challenge reached an ever-enlarging circle of his fellow citizens. He spoke the language of those who had fought and those whose sons had perished in the War—language rising out of deep feeling, impatient of horse-trading politics and half-measures, addressed to anxious and indifferent citizens alike who took shelter in the comfortable belief that "problems would take care of themselves" if "agitators" would only refrain from "stirring up trouble."

In taking to the lecture platform, Locke was using one of the most effective media of his time, for in 1867—the year in which "Cussid Be Canaan!" was first delivered—lecturing was still in its prime. An inner compulsion drove the lecturer to speak: he wanted to say the needful thing on Negro suffrage as strongly as it could be said, without any trifling. One can imagine that Henry Thoreau, had he not died some five years before, would in 1867 have been found speaking his mind in the same unequivocal tones, and that he might have seasoned his remarks with a similar brand of satirical hot-sauce. Locke was a man of Thoreauvian fibre. Mark Twain said of him that he had "the constitution of an ox and the strength and endurance of a prize-fighter."

Lecturing, at length, became a major occupation for Locke. He had little or no platform personality; his delivery was matter-of-fact and rather uninspiring; so he must have depended upon matter rather than manner for the wide public acceptance and substantial income he enjoyed for twenty years on the lecture circuits. On the occasion of his lecture at Hartford, Connecticut, he had missed a train connection and in order not to disappoint his audience, traveled nearly twenty-four hours on a freight train, in a cattle car. "He went from cattle car to his reading desk without dining," Mark Twain reported, "yet showed no sign of fatigue." Quite evidently he felt himself to be a man with a message, for he can hardly have needed the extra income badly enough to ride cattle cars and to read "Cussid Be Canaan!" hundreds of times. He must have felt, also, that an endemic resistance to any real changes in the status quo was so strong that a continuing assault with all his strength was his necessary contribution to help beat it back. Exasperation and altruism combined, surely, to produce such drive as this.

A hundred years later, we may assume, the older type of Scriptural exegesis to condone slavery is largely if not entirely gone—but not so the appeal to Scripture as a bulwark of racial segregation. In the early 1930s, for example, a segment of one of the great Protestant denominations hewed to the doctrine that national and racial lines are "ordained of God" and fought national church unity for this reason. Much more recently a Southern religious group was still saying that "The Almighty God saw fit, in His infinite wisdom, to segregate the races in the beginning, and we earnestly believe that the will of God will be best served by continuation of the total segregation of the black and white races." Though the argument, in short, had failed to perpetuate slavery, it might still be used to bolster coercive segregation: that was precisely what Locke perceived. Even during so critical a time as World War II, the publication of a book on racial friendship brought painful remonstrance from some theological circles. Political campaigns which drag in the issue of white superiority, it goes without saying, rely heavily upon certain forms of religious sanction for support, both in the Bible Belt and wherever else Nasbyan "red necks" are to be found.

The world, before which on the night of December 22, 1867, Locke declared we could not afford to say one thing and do another, was doubtless in his mind somewhat less of a political than a moral entity. He had no way of foreseeing that by an action taken a few weeks prior to his appearance at Music Hall, Boston, the United States had most providentially insulated itself (for a time) from the one nation whose presence in North America it would have the most to fear. The Alaskan Purchase was no more than a pretext for another Nasby letter. He did foresee, however, that without the resolution to do right, a moral weakness of the first magnitude must remain as working propaganda capital for whatever hostile regime might rise to employ it. His performance teaches us once more that in the long run the most useful patriot is the one who thinks hard and deeply and has the courage to say what he thinks.

The message of "Cussid Be Canaan!" is simple: put aside your preconceptions, your prejudices and give the Negro a fair deal. Simple, but not easy, for there lingered in the minds of South and North alike many vestiges of the old slaveholding mentality, and how should one exorcise these demons? Locke's attack is made upon the ground of essential Christianity against pseudo-Christianity, the elemental justice of the Sermon on the Mount against scholastic weaseling with hand-picked passages of Scripture. To reach this ground, he traverses the treacherous bogs of literalistic interpretation of the Bible, heaping ridicule upon favorite Old Testament verses to which pious defenders of slavery—curious as it may seem—once actually fled for refuge. How absurd it would be merely to take these holy theorists at their word, Locke reflects: how grotesque the great words of human history sound with a Jim-Crow proviso tacked on! And to remind his listeners of their own free heritage and its obligations, he fortifies his lecture at the outset and at the conclusion with that portion of the Declaration of Independence which autocrats have always found the most annoying: "We hold these truths to be self-evident, that all men are created equal; that they are endowed by their Creator with certain unalienable rights; that among these are life, liberty, and the pursuit of happiness." This "hard mystery of Jefferson's," as Robert Frost has termed it, was the line of defense upon which Locke proposed to fight it out—a line which, as history has proved, is more easily undermined than assaulted. Locke was of that succession of hard-thinking minds which in various ages have stood uncompromisingly for justice—men like Luther, Milton, Voltaire, Thoreau, Gandhi. He believed that the Declaration of Independence meant what it said; today he would be equally confident that the Constitution means what it says.

As a piece of satirical oratory, the speech is notably effective. It entertains its audience by pounding a formidable lie into a rubble of pitiful absurdities, and at the same time it develops a line of more serious thought that is thrust home in pointed references to current affairs. Locke intends to leave a hypocrite no corner to hide in: he searches into innumerable crannies of the larger question, making clear that the fundamental issue is not to be sidetracked by technicalities. One can feel in the astringency of the satire the depth to which Locke and others like him were stirred. He means to be as lethal as he can; there is no compromise to be made with the evil at which he launches his bolt, any more than there had been in the fiery days of ante-bellum Abolition. Yet there is a broad playfulness in the bur-lesque logic and pseudo-scholarship with which he brandishes the "Canaan" text; an ironic largeness in the amount of room he allows himself to handle the obviously picayune question. The final appeal is intellectual; the audience must be able to follow and appreciate a sustained *reductio ad absurdum,* as apparently his audiences could.

Locke was telling the North what it, along with the South, needed to be told. He had understood only too clearly, during his days of campaigning for the newborn radical Republican Party in rough-and-tumble Ohio politics, that not all the Americans who were unfriendly to the Negro lived south of the Mason-Dixon Line. He is not above making capital of the vexing (and still vexing) question of miscegenation, nor does he handle it with kid gloves; both races might wince a little at his satiric broadness, as he very likely intended. Neither of the major political parties escapes being measured against manifest justice and found wanting, though the Democrats take most of the battering. He feared that Republicans, smug in victory, might conveniently forget and at length lay completely aside their ideological birthright.

In more than a figurative sense, the circumstances of our own day have brought us back to Locke. And he confronts not merely a few interested radicals or reactionaries, but a whole nation of us. To be sure, at no time since the Civil War has there been anything like a complete quiescence of the American racial prob-lem. Novelists both black and white have used the theme re-peatedly, from Mark Twain to William Faulkner and Richard Wright; much poetry has been written about it; the plays of Eugene O'Neill and others have dramatized the issues. Important and effective as some of this literature may have been, however, it is after all still "literature," and to the pragmatic minds of many Americans it describes only a world of theory—perhaps only of fantasy, for all they are aware. That it is not fantasy, and that it can no longer be viewed from the armchair of theory, is now very evident. We are forced to face truth, and it is not to our credit that we have procrastinated the encounter. Like the ghost of Hamlet's father, this old-fashioned liberal whose views are so curiously up-to-date seems to say, "I come to whet your almost blunted purpose."

"Cussid Be Canaan!" is a vivid historic document from the

most turbulent era of our history—and more than merely historic. There is still point to it: nearly a century after its first delivery its irony still troubles the consciences of honest men, its ridicule still stings. And old Nasby's advice to his Confedrit × Roads congregation is pure gold: "Learn to spell and pronounce Missenegenegenashun. It's a good word."

I. Inside Nasby: Some Intimate Glimpses
Through the Years
(1862-1870)

NOTE TO THE CHAPTER

Politics of the Civil War era resembled the sphinx of the fable; it devoured the men who failed to solve its riddle. Petroleum Vesuvius Nasby escaped that fate, since he never allowed issues to confuse him in his dogged pursuit of his primary aim in life: a postmaster's commission. His vision of "that haven uv worn-out patriots" supplied an elastic political creed which equipped him to make "many sudden and rather 'strordinary changes in politix—some so very sudden that the movement perdoost conjestion uv the conshense." Undaunted by all his experience, he kept reminding his "Dimekratik brethrin" that he was in need of an office, and therefore should have one.

The logic of his reasoning as well as his years of faithful service recommended the loyal Democrat who had cast his first ballot for Andrew Jackson and continued voting "for every succeedin Dimocratic candidate ez many times ez possible." This master of the fine art of stuffing ballot boxes fondly recalled that no man "hez drunk more whisky than I hev for the party," and could honestly claim that "none hez dun it moar willingly." In 1856 he helped secure the pivotal electoral votes of Pennsylvania by appearing at the polls "twict or four times for that eminent and gilelis patriot, Jeems Bookannan," to defeat the first Republican presidential candidate, John C. Fremont. Nasby "wuz hauled up therfor, and sentenced by an Ablishen Judge to a year in the Western Penitentary." When he was discharged from prison, with a "tolable knowledge uv the shoemakin biznis," he hurriedly took up again the pursuit of his elusive goal.

The Civil War finally helped Nasby to the postmastership which two such eminent dispensers of Democratic patronage as Jackson and Buchanan had refused him. During the war the draft caught up with Nasby, who, after brief service in the 778th Ohio Kidnapt Melishy, escaped to the "Looisiana Pelicans . . . ez a deserter from the hordes uv the tyrant Linkin." After Appomattox he was pardoned by Johnson who still "didn't like to give the precious commission" to the politico. But the President, harassed by Radical Republicans, "wanted a party,"

Nasby gleefully related, "and, ez his appintments everywhere show, he coodn't be very pertikeler. I succeeded," the perpetual office-seeker rejoiced, and "bore with me to Kentucky a commission ez Post Master."

The accomplishment permanently placed Postmaster General Alexander W. Randall, who "signed the commission," in a special niche in Nasby's pantheon of Democratic idols. Andrew Johnson also occupied an elevated place in the hierarchy, as did John C. Calhoun, the eloquent defender of slavery and states' rights. Thomas Jefferson, Andrew Jackson, Thomas Hart Benton and Stephen A. Douglas, the standard bearers of Democracy, Nasby also revered dutifully, but he reserved his greatest sympathies for such truly mediocre Democratic presidents as Franklin Pierce and James Buchanan, who had proved manageable even by politicos of Nasby's caliber. Nothing could shake his faith in all great Democrats, and when the medium at a seance quoted from the opening passages of the Declaration of Independence, that all men are created equal, as the message of Jefferson's spirit, Nasby knew at once that this spirit was an imposter since he had "heerd a Abolishn preecher use the same language at a 4th uv July celebrashen."

The singlemindedness of purpose with which Nasby pursued his goal did not blind him to reality. Principles were valuable, to be sure, but only as far as they facilitated the orderly dispersal of patronage through a Democratic administration. A devoted champion of states' rights, Nasby never actually concerned himself with the vague wording of the Tenth Amendment or the lack of a definite boundary between federal and states' rights, but confidently followed the lead of his Southern friends of 1860 to whom the doctrine guaranteed the constitutional right to secede from the Union. No doubt he felt safe with the principle which at one time or the other had been embraced by every major political party. Like most politicians of his day, Democrats or Whigs, who raised the time-honored shibboleth when the other party was in power, Nasby cherished states' rights while he abhorred Douglas's squatter sovereignty, which left the fate of slavery in Kansas to the actual occupants of the territory.

Nasby easily passed the acid test of the true administration Democrat. He was safe on the question of slavery, which he saw justified in the Bible and the Constitution. "This nigger question is the problem uv the age," he pondered pensively after he had devoted his life to finding an answer to the challenge. Until Appomattox, he diligently combined the lessons of his childhood with his interpretation of Chief Justice Roger B. Taney's opinion in the Dred Scott case of 1857 that "the nigger hez no rites which the white man is bound to respeck." After the proclamation of the Fifteenth Amendment, providing for Negro citizenship, he applied himself with equal determination to the manipulation of the newly enfranchised colored voters.

Before the downfall of the Confederacy the ways of the Democratic party had filled Nasby with hope; after the Civil War the party supplied him with a Lost Cause. The Democracy always furnished him with a living. When "the wust comes to the wust," he speculated, there is always "the nigger left us." He felt certain that "Dimocrisy never yet failed to control all uv the lower orders uv sosiety." As long as the party could rely on such pillars of strength as the "sturdy old yeomanry who still swear that Bloo Lite Federalism ought to be put down . . . and who . . . don't know more what Bloo Lite Federalism wuz than an unborn baby does uv Guy Fawkes," he pontificated, "so long ez ther is a Pope and a distillery, so long will there be a Dimokratic party in the Yoonited States." (During the War of 1812, the Blue Lighters, extreme Federalists and advocates of peace, had been accused by Jeffersonians of traitorously making signals with a blue lantern to British vessels off the American coast. In the Gunpowder Plot, a conspiracy to blow up King, Lords and Commons—in revenge for the penal laws against Catholics—Guy Fawkes was seized on November 5, 1605, when he was about to fire the powder which had been placed under the House of Lords.)

Nasby had sufficient martyrs of his own Lost Cause to bewail, and while the ghosts of radical fire-eaters like Louis T. Wigfall and James M. Mason were "sheddin speritooal tears," he sadly realized that the shooting of Elijah Parish Lovejoy (the editor of an Abolitionist paper), the hanging of John Brown and the mobbings of William Lloyd Garrison, Gamaliel Baily and Benjamin Lundy were all in vain once the Fifteenth Amendment passed. The Devil himself rushed in to console his disheartened disciple after that "humble worker in the great field of Dimekratik reform," like his beloved Confederacy, almost found his last ditch when he was thrown off the night train of New Jersey's Camden and Amboy Railroad. The Devil was inspired by invectives which Benjamin F. Perry, Johnson's appointee as provisional governor of South Carolina, had impulsively hurled at the Radical Republicans, and other indications of the resurgence of the old spirit of the South. "We re-establish slavery in the South," he exhorted his fellow-conspirator, "and extend it all over the territories, and finally over all the Northern States, making it universal." Although the encounter "wuz only a dream," Nasby sadly realized, his newly gained hope in the Cause kept him from sinking to the position of an artfully crippled "Dimokratic organ grinder" on the sidewalks of Louisville and Frankfort, waiting for the return of John C. Breckinridge. A Confederate General and Secretary of War, Breckinridge, the presidential candidate of the Southern Democrats in 1860, had escaped to Cuba after the collapse, and had toured Europe and Canada before returning to Kentucky in 1869. There, he was received with unbounded enthusiasm, and might have obtained any elective position—had his right to hold office been restored, and had he been so inclined.

Turned out of office with the beginning of the Grant administration, Nasby found a temporary haven in another citadel of Democracy, New

York City's nefarious Sixth Ward. As "sole proprietor uv the Harp uv Erin Saloon," * he demonstrated again that very early in life he had come to appreciate the elementary lesson that in politics victories are won by votes cast. He captured the sympathy of his Irish patrons with portraits of the leaders of their Fenian Brotherhood, the secret organization aimed at overthrowing English rule in their native land and at the conquest of Canada. His "cabinet uv sakred relics" contained a piece of the rope which hung John Brown at Charlestown after the Abolitionist had been convicted of treason for his raid on Harper's Ferry, and mementoes of the New York Draft Riots in the summer of 1863. Among them was a bullet fired during the mob's attack on the offices of Horace Greeley's *Tribune*, which had advocated the suppression of the uproar with the greatest possible force.

In the congenial atmosphere of Manhattan's Five Points, Nasby gained new confidence in the Cause by reviewing the other strongholds of the Democratic party in the North. Behind his bar he felt content to wait for the eventual triumph of the "anshent Dimocrisy" which would bring him to his "rest in that haven uv worn-out patriots—a perpetooal Post Offis."

* ["Grocery," as Nasby uses the word, also customarily means "saloon." Ed. note.]

1. *"Nuthin Monotonous"*: *A Personal Record*

CONFEDRIT X ROADS
(Wich is in the Stait uv Kentucky,)
Jan. 29, 1872.

TO THE PUBLISHER:

Enclosed find photograff uv myself, ez you desired. To make a strikin picter, I flung myself into the attitood, and assoomed the expreshun wich mite hev bin observed onto my classikle countenance when in the act uv deliverin my justly celebrated sermon, "The wages uv Sin is Death." The $2.00 wich yoo remitted to kiver the cost uv the picter wuz, I regret to say, insuffishent. The picter cost 75 cents, and it took $1.50 worth uv Bascom's newest whisky to stiddy my nerves to the pint uv undergoin the agony uv sittin three minits in front uv the photograffer. I need not say that he is a incendiary from Massachoosets. Ez the deceased Elder Gavitt's son, Issaker, hez expressed a burnin desire to possess his apparatus, it is probable that public safety will very shortly require his expulsion. But I hed my re-

venge—in his pocket is none uv my postal currency. Sekoorin
the picter, I told him I wood take it home, and ef my intimit
friends, those who knowd me, shood decide it wuz a portrait, I
wood call and pay for it afore he left the Corners. Will I do it?
Will this picter-takin Ablishnist ever more behold me? Ekko
ansers.

Yoo may remit the odd twenty-five cents, either by draft on
Noo York, or money order, at my resk.

I wuz born in the year 1806, at—I will not say where. I hev
reasons for conceelin my birthplace. I don't want to set any town
in that State up in biznis. That town hez gone loonatic, and
gives Ablishn majorities friteful to contemplate, and I don't
want to benefit it by givin it a nashnel reputashen. I don't want
to double the price uv its property—to be the means uv erectin
a dozen, or sich a matter, uv fust class hotels to accommodate the
crowds ez wood make pilgrimages thither to visit my birthplace.
The present owner uv the house into wich I first opened my eyes
onto a world uv sin, is a Ablishnist of the darkest dye, and I hev
no desire to enrich him. Never, by word uv mine, shel he cut that
house up into walkin sticks and buzzum pins.

My boyhood wuz spent in the pursoot uv knollege and musk-
rats, mostly the latter. I wuz a promisin child. My parence wuz
Democrats uv the strictest kind, my mother in partikeler. She
hatid eny one that wuzn't Dimocratic with a hatred that I never
saw ekalled. When I say that she woodent borrer tea and sugar
and sich uv Whig nabers, the length, and breadth, and depth of
her Dimocrisy will be understood.

From sheer cussidnis I shood hev probably hev bin a Whig,
hed not a insident occurred in my boyhood days, wich satisfied
me that the Dimocrisy wuz my approprit and nateral abidin-
place. It wuz in this wise:

In a playful mood, wun nite, I bustid open a grosery, and ap-
propriatid, ez a jest, what loose change ther wuz in the drawer
(alars! in these degenerit days uv paper currency, the teterprisin
theef hez to steel at 10 per cent. discount), and sich other notions
ez struck my boyish fancy. I indoost a nigger boy, sumwhat
younger than myself, to aid me, and when we hed bagged the
game, I, feelin in my pride ez wun hevin the proud Anglo-Sack-
sun blood a coursin toomulchusly thro his vanes, what Cheef-
Justis Taney hez sence made law, to-wit: that the nigger hez no
rites which the white man is bound to respeck, whaled him till
he resined the entire proceeds uv the spekulashen to me. The de-

graded wretch, devoid uv every prinsiple uv honor, blowed on me, and we wuz both arrested.

The Justis uv the Pease wuz a Whig! and after a hurried eggsaminashen, he sentenst ME! wun uv his own race! uv his own blood! uv his own parentige! to impriznment for THIRTY DAYS! on bred and water, and the nigger to only ten, on the ground that I wuz the cheef offender!

My mother beggd and prayd, with teers a stremin down her venrable cheeks faster than she cood wipe em up with her gingum apern, that the arrangement mite be reverst—the nigger the 30 and I the 10—but no! Cold ez a stun, inflexible ez iron, bludlis ez a turnip, I wuz inkarseratid, and stayed my time.

Sullenly I emerged from them walls, on the evenin uv the 30th day, a changed indivijooel. Liftin my hands to heven, I vowd three vows, to-wit:

1. That I wood devote my life to the work uv redoosin the Afrikin to his normal speer.

2. That I wood adopt a perfeshn into wich I cood steel without bein hauled up fer it.

3. That the water I hed consoomed while in doorance vile, wuz the last that wood ever find its way, undilootid, into my stumick.

Hentz, I jined the Dimocrisy, and whoever eggsamines my record, will find that I hev kep my oaths!

Uv my childhood, I know but little. My father wuz a leadin man in the humble speer in which he moved, holdin, at different times, the various offices in the town up to constable, the successive steps bein road supervisor and pound master. He wuz elected constable, and mite probably hev gone higher, but for an accident that occurred to him the first month. He collected a judgment for $18, and the money wuz paid to him. The good man wuz a talented collector, but wuz singlerly careless in payin over what he collected. Ez showin the pekoolier bent uv genius uv the old man, I repeet a conversashen I wunst heerd. A man who hed an account to collect, wuz consultin one who knowd my father well, ez to the safety uv puttin a claim into his hands.

"Is he a good collector?" askt the man.

"Splendid!" sed the naber.

"Is he a man uv responsibility?" askt the man.

"Sir!" sed the naber, "he hez the ability, but yoo'll find, when yoo try to git yoor money out uv his hands, that he lacks the response."

Cood ther hev bin a more tetchin triboot?

He wuz like all men uv genius, unbalanced. His ability was all on one side. The grovelin plaintiff, who didn't admire sich erratic flites, raised a ruckshen about the paltry sum, and my father

> "Folded his tent like the Arabs,
> And ez silently stole away."

From that time out, the old gentleman migrated—in fact, he lived mostly on the road. He adopted movin ez a perfeshun, and a very profitable one he made uv it. When his hoss died, the nabors, rather than not hev him move, wood chip in and raise him another. Appreshiatin the compliment they pade him, he alluz went. I menshun these pekooliarities uv my ancestor, becoz

> "The lives uv all grate men remind us
> We may make our lives sublime,
> And, departin, leave behind us—"

ef our talent runs in that direckshun, ez many debts ez he did, though it does require espeshel talents.

This hed its inflooence upon my yoothful mind. I saw not only a great deal uv the country, but much uv mankind, and I acquired that adaptability to circumstances wich hez ever distinguished me. Even to this day, ef I can't git gin I take whiskey without a murmur and without repinin.

My politicks hez ever bin Dimocratic, and I may say, without egotism, I hev been a yooseful member uv that party. I voted for Jackson seven times, and for every succeedin Dimocratic candidate ez many times ez possible.

My Dimocrisy wuzn't partikerly confirmed until I arrived at the age uv twenty-four. My father wuz intimately acquainted with me, and knowd all my carakteristics ez well ez tho he hed bin the friend uv my buzzum. One day, ez I wuz a layin on my back under a tree, contemplatin the beauties uv nacher, my parent, sez he,—

"Pete" (which is short for my name), "ef yoo ever marry, marry a milliner!"

"Why, father uv mine?" replied I, openin my eyes.

"Becoz, my son," sed he, "she'll hev a trade wich'll support yoo, otherwise yoo'll die uv starvashen when I'm gone."

I thot the idea wuz a good one. Thro woman a cuss come into the world, wich cuss wuz labor; and I wuz determined that ez woman hed bin the coz uv requirin somebody to sweat for the bread I eat, woman should do that sweatin for me. That nite I perposed to a milliner in the village, and she rejectid my soot. I offered myself, in rapid succeshun, to a widder, who wuz a washerwoman, and to a woman who hed boys old enuff to work, with the same result, when, feelin that suthin wuz nessary to be done to sekoor a pervision for life, I married a nigger washerwoman wich didn't feel above me. Wood you blieve it? Within an hour after the ceremony wuz pronounst, she sold her persnel property, consistin uv a wash-tub and board, and a assortment uv soap, and investin the proceeds in a red calico dress and a pair uv earrings, insisted on my going to work to support her! and the township authorities not only maintained her in her loonacy, but refused to extend releef to me, on the ground that I wuz able-bodied.

Ez I left that nigger, I agin vowed to devote my life to the work uv gettin em down to where they wood hev to support us, and that vow I hev relijusly fulfilled. I hev never felt good, ceptin when they wuz put down a peg; I hev never wept, save when they wuz bein elevated.

The offices I hev held hev not been many. I hed signers to a petishun for a post-office in Jackson's time, but I killed my chances by presentin it in person. The old hero looked at me, and remarked that it wuzn't worth while throwin away post-offices on sich—that when he wanted em, he cood buy em at a dollar a dozen. Bookanan wuz agoin to appoint me, but somehow my antecedents got to his ears, and he wuz afeerd uv his respecktability; and I never succeeded till Androo Johnson returned to his first love and embraced us.

I hed bin drafted into the Federal army at the beginnin uv the war, and hed deserted to the Confederacy. Procoorin a certifikit to that effeck, I applied for a pardon and a place. He didn't like to give me the offis, but he wanted a party, and, ez his appintments everywhere show, he coodn't be very pertikeler. I succeeded! I bore with me to Kentucky a commishun ez Post Master, and I wuz livin in the full enjoyment uv that posishun, till ousted, and I may say, I wuz happy.

The society wuz conjenial. Ther is four groceries, onto wich I could gaze from the winder uv my offis, and jest beyond, enlivenin what wood otherwise be a dull landscape, is a distillery, from wich the smoke uv the torment ascendeth forever. I hed associates who reverenced me, and friends who loved me. There wuz nuthin monotonous there. I hev knowed ez many ez eight fites per day, though three or four is considered enuff to break the tedium. And in those deliteful pursoots, havin left behind me the ambishens uv wat mite be called public life, with my daily bread sekoored, with my other sustenance ashoored, with a frend alluz to share my bottle, or, to speek with a greater degree uv akkooracy, frends alluz willin to share ther bottles with me, I wuz glidin peacefly down the stream uv time, dodgin the troubles, and takin ez much uv the good uv life ez I could.

The twenty-five cents menshuned in the beginnin uv my letter, you may, ez I remarked, remit either in postal order or currency.

PETROLEUM V. NASBY, P. M.
(Wich wuz Postmaster).

P. S.—Don't remit the twenty-five cents menshund in postage stamps. I hev enuff to last me, ez they ain't in demand here. Send it in currency. P. V. N.

2. *"I Announse Myself ez a Candidate":* *A Veteran Still Available*

[1862]

TO THE DIMOKRASY UV THE COUNTY:
I announse myself ez a candidate for ary one uv the offices to be filled this autum, subgik, uv coarse, to the decishun uv the Convenshun.

In makin this anouncement, I feel it due my Dimekratik brethrin, that I stait the reasons for takin this step. They run ez follows:

1st. I want a offis.
2d. I need a offis.
3d. A offis wood suit me; therfore,
4th. I shood like to hev a offis.

I make no boasts uv what my speshel claims are, but I hev dun the party sum servis. My fust vote I cast for that old Dimekrat, Androo Jackson. For him I voted twict, and I hev also voted for every Dimekratik candidate sence. I hev fought and bled for the coz, hev voted ez often ez three times at one elekshun, and hev alluz wore mournin around my eyes for three weeks after each campane. I hev alluz rallid to the poles early in the mornin, and hev spent the entire day a bringin in the agid and infirm, and in the patryotik biznis uv knockin down the opposition voters. No man hez drunk more whisky than I hev for the party— none hez dun it moar willingly. Twict, in going thro campanes, hev I brot myself to the very verge uv delirium tremins a drinkin the terrific elekshun whisky pervided by our candidates, but the coz demandid the sacrifis, and I made it ez cherefully ez tho my stumic hed been copper-lined, which, unfortunitly, it is not. Ez for my services in this line, let my nose, which has trooly blossomed like the lobster, speak for itself.

> "Rum hez its triumphs ez the water hath,
> And this is wun uv em."

My politikle principles are sound. I am opposed to a nashnel bank, and am unmitigatedly in favor uv free trade. I approved uv the last war with Great Britain, and hev sence seen no reason to change my views on that subgik. On the war queshun my views are ez follows: Bein a naytiv uv this Republic, and hevin livd under the Stars and Stripes, I am in favor uv maintainin the Guverment, and puttin down the rebelyun, and will aid the Guverment in doin it, in all constitooshnal ways. But, after a keerful readin uv my papers, I kin find no constitooshnal warrant for half what is bein dun. I am in favor uv a war for the Union ez it used to was, and the Constitooshn ez I'd like to hev it; but a war uv subgugashen—never! Hents, I am opposed to all this military biznis. Ef a citizen uv Virginny shoots a citizen uv Ohio, let him be arrested, taken before the nearest Justis uv the Peese, and bound over to court. That's the only way to do it. I regard confistikashen as unconstitooshnel, and ez for emansipashen, words cant express my disgust at the bare ijee. Wat! is armies to march forth, under the good old flag, for the purpus uv destroyin an institooshn guaranteed by the Constitooshn, and wich hez enabled the grate Dimekratik party to controle the destinies uv this republic for mor'n thirty yeres? Ferbid it, hevin! The follerin resolushens, wich I drawd up, show percisely wat I bleeve:—

Resolved, That we are now, eggsackly as we alluz hev bin, the devoted friends uv the Union ez it used to be wen us uns and our breethrin uv the South run the masheen, and we'd be thenderin glad to see it restord agin.

Resolved, That evry dictate uv patertism reqwires that, in the fight we hev afore us, the Dimokrasy shood present a un-broken front; and therefore, ez differenses may arize amongst us, the General Committee shel, frum time to time, inform the county committies wat the people is expectid to beleve, that we may talk alike in all parts uv the country.

Resolved, That the Abolishn party, by ther denunsiashn uv President Davis, hev shown that they hev no regard for our feelins or hizn, and hev exhibited a bitterness towards our mis-gided Suthrin brethrin, that demonstraits their onfitness to hold eny place wer they kin hev an opportunity to injure them.

Resolved, That the stait uv Massychusits is ornery and cussed. That the annimosity exhibited by her men, in the lait fites afore Richmond, towards our misgided Suthrin brethrin, is wat mite be expektid frum a state that hez no Dimekrats, and where every body redes and rites.

Resolved, That, while rebels shood be punisht, we are op-posed to confisticashun er emansipashun in any shaip; becoz it isnt constooshnal; becoz the South wood be made more desprit, and moar uv em wood be killed, wich wood lessen Dimekratik majoritis in them states; and becoz it wood hev a tendency to make em madder nor they air.

On the absorbin question uv nigger I am sound. I am op-posed to amalgamashun, and am in favor uv prohibitin any wench from marryin any wun hevin a visable admixter uv white blud. I am ferninst allowin niggers to come into the North, and am in favor uv expellin the thirty-two milyuns now here. To force em away, I wood make it a pennytenshiary offence to be shaved by a nigger, and wood regulate the price uv barberin by law, that white men mite be indoost to go into the biznis. Ez for other pints uv nashenel and stait policy, my paper dident cum last nite, and consequently I am somewhat at a loss.

In county matters I shel follow closely the footsteps uv my predecessers. I shel be keerful uv the funds, and shel apply jest ez much ez possible to the grate work uv bildin up the Dime-kratik party; alluz, uv coarse, reservin enuff to buy me a mod-erit farm at the close uv my term.

I aint partickeler ez to wat offis I hev. I am willin to serve ez Treasurer, Sheriff, Commishener, or Coroner—tho I cood do the party more good ez Treasurer than in any other posishen. Money cozes the female hoss to amble.

In conclushen, fellow Dimekrats, I hev to say, ef nominated, all rite; ef not, I shel abide by the result ez cherefully ez my temper will allow.

PETROLEUM V. NASBY.

3. *"Squelch Them Tuppenny Pollytishns":*
A Spiritualist Seance

CHURCH UV THE SLAWTERD INNOCENTS
(Lait St. Vallandigum), December the 19th, 1863.

I hev bin for many years disposed to bleeve in speritooalism. Ther is suthin pleasant in the idee uv bein in communicashen with them ez hev gone before, as it may be reznably supozed that frum their stan-pint they kin see things in a more clearer lite than we who is encumbered with clay. Akordingly, I invited a distingisht mejum to visit my flock.

A circle wuz formed, and I wuz requestid to call for the sperit uv sum wun. Havin a few Abolishnists present, whom I wisht to enliten on politikle topics, I called for Thomas Jefferson.

"Thomas," sez I, "wuz yoo the father uv Dimokrasy?"

(I use my own language, ez them old fellers wuz not alluz elegant.)

"I wuz."

"Thomas, are the party now barin the name yoor child?"

"Not any. It's a mizable bastard, born uv John C. Calhoon, and that old hag, State-Rites, and a low-lived whelp it is. My heirs is them ez supports the guverment I helpt to make."

"But, Thomas, wood yoo hev us support a Abolishn war for the purpus uv freein niggers?"

The spirit rapt out with awful distinknis:

"We hold these trooths to be self-evident, that all men is creatid ekal, and endoud with certing inalianable rites, among wich is life, liberty—"

At this pint I stopt the mejum. I knew the sperit wuz not Thomas Jefferson, but a imposter, hevin heerd a Abolishn preecher use the same language at a 4th uv July celebrashen. I then called Androo Jaxon, who respondid.

"Androo," sez I, "woodent yoo like to be back on earth, jist now?"

"Yoo kin bet I wood," retortid he. "I'd like to hev bin President in the place uv that old, white-livered, black-cockade Fed-

ralist, Bookannon. Wat a hangin ther wood hev bin! Ther wood
hev bin vacancies in Congris, and jest es many funerals ez ther
wuz vacancies. As for South Carliny—"

The communicashen ceased, and I heerd a sound like the
grittin uv teeth. It resoomed:

"I'd string up Vallandigum, and Fernandywood, and Sam-
medary, et settry. It wood be a bad old joke on them indivijuels
ef I hed control of the habis corpus; I'd—"

I refoozed to hear further. This sperit wuz, also, ondoubtedly a imposter.

I called for Benton, who merely sed that Missoury wuz
comin to her senses in gittin rid uv slavery; and for Duglis, who
remarkt that he cood say uv the temple uv Dimokrasy ez the
Savior sed of the temple, "My house is cald a house of prayr, but
ye hev made it a den of theeves;" both of whom wuz onquestionably imposters. Another sperit (probably of a deceest Ablishnist)
sed that Benedict Arnold and Judis Iscariot hadent bin on
speekin terms for sum time, Iscariot hevin called Arnold a copperhead. Arnold sed he'd never stand that.

Duglis cum back, and sed he had jest wun word to say.
"The Dimekratik party wuz wunst grate, but it had got into bad
hands, and gone crazy as a drunken bed-bug. It needed new
managers—men uv suffishent sense and honesty to run the party
on old principles. In the old hands, it wuz a patriotic party—a
party that wuz alluz for the country. It whaled the British in
1812, and afterwards nockt the hind sites off uv the old Fedral
party for opposin it. It smasht Mexico, and afterwards smasht
the Whig party for not helpin. Now, for the Dimokrasy to oppose a war agin rebels who not only commenst it, but hed actooally bustid the party itself, is loonacy unekaled in the history uv
the world. Squelch them tuppenny pollytishns who hev thieved
the mantels wunst worn by Jaxon and Benton (they look in em
jest about as well as a orgin grinder's monky wood in a soljer's
overcoat, and fill em jest as much), get on to a war platform, and—"

I didn't care about persooin my investigashens enny further,
pertikelerly ez the Abolishnists wuz all a snickrin. It's my privit
opinion that ther's nothin reliable about it. Hed the sperits bin
reely them uv Jefferson, Jaxon, and sich, they woodent hev talkt
so much undilootid niggerism. However, it did me very well.
The mejum took up a colleckshun uv six dollars, wich, by a singler coincidence, was the eggsact amount I hed intendid to

charge him for the use uv my church. He grumbled, but finally sheld out. I am now warin a new pare uv pants.

PETROLEUM V. NASBY,
Pastor uv sed Church, in charge.

4. *"Settin on the Fence, the Figure uv Satan Hisself": Another Venture into the Supernatural*

SAINT'S REST (wich is in the Stait uv Noo Jersey),
September the 30th, 1865.

Nite afore last, I wuz at a gatherin uv the faithful, in the next town to Saint's Rest, and wuz a comin back on the nite train uv the Camden and Amboy, wich is the beauty and glory uv Noo Jersey. I wuz somewat elevatid, hevin hed a need uv inspirin flooids, there bein two or three returned soljers in the meetin, who kept a provokin me with irrelevant and irritatin remarks, sich ez pullin me off the stand, and pintin revolvers at me.

When the conductor cum around, I told him that I wuz a humble worker in the great field uv Dimekratik reform, and wuz, uv coarse, without funds, and that I expected to be passed to my home, FREE! The poor man wuz thunder-struck! Staggerin aginst the side uv the car, pale ez a ghost, and speechless, he beckoned to a brakesman, and pinted me out. In a instant I wuz seized and bundled out uv the car. The next mornin I saw the incident noticed in the daily papers, under the follerin hed lines:—

"THE BULWORKS UV SOCIETY A BRAKIN AWAY!—NOO JERSEY IN DANGER!—A FEEND DEMANDS TO BE DEAD-HEDED OVER THE CAMDEN AND AMBOY!—PROMPT AND HEROIC ACTION UV A CONDUCTOR!"

How long I lay alongside uv the track I know not; but when conshusnis returned, I saw, settin on the fence, the figure uv Satan hisself.

"Avant!" cried I. "Why comest thou to torment me afore my time?"

"Don't skeer," sez he; "I don't want yoo yet. Remember the old man's remark: 'Why shood men club apples off uv trees, when, ef they let em alone, they will fall off themselves?' I woodent take the trouble to *cum* after yoo, and sich ez yoo. I often take a toor thro Jersey. It's my best harvest-field. I'm pleasurin now."

Reassured, I asked the old gentleman some questions as to what kind uv biznis he wuz a doin these times, et settry.

He replied that biznis wuz good. The Suthern States hed bin his grate field uv labor, and when they rebelled agin the guverment he thot he hed dead wood on them localities. His soul expanded with joy ez he saw the Churches South plunge into the seceshn biznis, and their preachers throw off the sacerdotle robes and put on butternut uniform. They never hed much religion down there, anyhow; but when they went into seceshn, they threw away that little.

"Ez Linkin's hellions advanced," he sed, "my soul shrunk —only occasionally wuz I elevatid ez yoo Copperheds riz in the North. Finally, when Lee and Johnson surrendered, I give up all hopes. That, I thot, settled the question. The niggers will be emancipated and I'll lose them, for they'll learn to read, and they'll diskiver that virchoo is the best road to travel. Also—"

"Hold!" sez I; "do niggers go to hell?"

"Uv course, when they die in their sins," sez he.

"Farewell, hope!" exclaims I, in agony, "for all is lost! At the last end the entire Dimokrasy will be on a equality with the nigger, and will hev to mix with em."

"Also," sez he, a goin on, "I wuz satisfied I shood lose the whites South, for when they can't live on nigger labor, and hev to go to work, they won't hev time to gamble nor drink. They won't hev $2500 to pay for pretty octoroons, and, per consequence, one uv the commandments will be better observed. So I wuz lo-sperited, and conclooded that the Almity had taken that part uv the country out uv my hands."

"How, then," sez I, "is it that yoo feel so well to-night?"

"For two reasons," sez he. "I alluz feel at home in Noo Jersey; and besides that, things don't look so bad after all. You folks up North are doin things to soot me, and so they are South. Uv what account is Linkin's proclamashen, when sich men ez now controle the South, are in power? Them Sutherners are men I like. Guvner Perry talks uv 'Radikle Republikins,' wich shows he's bound to make head agin the only enemies I ever hed in the North. The nigger is free, but only in name. That blessid doctrin uv Stait Rites allows each wun uv the States to oppress jist which class they please, and ez the North will certainly pass all sorts uv laws agin their escapin in that direcshun, it seems to me ez tho Cuff wuz between the upper and nether mill-stun, after all. Five dollars a month they will agree to pay him, but that he'll never git. Then follers stealins, and stabbins, and shootins, and hangins, and arsons, and insurrections [here he rubbed his hands], and more sich fun than we ever saw. Then when the South gets strong agin, and they and yoo, united, make a majority in Congris, won't them Yankees git? Won't we (I speak uv yoo Northern Dimekrats and the South and me, wich hez alluz bin pardners) make the North pay the Suthern war debt? Won't we re-establish slavery in the South and extend it over all the territories, and finally over all the Northern Staits, makin it universal? I rather think so. Ef the North refuses, then agin, yoo and the South and I will make another war, and that time we'll succeed, for we'll know how, better, and the guverment overthrowd, we'll fix it jist ez we want it. And then—"

At this pint he threw his left arm about my neck in a extasy uv irrepressible love. It scorched ez tho a hot bar uv iron hed bin twisted around me, and, shreekin with agony—I awoke.

It wuz only a dream, and I found myself a lyin in the identikle ditch into wich I hed fallen when the conductor threw me off the trane.

I cood not help wondrin at the correctnis with wich my visitor guessed the purposes uv our party.

PETROLEUM V. NASBY,
Lait Paster uv the Church uv the Noo Dispensashun.

5. "Wat Kin I Do with Myself?": A Narrow Escape from Amputation

POST OFFIS, CONFEDRIT X ROADS
(wich is in the Stait uv Kentucky),
January 13, 1869.

The question "Wat kin I do with myself?" is not solved. My return from Noo York so ignomiously, on foot, wuz a serious disappointment to my friends at the Corners. They felt when I left em that they had me fixed for life, and their sorrer at my ontimely return wuz genuine. Bascom, ez soon ez he saw me enter his bar, weary and foot-sore, remarked, with a profane ejaculashen, that I'd be his rooin yet.

I am a man uv ackshun. To-wunst I called a meetin uv my friends to consider the situashen, and to arrange for another vencher. I remarkt to em that I had not lost faith in Noo York;

that I wuz certin that that wuz my field. I proposed that another outfit shood be furnished me, the same ez before, and that I shood hev one more trial. But they unanimously declined, feelin that I hedn't suffishent control uv my own appetite for a grocery keeper, and that investments in that direcshun wood be a waste uv capital which the Corners cood not afford.

Various methods uv makin a livin were sejested, but none met my approval. One wood sejest this thing in San Francisco; another in Alaska; and each one wood swear that every one wuz the very thing. Their readiness to agree, and the numerousnis uv the miles the places wuz away, satisfied me that distance was the main pint with em.

That misable wretch, Joe Bigler, happened in at a moment when they wuz a discussin the feasibility uv a conductership on a street railroad in Noo Orleans,—ez tho the directers uv the companies hadn't all got dissipated nephews to fill sich responsible places,—when he remarkt that the obtoosenis uv humanity wuz one uv the wonders uv the nineteenth century.

"Make uv him," sed Josef, "a Dimokratic organ grinder, saw off his rite leg, dress him in bloo, git him an instroment wich will play 'Dixie,' the 'Bonnie Bloo Flag,' and sich toons, and plant him on the side walks uv Louisville, Noo York, or any other Dimekratic city, and his forchoon is made."

"But why dress me in bloo? Why not in gray, ef I play Confedrit toons?"

"Innocense! Didn't the Dimocrisy always wear bloo while they wuz whistlin Confedrit toons? Even in the North they don't object to a bloo coat, so that they know that there's a Confedrit heart under it?"

"But," replied I, "I wuzn't a soljer; wich is, only ez a draftid man, and then only for a short time."

"That don't matter," remarkt Josef; "no more wuz the heft uv Dimocrisy. The bulk uv em wich served, did so as draftid men. But that circumstance is in yoor favor. The regler organ grinders, them wich wuz volunteers, put onto a placard wich hangs onto their instroment words to this effect:—

" 'Enlisted July 10, 1862—shot thro the leg at Anteetam.'

"Yoo kin put onto yourn this proud inscripshen:—

" 'Draftid September 6, 1863—desertid September 30, 1863; lost rite leg in an encounter with Provost Marshels, October 10, 1863.'

"Sich an inscripshen wood melt the heart uv every Dimokratic passer-by, and they'd fill your cigar-box with coppers. Wich uv em cood resist such an appeal? Think uv wat a harvest yoo'd reap in Louisville when Breckinridge comes home, and in Frankfort when he is inoggeratid Governor of Kentucky! It's the dodge for yoo, Parson."

I thot the matter over for a minnit, and it pleased me. The life uv an organ grinder is by no means to be despised. It's a dreamy, poetical, contemplative sort uv eggistence. Ez ther ain't no manyool labor in it beyond the mere turnin uv a crank, I am satisfied that it wood soot me. Then one sees so much uv life. Constantly before yoo is a ever changin panorama; yoo see humanity in all its phases; and when nite comes how sweet the rest, how inspirin the likker, wich yoo hev honestly earned by yoor manly exertions!

"Is it neccessary that I shel hev a leg ampitatid?" askt I.

"Certainly!" replied Josef.

"Then I decline!" sed I. "Aside from the pain, I hev regard for them legs. They saved my life in all the skirmishes I wuz in doorin my breef term uv servis ez a drafted man in '63. I will not part with one uv em."

"This is triflen with your friends, sir!" ejaculatid Bascom. "Yoo hev the way opened for a honist livin, and yoo refoose to walk ye into it. This cannot be permitted."

"It cannot be permitted!" ekkoed McPelter, Pennibacker, and the rest uv em.

"Joseph, hev yoo suffishent skill to ampetate a limb?" askt Bascom.

"I hev," replied Joseph, "ef yoo will furnish me a carvin knife and handsaw. I've seen it done in Confedrit hospitals. Troo, the victims didn't most alluz survive. Ef yoo do stand it, Parson, think uv the glorious life organ-grindin is; ef yoo die under it, console yourself by thinkin how much organ-grindin yoo've escaped! Bring the knife and saw, and somebody twist a handkercher about his leg."

And forthwith they ceazed me, throwd me onto the bar, and tied me there, and brot a dull knife and handsaw, and that cuss wood hev hackt into my leg hed it not bin for Deekin Pogram.

"Joseph Bigler!" sed this more than saint, "trooly tell us the chances uv his survivin this operashen?"

"About one in a thousand, I shood say; and that's why I am

so anxious to commence!" promptly replied Joseph, sharpnin the knife vishusly onto the sole uv his boot.

"Then let him up!" ejaculated the Deekin hastily; "let him up. He owes me thirty-seven dollars, with interest, sence the second day of his arrival in this place, wich he borrered. Ef he dies its gone; ef he lives he may strike suthin that'll enable him to pay it."

"Slash away, Bigler!" remarkt Bascom, vishusly; "he owes me seven hundred dollars for drinks sence he's bin here, and ef he lives he'll double it in a year."

There wuz an animatid discussion, ez to whether he shood go on or stay his eager hand. Fortunately I owed every one uv the bystanders, and wat wuz more fortunate, the most uv em wuz better fixed than Bascom. The heft uv my indebtedness to the others wuz for borrered money, clothin, and sich things wich a man kin git along without. Bascom knows that ez long ez I live I must hev his goods, money or no money; and hence his desire to see me either git lucrative employment or die.

But the majority wuz agin him; he yeelded, and I wuz saved. Thank Heaven for debt. Hed I bin less hefty on the borrer, I wood now be a cold corpse.

I must git out uv this ez soon ez possible.

Petroleum V. Nasby, P. M.
(wich is Postmaster).

6. *"The Guilloteen Hez Fallen!": A Patriot Loses His Reward*

On a Farm, Three Miles from Confedrit × Roads
(wich is in the Stait uv Kentucky),
June 29, 1869.

The die is cast! The guilloteen hez fallen! I am no longer Postmaster at Confedrit × Roads, wich is in the State uv Kentucky. The place wich knowd me wunst will know me no more forever; the paper wich Deekin Pogram takes will be handed out by a nigger; a nigger will hev the openin uv letters addressed to parties residin hereabouts, containin remittances; a nigger will hev the riflin uv letters addrest to lottry managers, and extractin

"The Guilloteen Hez Fallen!"

the sweets therefrom; a nigger will be.—But I can't dwell upon the disgustin theme no longer.

I hed bin in Washington two weeks assistin the Caucashens uv that city to put their foot upon the heads uv the cussid niggers who ain't content to accept the situashen and remain ez they alluz hev bin, inferior beins. To say I hed succeeded, is a week expreshen. I organized a raid onto em so effectooally ez to drive no less than thirty uv em out uv employment, twenty-seven uv wich wuz compelled to steel their bread, wich give us a splendid opportoonity to show up the nateral cussidness uv the Afrikin race, wich we improved.

On my arrival at the Corners, I knew to-wunst that suthin wuz wrong. The bottles behind the bar wuz draped in black; the barrels wuz festooned gloomily (wich is our yoosual method of expressin grief at public calamities), and the premises generally wore a funeral aspeck.

"Wat is it?" gasped I.

Bascom returned not a word, but waved his hand towards the Post Offis.

Rushin thither, I bustid open the door, and reeled almost agin the wall. At the general delivery wuz the grinnin face uv a nigger! and settin in my chair wuz Joe Bigler, with Pollock beside him, smokin pipes, and laffin over suthin in a noosepaper.

Bigler caught site of me, and dartin out, pulled me inside them hitherto sacred precinks.

"Permit me," sed he, jeerinly, "to interdoose you to yoor successor, Mr. Ceezer Lubby."

"My successor! Wat does this mean?"

"Show him, Ceezer!"

And the nigger, every tooth in his head shinin, handed me a commishn dooly made out and signed. I saw it all at a glance. I hed left my biznis in the hands uv a depetty. It arrived the day after I left, and Isaker Gavitt, who distribbited the mail, gave it to the cuss. Pollock made out the bonds and went onto em himself, and in ten days the commishn come all regler, whereupon Bigler backt the nigger and took forcible possession uv the office. While I wuz absent they hed hed a percession in honor uv the joyful event, sed perceshn consistin uv Pollock, Bigler, and the new Postmaster, who marched through the streets with the stars and stripes, banners and sich. Bigler remarkt that the percession wuzn't large, but it wuz talented, eminently respectable, and extremely versateel. He (Bigler) carried the flag and played the fife; Pollock carried a banner with an inscripshen onto it, "Sound the loud timbrel o'er Egypt's dark sea," and played the bass drum; while the nigger bore aloft a banner, inscribed, "Where Afric's sunny fountins roll down the golden sands," with his commission pinned onto it, playin in addishen a pair uv anshent cymbals. Bigler remarkt further that the perceshun created a positive sensashun at the Corners, wich I shood think it wood. "It wuzn't," sed the tormentin cuss, "very much like the grand percession wich took place when yoo received yoor commishn. Then the whites at the Corners wuz elated, for they spectid to git wat yoo owed em in doo time, and the niggers wuz correspondinly deprest. They slunk into by-ways and side-ways; they didn't hold up their heads, and they dusted out ez fast ez they cood git. At this percession there wuz a change. The niggers lined the streets ez we passed, grinnin exultinly, and the whites wuz deprest correspondinly. It's singler that at the Corners the two races can't feel good both at the same time."

My arrival hevin become known, by the time I got back to Bascom's all my friends hed gathered there. There wuznt a dry eye among em; and ez I thot uv the joys once tastid, but now forever fled, mine moistened likewise. There wuz a visible change in their manner towards me. They regarded me with solisitood, but I cood discern that the solisitood wuz not so much for me ez for themselves.

"Wat shel I do?" I askt. "Suthin must be devised, for I can't starve."

"Pay me wat yoo owe me!" ejakelatid Bascom.

"Pay me wat yoo owe me!" ejakelatid Deekin Pogram, and the same remark wuz made by all uv em with wonderful yoonanimity. Watever differences uv opinyun ther mite be on other topics, on this they wuz all agreed.

"Gentlemen!" I commenced, backing out into a corner, "is this generous? Is this the treatment I hev a right to expect? Is this—"

I shood hev gone on at length, but jist at that minnit Pollock, Joe Bigler, and the new Postmaster entered.

"I hev biznis!" sed the Postmaster; "not agreeable biznis, but it's my offishel dooty to perform it."

At the word "offishel," comin from his lips, I groaned, wich wuz ekkoed by those present.

"I hev in my hand," continyood he, "de bond giben by my predecessor, onto wich is de names uv George W. Bascom,

Elkanah Pogram, Hugh McPelter, and Seth Pennibacker, ez sureties. In dis oder hand I hold a skedool ob de property belongin to de 'partment wich wuz turned ober to him by his predecessor, consistin of table, chairs, boxes, locks, bags, et settry, wid sundry dollars worf of stamps, paper, twine, &c. None ob dis post offis property, turned over to my predecessor by his predecessor, is to be found in de offis, and de objick ob dis visit is to notify yoo dat onless immejit payment be made uv the amount thereof, I am directed by de 'partment to bring soot to-wunst against the sed sureties."

Never before did I so appreciate A. Johnson, and his Postmaster-General Randall. Under their administrashen wat Postmaster wuz ever pulled up for steelin anythin? Eko ansers. This wuz the feather that broke the camel's back.

"Wat!" exclaimed Bascom, "shel I lose wat yoo owe me, and then pay for wat yoo've stole?"

"Shel I lose the money," sed Pogram, "wich I lent yoo, and in addishen pay a Ablishen government for property yoo've confiscated?"

"But the property is here," I remarkt to Bascom; "yoo've got it all. Why not return it, and save all this trouble."

"Wat wood I hev then for the whiskey yoo've consoomed?" he ejakelated vishusly. "It's all I've ever got from you; and I've bin keepin yoo for four years."

"Didn't that property pay yoo for the likker?" I asked; but Bascom wuz in no humor for figgers, and he pitched into me, at wich pleasant pastime they all follered soot. But for Joe Bigler, they wood hev killed me. Ez it wuz they blackt both my eyes, and rolled me out onto the sidewalk, shuttin the door agin me.

Ez I heard that door slam to, I felt that all wuz lost. No offis! no money! and Bascom's closed agin me! Kin there be a harder fate? I passed the nite with a farmer three miles out, who, bein sick, hedn't bin to the Corners, and consekently knowd nothin uv the changes.

I heard the next day the result uv the ruckshun. Bascom returned sich uv the property ez hedn't been sold and consoomed, wich consisted uv the boxes. The chairs hed bin broken up in the frekent shindies wich occur at his place; the locks hed bin sold to farmers who yoozed em on their smoke houses; the bags hed bin sold for wheat, and so on. The stamps, paper, twine, and sich, figgered up three hundred and forty-six dollars, wich wuz three hundred more dollars than there wuz in the Corners. Bascom advanced the forty-six dollars, and the three hundred wuz borrowed uv a banker at Secessionville, who took mortgages on the farms uv the imprudent bondsmen for sekoority. Uv course I can't go back to the Corners under eggsistin circumstances. It wood be uncomfortable for me to live there ez matters hev terminated. I shel make my way to Washinton, and shel see if I can't git myself electid ez Manager of a Labor Assosiation, and so make a livin till there comes a change in the Administrashen. I wood fasten myself on A. Johnson, but unforchnitly there ain't enuff in him to tie to. I would ez soon think uv tyin myself to a car wheel in a storm at sea.

Petroleum V. Nasby
(wich wuz Postmaster).

7. The Dove Alights: "I Shel Be Happy Here"

In the 6th Ward uv Noo York,
December 10, 1869.

The dove wich Noah sent out come back to the Ark becoz the waters kivered the land; when the dove found a dry spot it come back no more. I am a dove. I wuz sent out from the Corners, but the prevalence uv water druv me back, time and agen. Now, thank Heaven, I hev found a spot wher ther is no water (at least I've never seen any used here for any purpose), and here I stay. My foot hez found a restin-place.

I am the sole proprietor uv the "Harp uv Erin" saloon. The original proprietor uv the "Harp uv Erin" died the evenin uv the last eleckshun, much regretted by his politikle assoshates. He hed only voted thirteen times, when in an argyment techin the merits uv his candidate, ez compared with his opponent for the nominashen, he wuz hit with a brickbat, and died with his day's work half done. The man who struck him wuz expelled from the society to wich he belonged for killin an able-bodied Democrat before the closin uv the polls.

How I got possesshen uv the s'loon I shel not state. Suffice it to say, it became mine, and the stock likewise, and that I shel never hev occashen to leave it. Here I shel live, and here I shel die. Uv course I've decorated it to soot the tastes uv my patrons. I took down the portrate uv Jackson, and cut off uv the bottom the words, "The Yoonyun, it must and shel be preserved!" and substitootid, "He serves his party best who votes the most," wich I read to those who drop in ez the last words uv the Hero uv Noo Orleens. I hev an Irish flag turned round an Irish Harp over the bar, and portrates uv the Head Centres uv the Fenian Brotherhood, properly wreathed, all about the room. On the end uv the bar, in the spot where in other neyborhoods the water-pitcher stands, I hev a box with a hole in the top uv it, inscribed, "Contribushens for the benefit uv our suffrin brethren in English Basteels may be dropped in here." That box more than pays my rent. Then I hev quite a cabinet uv sakred relics. I hev a piece uv the rope wich hung John Brown; the identicle club wich killed the first nigger in the riots uv July, 1863; a bullit fired at the Triboon offis at that time, with other sooveneers dear to the Democratic heart, wich attract many. These hang onto the walls, and underneath them I hev the prices uv drinks inscribed, with the stern, cold words, "No Trust."

I inoggeratid my establishment last Wednesday nite. Rememberin the terrible endin uv all my other innogerashens, I declined at fust to make any formal openin; but my friends insisted that it wuz the custom uv the ward, and that I must do it.

"Nobody will buy yoor likker," sed one, "ef yoo don't make a regler openin."

"Ef I make a regler openin," sed I, "I won't hev a drop to sell em. Stay—I hev it. I'll go before a Justis uv the Peece and take a solemn oath not to drink anything myself that nite."

" 'Twon't do," sed my friend. "Oaths don't count in this ward."

Various plans were sejestid. One gentleman proposed that I shood be tied down so that I coodn't git at the likker, and that he shood do the honors. His nose wuz agin him, and I declined his proposishen. Finally I hit upon a plan. I calkilated that twenty gallons wood anser, and I put that amount in a barrel. The balance uv the stock I locked in a room, and then put the key away in a drawer.

"There," sed I, triumphantly, "afore that twenty gallons is eggsausted I shel be too far gone to know where the key to the room holdin the balance uv the stock is. Saved! saved!"

It resultid ez I anticipatid. At first we hed speeches and toasts. Mr. O'Rafferty replide to the toast, "Our adoptid country." He sed the term, "Our adoptid country," wuz a happy one, fur so fur ez Noo York wuz conserned, the sons uv Erin hed adoptid it. He hed bin charged with a lack uv love fur this country. He repelled the charge with skorn. Why shoodn't he love this country? In wat other country wuz votes worth a dollar apeece? Where else cood sich a man ez he hev so high a posishen ez Alderman, and only two yeers on the grounds.

Mr. O'Toole jined in the sentiment. Where else under the canopy cood a man like hisself, who coodn't read, be a skool direcktor? He hed often bin thankful that he hed turned his face toward Ameriky the minit his time wuz out in the prison at Liverpool. Ther wuz less risk in holdin offis in Noo York than in burglary in England, and the results wuz shoorer.

Ther wuzn't much more speech-makin. The drinkin went on fast and furious tho, and ez I antissipatid, before the twenty gallons wuz eggsaustid I wuz very drunk, and incapable uv any effort, mental or physikle, and the others were in very much the same predicament. Four or five uv em did try to rouse me to git more, but it wuz uv no use; they mite ez well hev whispered Grey's elegy in the ear uv a dead mule. The most uv em slept, ez I did, on the floor till mornin.

I shel be happy here. I hev the steddy patronage uv two Aldermen, three skool direcktors, and four contractors, and when the Mayor gits the appintin uv the poleece there will be twelve poleecemen whose trade I kin count on. There in my back room is where the preliminary caucuses fur the ward is held, and I shel be paid fur wat the managers drink till I git an offis myself. At last my lines is cast in pleasant places.

PETROLEUM V. NASBY
(wich wuz P. M.).

8. *"A Period uv Gloom Rarely Ekalled, and Never Surpast": The Patriot's Farewell*

CONFEDRIT × ROADS
(wich is in the Stait uv Kentucky),
May 12, 1870.

Poets hev remarked a great many times, too tejus to enoomerate, that "farewell" is the saddist word to pronounce wich hez to be pronounst. It may be so among poets, wich are spozed to be a continyooally carryin about with em a load uv sadnis, and sensibilities, and sich; but I hev never found it so. The fact is, it depends very much on how yoo say it, under wat circumstances, and to whom. Wen, in my infancy, I wuz in-karseratid in the common jail uv my native village, in Noo Jersey, a victim to the prejudisis uv twelve men, who believed, on the unsupportid testimony uv three men, and the mere accident uv the missin property bein found in my possession (notwithstandin the fact that I solemnly asshoored em that I didn't know nothin about it, and if I did it, it must hev bin in a somnamboolic state), that I hed bin guilty uv bustin open a grosery store, and takin twelve boxes of cheroot cigars, I asshoor yoo that, at the end uv the sentence,—hevin bin fed on bread and water,—the sayin of farewell to the inhuman jailer wuzn't at all onpleasant. Likewise, when, in the State uv Pennsylvany, in the eggscitin campane uv 1856, I votid twict or four times for that eminent and gilelis patriot, Jeems Bookannon, and wuz hauled up therefor, and sentenced by a Ablishn Judge to a year in the Western Penitentiary, after an elokent speech, in wich I reviewed the whole question at issue between the parties, and ashoored him that my triflin irregularity in the matter uv votin grew out uv an overweenin desire for the salvashen of my beloved country,—that, feelin that rooin wuz ahead uv us, onless that leveler Fremont wuz defeated, I felt that my conshence wood not be easy onless I did all in my power to avert the evil,—when I emerged from them gloomy walls, with one soot of close, and a tolable knowledge uv the shoemakin biznis, wuz it a sad thing for me to say "Farewell" to the grim jailer, whose key turned one way wuz liberty, and tother way wuz captivity? Nary.

These two instances, I beleeve, is the only ones in wich I hev ever hed to say farewell. In the course uv my long and checkered career (I do not here allood to the style uv clothin in the Penitentiary), I am, when I think uv it, surprised at the comparatively few times wich I ever left a place at wich I hed bin stayin, in daylite! I ginerally went in the nite,—

> "Foldin my tent like the Arab,
> And ez silently steelin away,"

hevin too much sensibility to be an onwillin witnis uv the agony of landladies, when they diskivered that I cood not pay. Knowin the softnis uv my heart, I hev alluz hed a great regard for my feelins.

I bid my readers farewell in a period uv gloom rarely ekalled, and never surpast, for the Democrisy. Never in my recollekshun wuz the party in sich a state uv abject cussitood. The

Northern States have slipt from our grasp one by one, ontil none remains wich we kin fondly call ourn. The Border States are losin their Dimocrisy, and rallyin under the black banner uv Ablishinism; and the States which we kin control hevent got strength enuff to do any more than to send a few Senators and Representatives to Congress, wich don't do us no good. They are very like the itch,—they irritate, but don't kill.

The Fifteenth Amendment is now a law, and the nigger votes. THE NIGGER VOTES! Ther ain't no doubt about it. The Dimocrat uv Kentucky, uv Ohio, uv Noo York, and Injeany must, from this time hentzforth and forever, go to the poles beside niggers, and must stand by calmly, and put his ballot into the box beside theirn! Wat degredashen! Lovejoy wuz killed in vain, and the mobbins uv Garrison, and Baily, and the other apossels uv Ablishnism goes for naught. Methinks I see the gosts uv Lovejoy, and Lundy, and John Brown, a hoverin in the air, and clappin their sperit hands, and shoutin in sperit voices, Halleloojy! Methinks I see over agin em the gosts uv Wigfall, and Mason, and the other worthies, wringin their sperit hands, and sheddin speritooal tears! Niggers at the ballot-box—niggers on joories—niggers in offis—niggers on railroads—niggers in churches—niggers everywhere! Thank Heaven I am an old man, and can't live long, anyhow. I hev fought a good fight—but, Heavens! how I hev bin walloped.

Nevertheless, Dimocrisy will not die. It hez endoored sich defeats afore, and hez survived. So it will this time. It is passin through the valley and the shadder now, but it will emerge yit in the sunlite uv victry. Suthin will come in time,—what, I can't, with any degree uv certinty, now state; but suthin will come. The Ablishnists cannot alluz rool. The cuss uv the old Whig party wuz, that the respective individooal members thereof cood read and write, and hed a knack uv doin their own thinkin, and therefore it could not be brot into that state uv dissipline so nessary to success ez a party. That same cuss is a hanging onto the Ablishnists. They hung together from 1856 to 1860 coz there wuz wat they called a prinsipple at stake; and on that prinsipple they elected Linkin. They wood hev fallen to peeces then, but our Southern brethren decided to commence operashens for the new goverment it hed so long desired; and the overwhelmin pressur uv the war smothered all miner ishoos and all individooal feelin, and they hung together long enough to see that thro.

But now that question is settled. The nigger—cuss him—is free, and hez the legitimit result of freedom, the ballot. The iron bond wich held em together is gone, and they will split, and our openin is made.

We hev a solid phalanx, wich they can't win over or detach from us. We hev them old veterans who voted for Jaxon, and who are still votin for him. We hev them sturdy old yeomanry who still swear that Bloo Lite Fedralism ought to be put down, and can't be tolerated in a Republikin Goverment, and who, bless their old souls! don't know no more what Bloo Lite Fedralism wuz than an unborn baby does uv Guy Fawkes. We hev that solid army uv voters whose knees yawn hidjusly, and whose coats is out at elbows, and whose children go barefoot in winter, while their dads is a drinkin cheap whiskey, and damin the Goverment for imposin a income tax. We hev the patriotic citizins whose noses blossom like the lobster, and we hev Ireland. There is ships a sailin the bloo sea forever, and so long ez a Irishman kin git to the coast with money enuff to pay a passage to Ameriky, so long we kin depend on reinforcements. The Pope uv Rome is our friend, and so long ez ther is a Pope and a distillery, so long will there be a Dimokratic party in the Yoonited States.

These classes argyment won't move, and reasonin won't tetch. They alluz hev ben ourn, and they alluz will. In this country ther will alluz be two parties, and these elements will alluz act with us, becoz they are naterally ourn. They belong to our organizashen, and woodent be comfortable anywhere else. They will be with us in obejence to that law in Nacher wich puts evrything in its proper place. We hev the proper assosiashens for these classes, and no others. Nacher never wastes nothin—she gives us all we kin enjoy. The bird that soars into the bloo empyrium wuz made to soar into the bloo empyrium, and consekently wuz provided with holler bones and wings. Sposn the elefant shood hev a cravin to soar into the bloo empyrium (I like that word—its hefty), woodent it be continyooally mizable becoz it coodent sore into the bloo empyrium?

Likewise. Nacher alluz makes a stingy man lean and thin. Why? Becoz. Spozn nacher shood give a mean man the entrales and stumick uv a liberal man and a good liver. Don't you see that his hevin the sed entrales and stumick, and the desires appertainin, and the meanness that prevented his fillin em, wood make him mizable? So, ez nacher didn't give him the disposition to fill stumick and entrales, she didn't also give him the stumick and entrales to fill. All uv wich goes to show that he who is fitted to be a Dimekrat will be a Demokrat, and that ez the Millenium is a long way off, there will alluz be enuff so fitted to make a tollably strong party.

The discouraged Dimokrat may say that preechers, and noosepapers, and Sundy skools, and sich, are underminin their party. In time they will, but not yet. Uv wat danger is preechers to these men, when yoo coodent git one uv em within gun-shot uv one? and wat harm is noosepapers to em, when they can't read? Besides, we are not at the end uv our resources yet. When the wust comes to the wust, there is the nigger left us. It isn't certin that we won't control him evenchooally. They ain't educated ez yit, and Dimocrisy never yet failed to control all uv the lower orders uv sosiety. They hev the lowest grade uv the furriners; they hev Delaware and Maryland; they hev Noo York city and Suthern Illinoy; and ef we kin git at him afore he reaches the spellin-book, he's ourn beyond peradvencher.

Then there's new territory to be acquired, wich is full uv material for us. There is Mexico a ripenin for us. That country wood cut up into at least twenty States, wich, added to the ten we hev, wood make a clean majority wich we cood hold for years. Massachoosets cood do nuthin in Mexico. The Greasers ain't adapted to Massachoosets. Ef they sent their long-haired teachers there with their spellin-books, they'd end their labors by lettin a knife into their intestines for the clothes they wore, wich wood put a check on the mishnary biznis. They are, it is troo, several degrees lower in the skale uv humanity than the niggers, but then they ain't niggers, and we cood marry em without feelin that we'd degraded ourselves. Mexico affords us room for hope; we never shel run out uv material for Dimocratic votes until she is convertid, and but few mishnaries wood hev the nerve to tackle her.

Therfore I say to the Dimocrisy, be uv good cheer! Ther's a brite day a dawnin. Ef we are laid out agin and agin, we kin console ourselves with the reflection that we're yoost to it, and we kin go on hopin for the good time that must come.

Let us hold onto our faith, and continyoo to run, hopin eventooally to be glorified. Let us still cherish the faith that evenchooally the American people will not refooze the boon we offer em, and persevere even unto the perfeck end. When this good time is come, then will the anshent Dimocrisy, uv wich I hev bin to-wunst a piller and ornament for thirty years, triumph, and layin off the armor of actooal warfare, I shel rest in that haven uv worn-out patriots,—a perpetooal Post Offis. May the day be hastened! Farewell!

PETROLEUM V. NASBY, P. M.
(wich wuz Postmaster).

II. Copperhead's Progress: The War Years

(1861-1865)

NOTE TO THE CHAPTER

The split of the Democrats in the campaign of 1860 foreshadowed the blurred party lines of the new decade. The factionating slavery issue finally broke the party which had linked Northern and Southern men as a national institution since the Whig party's disintegration following first the campaign of 1852, then the deaths of Henry Clay and Daniel Webster and the debates over the Kansas-Nebraska bill.

Men's views on slavery determined the rallying cries of the factions within the Democratic party and furnished their names. During the administration of the two Democratic presidents of the 1850s, Franklin Pierce of New Hampshire and James Buchanan of Ohio, Curlyheads and Doughfaces insisted that the national government was obligated to protect slavery. Anti-slavery Democrats were called Barnburners after the radical reform faction of New York's Democrats, which, in the eyes of the conservative Hunkers, resembled the Dutch farmer who set fire to his barn in order to get rid of the rats.

The Jacksonian Era had produced the Locofocos, the anti-monopolist wing of New York City's Democratic party, who seceded from Tammany Hall. The ensuing years of party struggle obscured the fine distinctions between the nicknames. For a while Whigs called any Democrat a Locofoco, and the Locofoco marshal, nostalgically remembered by Nasby's planter friend after the passage of the Thirteenth Amendment, was just another Democratic officeholder who had enforced the Fugitive Slave act.

In 1860 the Republican party, still far from grand or old, was a loosely knit aggregation of former anti-slavery Democrats, Conscience Whigs, Know Nothings and Abolitionists. A common hatred of slavery and a common love of the Union held these groups together. In the opening days of the Civil War, extreme partisanship waned and Northerners, regardless of party, rallied behind Lincoln in defense of the Union. Northern Democrats, or War Democrats, loyally supported the administration and generally joined Republicans on a Union ticket. They followed Stephen A. Douglas and, after his death on June 3, 1861, Andrew Johnson and John Brough. Together with the more conservative Republicans, these Union Democrats aimed at preserving the Union without interfering with slavery.

32

The extremists of both parties bitterly opposed the coalition of moderate Democrats and Republicans. The animosity of regular Democrats and Peace Democrats toward the Union Democrats paralleled the contempt of Radicals for the moderate element in the Republican party. The Peace Democrats, who were called traitors by their opponents, advocated the restoration of the Union by negotiation rather than force after the secession of South Carolina on December 20, 1860. They denounced military arrests, conscription, emancipation and other war measures. The Radical Republicans, frequently depicted as extremists, pursued their aims with fanatic zeal and ferocity—the chastising of the South, the abolition of slavery and the tightening of their hold over the country. Among their leaders were Benjamin F. Wade, Charles Sumner, Zachariah Chandler and Thaddeus Stevens.

Horace Greeley's *Tribune* applied the term "Copperhead" on July 20, 1861, to Peace Democrats who opposed Lincoln's war policies. The nickname stuck and became a household word within a year when Democratic successes in the elections of 1862 strongly encouraged Copperheads throughout the Midwest. Cutting out the head of Liberty from a copper penny and wearing it as a badge, these Democrats turned into a party symbol the label of reproach which originally had recalled the venomous copperhead snake that struck from behind without warning. At times they and all Confederate sympathizers were called Butternuts, after farmers in backwood areas who wore garments dyed with butternut bark having the same brown color as the homespun clothes of Confederate soldiers. However, Copperheads and Butternuts differed in their sympathy toward the South, as General John Morgan and his raiders discovered when they crossed from Kentucky into the Union to test Northern temper and encountered vigorous opposition from Copperheads in Indiana and Ohio.

Negrophobia, anti-abolitionism, fear of conscription and draft, resentment of arbitrary arrests and of Washington's centralising policies —all these explained the growth of Copperheads in the tangle of political, religious, social and personal issues. Their opposition to Lincoln's administration also owed much to economic conditions, the rebirth of western sectionalism and a belief that eastern industry and capital were writing their wishes into law. Democratic politicos skillfully cultivated these seedbeds of discontent. Nasby's anti-abolitionist speeches were of the kind that appealed to the traditional prejudices of small homesteaders who had crossed the Ohio River from the South to pre-empt the poorer soils of Ohio, Indiana and Illinois.

In the cities, the anti-abolitionist argument roused Irish and German immigrants who filled the factories and worked on construction jobs. They feared that emancipation would flood the North with cheap labor. Both groups also recognized the Know Nothing taint of the Republican party which struck Democrats and Catholics as a gathering of Protestants, Abolitionists and Whigs. The Irish in particular detested the Abolitionists. They voted the straight Democratic ticket and formed the backbone of the Copperhead movement in urban centers. When employers used free Negroes as strikebreakers, Irish workingmen became vociferous and violent and brought about anti-Negro riots in Detroit, Chicago, Cincinnati and New York.

Conscription and draft hit these workingmen as hard as Nasby, who felt safe only in Canada "under the protectin tail uv the British Lion," the same tail the Democratic politicians had regularly twisted to rally Irish voters to their cause. The laborers preferred the volunteer system, which depended on large bounties and which would primarily plague taxpaying Republican businessmen, to a conscription system that offered no tangible rewards. The $300 exemption clause, bitterly assailed by Copperheads, made no distinction between rich men's money and poor men's blood. The idea of sacrificing life and job for the liberation of their prospective competitors upset immigrants, many of whom had come to America to escape militarism and failed to understand the meaning of the events shaking the country.

Only minor disturbances accompanied enrollment; actual violence waited for the draft itself. Even New England saw rioting, but no disturbance equalled in length and destructiveness the draft riots in New York in the summer of 1863. The uproar began as a protest against the draft, but it soon turned into an insurrection of asocial elements against established order. For several days, a mob fanned by Copperhead agitators pillaged the city while Democratic members of the Board of Aldermen and the State Legislature seized the opportunity to assail the Republican president and mayor. The rioters hunted down Negroes and burned the Colored Orphan Asylum. Casualties climbed beyond the thousand mark and property losses amounted to $1,500,000.

Copperhead opposition to the administration was in a large measure intimately aligned with the Democratic party's struggle for survival. Desperate Democrats made votes out of the defeat of Federal armies and repaid the rank partisanship of their opponents by blaming Republicans for all the ills besieging the country. Secret organizations sprang up through which Democrats hoped to check the influence of the Union Leagues, the secret and militant arm of the Republican party. The attempt miscarried, but the Knights of the Golden Circle, the Sons of Liberty, the Order of American Cincinnatus and the Order of American Knights captured the imagination of the nation.

The rank and file of the Copperheads found their martyr in Clement L. Vallandigham, the patron saint of Nasby's "Church uv the Slawtered Innocents." A congressman from Ohio, he was defeated for re-election in 1862 after the Republicans gerrymandered his district. He had always considered himself a spokesman for principles and liberties, and made his final bid for martyrdom on May 1, 1863, when he boldly defied General Ambrose E. Burnside's "General Order No.

36" which restricted the freedom of speech and of the press in Ohio and implied that critics of the administration were traitors. Arrested and tried, Vallandigham was sentenced to close confinement in a Federal prison for the duration of the war by a military commission whose rights he refused to recognize, since the trial took place in a state where the civil courts were open. Lincoln's political master stroke changed the sentence into banishment to the Confederacy. Somehow a Union officer accomplished the difficult task and got rid of Vallandigham, who complicated the transfer at the line of pickets by insisting that he be classified as a prisoner of war when ushered into the Confederacy. As soon as possible the exile left Southern soil. After a short interrogation at Richmond by Confederate officials, who had not much love for him themselves, he hurried to North Carolina, left Wilmington on a blockade runner for Bermuda, and from there reached Halifax on a British boat.

In the fall elections of 1863, Ohio Democrats nominated the exile in Canada for governor. The essence of the contest, they clamored, was the struggle between the forces of liberty and oppression. The Republicans named a War Democrat, John Brough, and effectively mobilized the Union party, reducing the issue to a choice between patriotism and treason. Inspired by the timely victories at Gettysburg and Vicksburg, the voters of Ohio overwhelmingly endorsed the administration. Republicans interpreted their widespread election victories of the year as a repudiation of Copperheadism, while Democrats found in Vallandigham a convenient scapegoat for the party's calamities.

Vallandigham and other Peace Democrats continued to damage the prospects of the Democratic party. Daniel Voorhees and Jesse Bright of Indiana, Samuel Medary, founder of the Columbus *Crisis*, of Ohio, and other midwestern politicians had their eastern counterparts in two chieftains of Tammany Democracy—Fernando Wood, Mayor of New York during the first two years of the war and congressman during the last two, and John Morrissey, pugilist, gambler and party strongman.

Morrissey's career overshadowed the ventures of his comrades in politics. Born in Ireland, he came to America as a young boy. In the early 1850s he made his debut in New York politics as gang leader in the constant brawls between Tammany thugs and Know Nothing gladiators. California attracted his talents briefly, but unlike his pugilist friend Yankee Sullivan, alias Francis Murray, who ended in a Vigilante prison, Morrissey returned East and combined fist fighting and Tammany politics to his advantage. He operated gambling halls in New York and Saratoga, became champion heavyweight boxer of the world in 1858, gained the friendship of Commodore Vanderbilt, purchased the controlling interest in the Saratoga race track in 1863, and later served as congressman, state senator and co-leader of Tammany Hall—whenever his business interests allowed.

Like Morrissey, many other Copperhead politicians weathered the ascendancy and the reign of Radical Republicans in the strongholds of the Democratic party. Republican victories at the polls and the disintegration of the Confederacy swept away the mass of their followers. In these dark hours Nasby reflected on the party's decline from the "pammy days uv Dimokrasy" under Andrew Jackson. During the administration of William Henry Harrison, the first Whig president, "we wuz . . . still strong and viggerous, knowin that we cood manage to live . . . on what we hed stolen" during the reign of Martin Van Buren. In these good old days, Nasby felt, "a gloreous galaxy uv intellectooal and muskuler Dimokrasy" had guided the party's fortune. The aging politico fondly recalled the influence of Southerners like John C. Calhoun, Jefferson Davis, Robert Toombs, Thomas Ritchie and Henry A. Wise, and the contributions of Thomas H. Benton of Missouri, William Allen of Ohio, Stephen A. Douglas of Illinois, Daniel S. Dickinson of New York, Isaiah Rynders of Tammany Hall and Yankee Sullivan of the Sixth Ward.

In Nasby's memory these bygone years had seen great events. "O, with what arder Lovejoy wuz shot at Alton," Nasby reminisced on the riot of November 7, 1837, when a mob killed the "martyr abolitionist" who had tried to protect his latest printing press from the fate his other presses had suffered. "But, alas," Nasby sighed, "heresies crep into our ranks" and "since, it hez been nothin but disaster." In 1848, Van Buren's candidacy on the Free Soil party's platform, which opposed the extension of slavery into the territories, split the Democratic ticket and helped to defeat Lewis Cass. Salmon P. Chase, who had been elected to the Senate in 1848 by a coalition of Free Soilers and Democrats in the Ohio Legislature, subordinated party interests to the central issue of slavery and cast his lot with the Republican party. Jacob Brinkerhoff, another Ohio politician, also passed from the ranks of the anti-slavery Democrats to the Free Soil party and then to the Republican party. The agitation over the Kansas-Nebraska bill, the fight between Buchanan and Douglas, Lincoln's election, and the secession of South Carolina "hez elevated men we despised, and adoptid idees we scoft at." Once Cass had urged enlistment for the Federal army in his last public speech in 1862, and former Democrats like Benjamin Butler, Daniel S. Dickinson, John A. Dix, David Tod and John A. Logan had joined the cause of Horace Greeley, Joshua Giddings and other Abolitionists, Nasby was left to ponder the "singular fact that every leader we used to trust is now agin us."

The presidential election of 1864 offered the last chance for Nasby to restore the "anshent glory uv Dimokrasy." The leaders of the Democratic party speculated on the war weariness of the country and hoped to win the contest on a platform which declared the war a failure and demanded the immediate cessation of hostilities. General George B. McClellan seemed the ideal candidate to be presented to the nation as a victim of the administration's injustice. However, the extreme demands of the platform which Vallandigham had pushed through the convention only embarrassed the party and McClellan, who had always advocated the vigorous prosecution of the war. Victories on the battlefields proved beyond doubt that the South could be defeated; the election showed equally decisively that the nation preferred the incumbent administration. McClellan carried only New Jersey, Delaware and Kentucky with 21 electoral votes against Lincoln's 212.

Lee's surrender topped the long list of misfortunes which Nasby had endured since the defeat of John C. Breckinridge, the Southern Democrat's candidate in the presidential election of 1860. Nasby had anxiously followed the ups and downs of military fortune and Lincoln's stratagems. He wrongly assumed that the President's tactics would force the South to arm its slaves. "Imagine entire regiments uv blooded men," he speculated, "men uv the physicle strength uv the native Afrikin, animated with the spirit uv the hawty Southron." These soldiers struck Nasby as a combination of "a goriller with the sole uv Chevaleer Bayard," the fearless and faultless knight of French kings. However, the Confederacy never armed what he considered the colored counterparts of generals and diplomatists like P. G. T. Beauregard, James Mason, John Slidell and "Kernel" John L. Peyton, who had recruited a regiment mainly at his own expense before he went to England as North Carolina's agent.

Lincoln's assassination turned Copperheads who had bitterly assailed the President into mourners. Men who had hoped for Lincoln's assassination in the summer of 1864 now denounced John Wilkes Booth's deed. "The tragedy," Nasby wailed, "cum at the wrong time." He was eager to forget the heritage of the Copperheads who, after their failure, tainted the prospects of the re-emerging Democratic party unnecessarily. After all, "revenge is a costly luxury," the strategist counselled, "and a party so near bankrupt ez the Dimokrasy cannot afford to indulge in it."

1. "Nothin Short of Seceshn": As Wingert's Corners Goes, So Goes Petroleum V. Nasby

WINGERT'S CORNERS, OHIO, March the 21st, 1861.

South Carliny and sevral other uv the trooly Dimikratic States hevin secesht—gone orf, I may say, onto a journey after ther rites—Wingert's Corners, ez trooly Dimecratic ez any uv em, hez follered soot.

A meetin wuz held last nite, uv wich I wuz chairman, to take the matter uv our grievances into consideration, and it wuz finally resolved that nothin short uv seceshn wood remedy our woes. Therefore the follerin address, wich I rit, wuz adoptid and ordered to be publisht:

TO THE WORLD!

In takin a step wich may, possibly, involve the state uv wich we hev bin heretofore a part into blood and convulshuns, a decent respeck for the opinion uv the world requires us to give our reasons for takin that step.

Wingert's Corners hez too long submitted to the imperious dictates uv a tyranikle goverment. Our whole histry hez bin wun uv aggreshn on the part uv the State, and uv meek and pashent endoorence on ours.

It refoosed to locate the State Capitol at the Corners, to the great detriment uv our patriotic owners uv reel estate.

It refoosed to gravel the streets uv the Corners, or even re-lay the plank-road.

It refoosed to locate the Penitentiary at the Corners, not-with-standin we do more towards fillin it than any town in the State.

It refoosed to locate the State Fair at the Corners, blastin the hopes uv our patriotic groserys.

It located the canal one hundred miles from the Corners.

We hev never hed a Guvner, notwithstandin the President uv this meetin hez lived here for yeers, a waitin to be urgd to accept it.

It hez compelled us, yeer after yeer, to pay our share uv the taxes.

It hez never appinted any citizen uv the place to any offis wher theft wuz possible, thus wilfully keepin capital away from us.

It refoosed to either pay our rale-rode subscripshun or slack-water our river.

Therefore, not bein in humor to longer endoor sich out-rajes, we declare ourselves free and independent uv the State, and will maintain our position with arms, if need be.

There wuz a lively time next day. A company uv minit men wuz raised, and wun uv two-minit men. The seceshn flag, musk-rat rampant, weasel couchant, on a field d'egg-shell, waves from both groserys. Our merchant feels hopeful. Cut orf from the State, direct trade with the Black Swamp follers: releest from his indebtedness to Cinsinati, he will agin lift his head. Our representative hez agreed to resine—when his term expires.

We are in earnest. Armed with justice and shot-guns, we bid the tyrants defiance.

P. S.—The feelin is intense—the childern hev imbibed it. A lad jest past, displayin the seceshn flag. It waved from behind. Disdainin concealment, the noble, lion-hearted boy wore a roundabout. We are firm.

N. B.—We are still firm.

N. B., 2d.—We are firm, unyeeldin, calm, and resoloot.

PETROLEUM V. NASBY.

2. *"Ez for Me, I Cant Go": Nasby Feels a Draft*

August the 6th, 1862.

I see in the papers last nite that the Goverment hez institooted a draft, and that in a few weeks sum hundreds uv thousands uv peeceable citizens will be dragged to the tented field. I know not wat uthers may do, but ez for me, I cant go. Upon a rigid eggsaminashen uv my fizzlekle man, I find it wood be wus nor madnis for me to undertake a campane, to-wit:—

1. I'm bald-headid, and hev bin obliged to wear a wig these 22 years.

2. I hev dandruff in wat scanty hair still hangs around my venerable temples.

3. I hev a kronic katarr.

4. I hev lost, sence Stanton's order to draft, the use uv wun eye entirely, and hev kronic inflammashen in the other.

5. My teeth is all unsound, my palit aint eggsactly rite, and I hev hed bronkeetis 31 yeres last Joon. At present I hev a koff, the paroxisms uv wich is friteful to behold.

6. I'm holler-chestid, am short-winded, and hev alluz hed pains in my back and side.

7. I am afflictid with kronic diarrear and kostivniss. The money I hev paid (or promist to pay), for Jayneses karminnytiv balsam and pills wood astonish almost enny body.

8. I am rupchered in nine places, and am entirely enveloped with trusses.

9. I hev verrykose vanes, hev a white-swellin on wun leg and a fever sore on the uther; also wun leg is shorter than tother, though I handle it so expert that nobody never noticed it.

10. I hev korns and bunyons on both feet, wich wood prevent me from marchin.

I dont suppose that my political opinions, wich are aginst the prossekooshn uv this unconstooshnel war, wood hev any wate with a draftin orfiser; but the above reesons why I cant go, will, I make no doubt, be suffishent.

PETROLEUM V. NASBY.

3. Sanctuary: "Under the Protectin Tail uv the British Lion"

BREST, KANADA WEST, August the 20th, 1862.

After more advenchers than wood fill a book, I am here in Kanada, safe under the protectin tail uv the British Lion, where no draftin orfiser kin molest nor make me afraid. Halleloogy!

I never shood hev taken this step hed a good, sound, constooshnel doctor bin appinted Medical Eggsaminer; fer I hev twict ez menny diseases ez wood hev eggsemptid me, but I wuz afeerd the Eggsaminer woodent see em, ez he aint much uv a physician anyhow; besides, he votes the Union tickit, and hez, uv coarse, prejudisis. The Commissioner is a bloody Ablishnist; and I owe him a store bill wich hez stood about 8 years. I protest agin all sich appintments.

I left, in company with five other invalids, wun nite, a little after the "witchin hour uv 12 M.," ez Shakspeer hez it, and any wun beholdin our faces wood hev bin satisfide that sum "churchyard yawned" jest previously. We traveld all nite, "sustaned and soothed by an unfaltrin trust" in a bottle wich I, with my usual foresite, took along, together with two and one third yards uv bolony sassige, wich I alluz use ez a thirst-provoker. We met no interrupshen till we got within five miles uv Toledo (wich we did by 5 P. M. uv the next day—wich, permit me to remark, wus good travelin fer sich debillytatid cusses), when we wuz stopt by a pickit-gard uv the "Anti-draftin Invalid League," who remarkt:

"Who goes there?" "A invalid," sez I. "A Peece invalid?" sez he. "Ther aint no other kind," sez I; whereupon sez he, "Yoor a man uv sence"; a fact uv wich I hed been long aware. I presented my liquid consiliater, when he informed me that Toledo wuz closely watcht, that escape by steemer was impossible, and that a small boat was our only chance. He took us to the lake shore, furnisht us a boat, and, jest as the sun wuz a sinkin behind the golden horizon, I bid my nativ land adoo.

I need not dwell upon the perils uv that terrible passage. Suffice it to say, that, for invalids, we rowed well, and finally landed at the little village uv Brest, wher we now are.

Two hundred peece men are here, and I must acknowledge that we are not treeted with that distinguished consideration usually accordid political eggsiles. Fer instance, at the tavern where I board, the parlor is partikelerly pleasent, and I wuz a settin into it. In trips a girl, purty enuff for a man whose taste wuz not vishiated to eat. "Shel I shet down this window, sir?" sez she. "Why shet it down, gentle maid?" retorts I, lookin sweet onto her. "Because," replide she, "I thot perhaps, the DRAFT was too much for ye." A few slavish Kanajens, who set there, laft. The landlord required a month's pay in advance, and a further deposit uv 25 cents per eggsile, as sekoority fer the pewter spoons wich we hev at table. To cap the climacks, last nite a big nigger was put into eech uv our rooms, and we were forced to sleep with em, or okkepy the floor, wich I did. The cussid nigger laft all nite, in a manner trooly aggravatin to hear.

PETROLEUM V. NASBY.

P. S.—Tell my wife to send sich money as she earns, to me, as livin is high, and ther aint no tick. The township kin support her and the childern.

4. Drafted at Last: "Clad in the Garb uv Slaivry!"

CAMP UV THE 778TH OHIO KIDNAPT MELISHY,
TOLEDO, October the 17th, 1862.

I am here, clad in the garb uv slaivry! Nasby, clothed in a bobtailed bloo coat, a woolin shirt, and bloo pants, with a Oysteran muskit in his hands, a going thro the exercise! Good hevings! wat a spectacle!

The draft was over, and I thot that wunst more I'd visit my native land. Gaily I stept abord the boat that was to carry me from British shores—gaily I say, for my money hed given out some weeks afore, and I hed earned a precarious subsistence a sawin wood in pardnership with a disgustin mulatto, and I lookt forward with joyful antisepashens to the time when I should agen embrace Looizer Jane (the pardner uv my buzzum), and keep my skin perpetooally full uv the elickser uv life, out uv her washin money. Joyfully I sprang off the boat onto the wharf at Toledo, when a hevy hand was laid onto my shoulder. Twas a soljer! The follerin conversashen ensood:

"Wat wantest thow, my gentle friend?"

"I want yoo, my gay Kanajen."

"On wat grounds?" retortid I.

"On the ground uv eloodin uv the draft," sez he.

"Yoor mistaken," sez I; "I'm a Ablishnist—a emissary. I hev bin a spredin the bread uv life among the poor colored brethrin in Kanady, and am jest returnin to run thro another lot. Let me pass, I entreat thee, nor stay me in my good work."

"Not much," sez he. "I know better. Yoor a butternut."

"How knowst thou?" sez I.

"Yoor nose," sez he. "That bucheus beekun lite wuz never got out uv spring water."

"Yoor knowledge uv men and things is too much for me. I confess, and surrender at discreshun—do with me ez thou wilt."

And he did. I wuz led out to camp, and wuz allowed to volunteer to fite against my convickshens—against my brethren, who hev taken up arms in a rightous coz. So be it. Hentzforth the name uv Nasby will shine in the list uv marters.

Amid the dark, deep gloom that envellups me, wun ray uv light strikes me. I hev seen the eleckshun returns, and wen I seed em, I yelled Hallelogy! Me and another victim uv Linkin's tyranny, who is a Dimekrat (he wuz a postmaster under Bookannon, and wen removed by Linkin, dident give up the balance uv money he had on hand, fearin twood be used to subvert our free instooshns), hed a jubilee. We smuggled a bottle uv condenst ekstasy, and celebratid muchly.

"The North's redeemed!" showtid I.

"Let the eagle screme!" yelled he.

"The Quakers hev votid!" showtid I.

"Ablishnism dead!" screemed he.

"Dimokrasy's triumphed!" laft I; and so on, until after midnite, when, completely eggsaustid, we sank into slumber, with a empty bottle atween us.

PETROLEUM V. NASBY.

P. S.—Tell Looizer Jane that I may never see her again—that shood it be my fate to perish on the battle-field, amid the rore uv battle and the horrors uv missellaneous carnage, my last thot, ez life ebbs slowly away, shall be uv her; and ask her if she can't send me half or three quarters uv the money she gits fer washin, ez whisky costs fritefully here.

P. V. N.

5. *"Soljer uv the Confederacy": Deserter among the Pelicans*

CAMP UV THE LOOISIANA PELICANS,
November the 1st, 1862.

I hev deserted, and am now a soljer uv the Confederacy. Jest ez soon ez our regiment struck Suthrin sile, I made up my mind that my bondage wuz drawin to a close—that I wood seeze the fust oppertoonity uv escapin to my nateral frends,—the soljers uv the sunny South. Nite before last I run the guard, wuz shot at twice (reseevin two buck-shot jest below the hind buttons uv my coat), but by eggstrordinary luck I escaped. Had infantry bin sent after me I shood hev bin taken, for I am not a fast runner; but the commandant uv the post wuz new at the biznis, and innocently sent cavalry. Between the hossis they rode, and the stoppin to pick up them ez coodent stick onto ther flyin steeds, I hed no difficulty in outrunnin em.

At last I encounterd the pickits uv the Looisiana Pelicans, and givin myself up ez a deserter from the hordes uv the tyrant Linkin, wuz to-wunst taken afore the kernel. I must say, in this conneckshun, that I wuz surprised at the style uv uniform worn by the Pelicans. It consists uv a hole in the seet uv the pants, with the tale uv the shirt a wavin gracefully therefrom. The follerin colloquy ensood:—

"To what regiment did yoo belong?"

"776th Ohio."

"Volunteer or draftid?"

"Draftid."

"Yoor name?"

"Nasby, Petroleum V."

I notist all this time the kernel wuz eyein my clothes wistfully. I had jest drawd em, and they wuz bran-new. Sez the kernel:—

"Mr. Nasby, I reseeve you gladly ez a recroot in the Grand Army uv Freedom. Ez yoo divest yoorself uv the clothes uv the tyrant, divest yerself uv whatever lingrin affecshuns yoo may hev fer the land uv yer nativity, and ez yoo array yerself in the garb uv a Suthrin soljer, try to fill yer sole with that Suthrin feelin that animates us all. Jones," sed he, addressin his orderly, "is Thompson dead yit?"

"Not quite," sez the orderly.

"Never mind," sez the kernel, "he cant git well uv that fever; strip off his uniform and give it to Nasby, and berry him."

I judgd, from the style uv the uniforms I saw on the men around me, that I wood rather keep my own, but I sed nothin. When the orderly returned with the deceest Thompson's uniform, I groaned innardly. There wuz a pair uv pants with the seat entirely torn away, and wun leg gone below the knee, a shoe with the sole off, and the straw he had wrapped around the other foot, and a gray woolen shirt. Sez the kernel:

"Don't be afeered uv me, Nasby. Put on yer uniform rite here."

Reluctantly, I pulled off my new dubble-soled boots, and I wuz petrified to see the kernel kick off the slippers he wore, and pull em on. I pulled off my pants—he put em on, and so on with every article uv dress I possest, even to my warm overcoat and blankit. Sez the kernel:

"These articles, Nasby, belongs to the Guvment, to which I shel akount for them. Report yoorself to-wunst to Captin Smith."

Ez I passed out, the lootenant-kernel, majer, and adjutent pulled me to wun side, and askt me "ef I coodent git three more to desert." Wun glance at their habillyments showd why they wuz so anxious fer deserters.

I candidly confess that Linkin takes better care uv his soljers than Davis does. The clothin I hev described. Instid uv reglar rashens, we are allowed to eat jest whatever we can steal uv the planters, and, ez mite be expectid, we hev becum wonderfully expert at pervidin; but, ez the Pelicans hev bin campt here three months, the livin is gittin thin. Yet a man kin endoor almost any thing for principle.

PETROLEUM V. NASBY.

6. The Art of Survival: "Ha! A Turkey! Wher Gottist Thow Him?"

CAMP UV THE LOOISIANA PELICANS,
November the 15th, 1862.

Nasby still lives, though I must say its rayther tite nippin. The servis uv the Suthrin Confedracy wood be ez pleasent ez any military life cood be, were it not for three things, to-wit:

1. We hev nothin to eat.

2. Our clothes is designed more for ornament than use, consistin cheefly uv holes with rags around em—an appropriate summer costoom, but rayther airy for this season.

3. Our pay is irreglar, and not jest ez good in quality ez cood be wished.

Fer instance. Our regiment hezzent reseevd a cent fer eight months, and ther wuz much grumblin, wich cum to the ears uv the kernel.

"The men murmur, do they?" sed he to his adjutent. "Their complaints is just, and they shel be paid their just dooze. Is ther a printin offis in the town?"

"Ther is," retorts the adjutent.

"Go take possession uv it in the name uv the Confedrit States, and seeze whatever paper he may hev on hand. The faithful Pelicans must be paid."

The next day every wun uv the men hed his haversack stufft with money, each wun takin ez much ez he judgd he cood use. It does very well, except that it gives the grocery-keepers much trouble, as they take it by weight—a $1 bein wuth ez much ez a $20, ceptin that the $20 is a trifle the largest, and weighs more.

An incident. I wuz out on pikkit dooty, in the immejit visinnity uv a planter's barn, who hed bin suspectid uv Unionism. I saw a turkey, capchered it, and indulged all the way into camp into the pleasant idee that, fer the fust time in two months, I wood hev a stumic-distendin dinner. Ez I entered camp I met the kernel, who, ez his eagle eye caught the proud bird I held, spoke, sayin,—

"Ha! a turkey! Wher gottist thow him?"

"I capcherd him at Johnson's," replied I.

"Fat and young," mused he, feelin uv him; and then, lookin up, thus he did say: "My venerable patriot (he allooded to my gray hairs), this bird belonged to a Union man, and all sich property taken by the army belongs, uv coarse, to the goverment. Yoo will forthwith take it to my quarters."

Not hevin eaten any thing for 18 hours, I determined to make wun effort for my turkey. Sez I: "Admittin the bird belongs to the goverment," sez I, "I may retane him, I suppose, by payin his valyoo," and I tendered him a handful uv the money we hed reseeved that mornin.

"Not so fast, my aged hero," sed he. "The goverment needs turkeys more than it does money. Money we kin make, but yoo must be aware that, without a material alterashen in our anatomikle structure, the makin uv a turkey by us is a impossibility. Leave the property at my quarters."

That nite I passed the kernel's quarters. Ther wuz a sound uv revelry within, and the odor uv a Thanksgivin dinner assailed my nostrils. The next mornin I saw the kernel's dorg a chawin the bones uv that goverment turkey.

PETROLEUM V. NASBY.

7. *"Linkin, Scorn Not My Words": Interview with Old Abe*

CHURCH UV ST. ———,
November the 1st, 1863.

I felt it my dooty to visit Washinton. The miserable condishon the Dimokrasy find themselves into, since the elecshen, makes it necessary that suthin be did, and therefore I determined to see wat cood be effectid by a persnel intervew with the President.

Interdoosin myself, I opened upon him delikitly, thus:—

"Linkin," sez I, "ez a Dimekrat, a free-born Dimekrat, who is prepared to die with neetnis and dispatch, and on short notis, for the inalienable rite uv free speech—knowin also that you er a goriller, a feendish ape, a thirster after blud, I speek."

"Speek on," says he.

"I am a Ohio Dimekrat," sez I, "who hez repoodiatid Vallandigum."

"Before or since the elecshin did yoo repoodiate him?" sez he.

"Since," retortid I.

"I thot so," sed he. "I would hev dun it, too, hed I bin you," continnered he, with a goriller-like grin.

"We air now in favor uv a viggerus prosecushen uv the war, and we want you to so alter yoor policy that we kin act with you corjelly," sez I.

"Say on," sez he.

"I will. We don't want yoo to change yoor policy materially. We are modrit. Anxshus to support yoo, we ask yoo to adopt the follerin trifling changis:—

"Restore to us our habis corpusses, as good ez new. Arrest no more men, wimmin, and children for opinyun's saik. Repele the ojus confisticashen bill, wich irritaits the Suthern mind and fires the Suthern hart. Do away with drafts and conskripshens. Revoke the Emansipashen Proclamashen, and give bonds that you'll never ishoo another. Do away with treasury noats and sich, and pay nuthin but gold. Protect our dawters from nigger equality. Disarm yoor nigger soljers, and send back the niggers to their owners, to conciliate them. Offer to assoom the war indetednis uv the South, and pledge the guvernment to remoonerate our Suthern brethren for the losses they hev sustaned in this onnatrel war. Call a convenshen uv Suthern men and sech gileless Northern men ez F. Peerce, J. Bookannun, Fernandywood, and myself, to agree upon the terms uv reunion."

"Is that all?" sez the goriller.

"No," says I, promptly. "Ez a garantee uv good faith to us, we shel insist that the best haff uv the orifises be given to Dimekrats who repoodiate Vallandigum. Do this, Linkin, and yoo throw lard ile on the troubled waters. Do this, and yoo rally to yoor support thowsends uv noble Dimokrats who went out uv offis with Bookannon, and hev bin gittin ther whisky on tick ever sinse. We hev made sakrifises. We hev repoodiatid Vallandigum —we care not ef he rots in Canady; we are willin to jine the war party, reservin to ourselvs the poor privilidge uv dictatin how and on wat principles it shel be carried on. Linkin! Goriller! Ape! I hev dun."

The President replide that he would give the matter serious

considerashen. He wood menshen the idee uv resinin to Seward, Chase, and Blair, and wood address a circular to the postmasters, et settry, and see how menny uv um wood be willin to resine to accommodait Dimekrats. He hed no dout several wood do it towunst.

"Is ther any littel thing I kin do for you?"

"Nothin pertikler. I wood accept a small post-orifis, if sitooatid within easy range uv a distilry. My politikle days is well-nigh over. Let me but see the old party wunst moar in the assendency; let these old eyes wunst more behold the Constooshn ez it is, the Union ez it wuz, and the nigger ware he ought to be, and I will rap the mantel uv privit life around me, and go into delirum tremens happy. I hev no ambishen. I am in the seer and yellow leef. These whitnin lox, them sunken cheek, warn me that age and whisky hev done ther perfeck work, and that I shel soon go hents. Linkin, scorn not my words. I hev sed. Adoo."

So sayin, I waved my hand impressively, and walkd away.

PETROLEUM V. NASBY,
Paster uv sed Church, in charge.

8. "A Trane uv Refleckshen": O Tempora! O Mores!

CHURCH UV THE SLAWTERD INNOCENTS
(Lait St. Vallandigum), December the 11th, 1863.

Yisterday I heerd a Ablishnist remark, "The world moves." The observashen (wich I hev heerd frequently uv late) set me into a trane uv refleckshen. My comprehensive mind sprang back into the misty days uv the past, and I wuz a boy agin. Twenty-six years ago I wuz a splittin my symetrikle throte a hollerin for Van Booren. Them wuz the pammy days uv Dimokrasy. Androo Jaxon hed left us his name ez capital for us to do biznis on wile he wuz out uv the way, and coodent interfere with our steelin, wich wuz comfortable. We wuz beaten, but wuz still strong and viggerous, knowin that we cood manage to live doorin Harrison's reign on wat we hed stolen doorin Van Booren's, the facilites havin been unlimitid. O, them times! Ther wuz Cass, and Davis, and Dickinson, and Calhoon, and Tooms, and Bill Allen, and Duglis (who wuz jest comin in), and Ritchy, and Benton, and Isaer Rynders, and Wise, and Yankee Sullivan—a gloreous galaxy uv intellectooal and muskuler Dimokrasy, sech ez the world never seed afore, and never will agin. Wuz Abolishnism tolratid in them happy daze? Not enny. O, with what ardor Lovejoy wuz shot at Alton! How viggerusly the Dimokrasy laberd to throw his press into the turbid waters uv the Missisipi! Wood, O wood that we cood hev sunk his doctrines with his press! Did we allow Abolishn talk? Nary. These stalwart arm hev hurled baskitfuls uv unsavry eggs at the pedlers uv polittikle heresy, and my skill in eggin Abolishn lecturers wunst made me justis uv the peese in my native township.

In the South, every hill-side wuz dottid with the carcasses uv Noo Ingland skoolmarms, who, hevin bin suspected uv teechin niggers to rede, wuz justly hung; and the pleasant crack uv the whip wuz heard all over the land. O, them Arcadian days, wen it only took 20 minits to arrest, try, sentence, hang, and divide the close uv a Yankee skool-teacher!

But, alas! heresies crep into our ranks, and ther wuz confooshun. Van Booren bolted and beat Cass; and, notwithstandin he repentid afterwards, the Abolishn pizon he interdoost into the Dimekratik body pollytik, remaned. It broke out in ugly sores in Ohio in 1848, in the shape uv the feendish Freesile party. Then Chase and Brinkerhoff sluffed orf, and jind with our anshent enemies. Jest afterward the Anti-Nebrasky excitement, cuppled with No-nothinism, whaled us, and it wuz only by sooperhooman eggsershens that we electid Bookannon. Since, it hez bin nothin but disaster. Bookannon and Duglis got by the ears; Duglis refoosed to cave to his Suthrin brethrin; Linkin wuz electid; war ensood; and now wat do these old eyes behold? Cass, and Ben Butler, and Logan, and Dix, and Dickinson, and Dave Tod, striken hands with Josh Giddins and Horris Greely! It is a singular fact that every leader we used to trust is now agin us. And wuss. Abolishn papers is being publisht in South Karliny, in Tennisee, Kentucky, and Loozeaner, and a million uv men, led by the ghosts and ghostesses uv them hung schoolmasters and schoolmarms aforesaid, assisted by John Brown's soul, wich is litterally a marchin on, is enforcin a proclamashen freein all the niggers at wun stroke, and the Dimokrasy, bein sum hundreds uv thowsands in the minority, is powerless to prevent it.

Trooly, the world moves. It hez moved the Dimokrasy from the pedestal uv power it wunst okepide, and laid it prostrate. It hez elevatid men we despised, and adoptid idees we scoft at.

Yunger men may shift and git into the tide agin, but ez for me, I cant. I shel make wun more effort, and if we fail—why, then, I shel withdraw from public life, and start a grocery, and in that umble callin will flote peecefully down the stream uv time, until my weather-beten bark strikes on the rocks of death, gittin my licker in the meantime (uv wich I consume many) at wholesale prices.

PETROLEUM V. NASBY,
Paster uv sed Church, in charge.

9. The 1864 Election: "Micklellan, the Nashun's Pride"

CHURCH UV THE NOO DISPENSASHUN,
September the 1st, 1864.

Glory! Micklellan, the nashun's pride, is nominated! Bein a orthodox Dimekrat, the nominashen soots me! Nominashens alluz soots orthodox Dimekrats! In 30 years' experience, I never knew a nominashen that dident.

Me and my Church wuz for peace. We wuz for Suthern rites. We wuz opposed to drafts, and had purchast revolvers. Therefore the incomparable Micklellan wuz not our fust choice. The fact is, the grate George wuz a war man wunst, and wuz the original inventor uv drafts, wich don't make him ez acceptable to us ez he mite be. But ther's a excoose for him. The Dimokrasy must bare in mind that the unforchnit man hed sunk sum 85,000 Ablishnists sumwher about Richmond, and ez he knew uv the prejoodice existin agin volunteerin under him, he insistid on hevin uv em brot in by draft. It wuz all dun for the benefit uv the Dimokrasy, becoz: The Dimekrats drafted wood resist to run to Kanady—the Ablishnists wood go, and, halleloogy! but few uv em wood ever return.

On receet uv the news I immejitly called my flock together, announst it to em, and give em the follerin brief biographical sketch uv our candidate, ez follers:

George B. Micklellan wuz born uv rich but honest parence, sumwher, in the yeer 18—. (I love accooracy.) The nationality uv his parence I am not shoor uv, but from the fact that all the bitter old Know-Nothins is a supportin him, I shood think he wuz uv Irish extraction. His great pint was promptnis and decision uv character, wich qualities displayed themselves at a early period. It is on record in the arkives uv the family, that he cried immejitly after he wuz borned, and commenced nursin within a hour. He wuz remarkable at school for the same quality.

No sooner did the clock strike noon, than young George wood promptly leave the house. The fucher general wuz foreshaddered in the skill with wich he robbed melon patches. He made reglar approaches, wich wuz skillful, but his retreats wuz magnificent. He cood change his base bootiful—shiftin from melon patches to orchards with neatnis and dispatch. Another peekooliarity uv young George shows how troo is the sayin, "The child is father uv the man." While George cood alluz very elaboritly stratejise hisself into a melon patch or orchard, he never stratejised hisself out with any melons or apples.

He wuz edikatid at West Pint, and wuz finally made President uv the Ohio and Mississippi Railroad. Here his decishun agin showd itself. He conseeved the bold ijee uv gravelin the road, wun mornin, at 31 minutes past 11. Wun yeer from that time he announst to the Drektors that 17 laborers and an ekal number uv wheelbarrers hed bin prokoored, and he wuz bizzy, at that time, perfectin a plan for organizin uv em. Two months after he announced his plan perfected, and that operations hed commenst on a gravel-pit. Four days uv brilliantly successful work follered, wen he announct that he wuz obleegd to suspend operations, that five wheelbarrers wuz broke, and seven laborers hed the diarrear. He wood reorganize promptly, and proceed. Reorganizin his force, and perfectin a new plan uv approach, only occupied eight months, and the work wood hev bin commenst by this time, had not the war broke out. The pay uv the Fedral Guvment bein larger and more surer than the Confederacy, he relinquisht railroadin and entered the Fedral service.

His military career is knowd by all uv us. Suffice it to say, that no general wuz ever so beloved South, and so hated North, wich wuz wat prokoord his nominashen.

Sich, my brethrin, is our candidate. Let us all sink our prejoodices, and elect him. The platform on which he stands I endorse with my whole heart. I hevent read it yet, but it must be good, for Vallandigum made it. The post-orfises, the treasury, for wich we hev bin waitin four long, dreary years, is within our reach. Let us, my brethrin, go in and win. The cheerin for me will now commence.

A collekshun wuz taken up to defray expensis uv the campane. $8 wuz realized, wich wuz paid over to me. I shel probably appear on the stump in a new pair uv pants.

PETROLEUM V. NASBY,
Paster uv sed Church, in charge.

10. Arming the Slaves: "I Hev Prayd That Linkin Will Spare the South This Bitter Cup"

SAINT'S REST (wich is in the Stait uv Noo Jersey),
November the 21st, 1864.

The brave and chiverlus South hev at last desided upon armin their niggers. Ef they do it, it settles the question. The Ablishn party is neerly eggsaustid, and can not hope to cope successfully with three millions uv fresh niggers, the most uv em decendid drekly frum the fust families uv the South. The nigger will fite! I may hev sed at diffrent times, when the goriller Linkin wuz armin uv em, that they woodent fite, but it wuz a lie uv the basest character, that I got up to deseeve the people. Does Boregard fite? Does the younger Masons, and Peytons, and Ruffins, and Slidells, and sich? Where do they get their chiverlus darin from? Onqueschenably frum the old Boregard, Mason, Peyton, Slidell, et settry. Very good. Admittin it's blood that does it, won't the same blood that makes Kernel Peyton chivelrus, operate the same way when coursin thro the vanes uv Sam, his half-brother? Uv coarse. Like causes perdoose like effex. Ef Kernel Peyton takes a dose uv pills, wat's the result? Precisely the same ez wen Pomp takes em. Blood, like pills, operate the same on all constooshns.

The mizrable hirelins uv Linkin will rue the day they meet these dark knites. The Suthern white soljer is, I am aware, a mizrable cuss. He wuz born a serf; nacher made him expressly for that system uv society, and he coodent eggsist nowhere else. The Suthern lord uv the sile requires various serviss. Manual labor is dun by the black, but votin must be dun by whites. Nacher steps in and furnishes him a man white enuff to vote, and low enuff to be owned. He hez no chiverlry, and woodent fite at all ef 'twant for the blooded offisers. Imagine entire regiments uv blooded men—men uv the physikle strength uv the native Afrikin, animated with the spirit uv the hawty Southron—a goriller with the sole uv Chevaleer Bayard.

I hev prayd that Linkin will spare the South this bitter cup. Hez the wretch no sole? Imagin a Suthern offiser a leadin his regiment into battle. He drors nigh to the enemy. Whiz! sings a shell. It explodes! He is safe, but, alas! dispersed into inch pieces is Scipio, his nigger, and perhaps the son uv his grandfather's son, or, may be, the uncle uv his own children! That shell cost him $1500. A rifle pops, and Pompey dies, who, livin, wood hev bin dirt-cheap at $1200. And so he goes. He treads the path uv glory over the dead bodies uv his blood relashens, which is also his forchune.

Agin. Ef the nigger fites alongside uv the white man, he is acknowledged ez his ekal, and away goes the corner-stun uv Dimokrasy. It hez alluz bin a consolashen to the Northern Dimekrat to feel that ther wuz a race meaner than they are. Shel this pleasin deloosion be roodly dissipatid? Forbid it, Hevin!

This sacrifis may be avoidid. Linkin hez bin slitely electid, and inasmuch ez he hez control uv suthin over a million muskits, with artilry to match, we Dimekrats, hevin alluz bin a law-abidin people, shel submit quietly to the popular voice. But we kin advise. Linkin hez it in his hands. Let him make peace immejitly and to-wunst. Let him send commishners to Richmond, under same pay ez members uv Congris (I will go for wun), to treat and be treated. Let us act upon the Micklellan ijee. Let us offer them all they want to kum back, and ef they refooze—why then fite it out, on constooshnel, conservative principles. Ef they do refooze, and the war shood be properly conductid, I shood sacrifice all for my bleedin country, and go into the service ez a sutler. I cood not hesitate for a moment.

PETROLEUM V. NASBY,
Lait Paster uv the Church uv the Noo Dispensashun.

11. Lee's Surrender: "Why, This Ends the Biznis"

SAINT'S REST (wich is in the Stait uv Noo Jersey),
April the 10th, 1865.

I survived the defeat uv Breckinridge in 1860, becoz I knowd the Dimokrasy cood raise up in arms agin the unconstooshnality uv electin a seckshnal President, who wuz impregnatid with any seckshnal ijees that he got north uv Mason and Dixon's line.

I survived the defeat uv Micklellan (who wuz, trooly, the nashen's hope and pride likewise), becoz I felt ashoored that the rane uv the goriller Linkin wood be a short wun; that in a few months, at furthest, Ginral Lee wood capcher Washinton, depose the ape, and set up there a constooshnal guverment, based upon the great and immutable trooth that a white man is better than a nigger.

I survived the loss uv Atlanty, and Savanner, and Charleston, becoz, dependin on Suthern papers, I bleeved that them places wuz given up—mind, *given up*—becoz the Confedrits desired to concentrate for a crushin blow.

I survived the fall uv Richmond, tho it wuz a staggerer; becoz I still hed faith that that grate and good man, Lee, did it for stratejy, that he mite concentrate hisself sumwhere else; and when the Ablishnists jeered me, and sed "Richmond," and "Go up, bald head," to me, I shook my fist at em, and sed, "Wait, and you'll see."

I wuz a lookin for the blow that wuz to foller this concentratin. It cum!

But it wuz us who reseeved it, and a death blow it wuz. Ajacks defied the litenin; cood he hev bin a Northern Dimekrat, and stood this lick unmoved, he mite hev done it with perfect safety.

"Lee surrendered!"

Good hevins! Is this the end uv the concentratin? Is this the dyin in the last ditch? Is this the fightin till the last man wuz a inanimate corpse? Is this the bringin up the childrin to take their places, ez the old ones peg out under Yankee bullets?

"Lee surrendered!"

Why, this ends the biznis. Down goes the curtain. The South is *conkered!* CONKERED!! CONKERED!! Linkin rides into Richmond! A Illinois rail-splitter, a buffoon, a ape, a goriller, a smutty joker, sets hisself down in President Davis's cheer, and rites despatches! Where are the matrons uv Virginia? Did they not bare their buzzums and rush onto the Yankee bayonets that guarded the monster? Did they not cut their childern's throtes, and wavin a Confedrit flag in one hand, plunge a meat-knife into their throbbin buzzums with the tother, rather than see their city dishonored by the tread uv a conkerer's foot? Alars! not wunst.

Per contrary! I read in the papers that they did rush wildly thro the streets, with their childern in their arms.

But it wuz at the Yankee commissary trains, who give em bread and meat, wich they eat vociferously.

Their buzzums was bare.

But it wuz becoz their close hed worn out, and they didn't know how to weave cloth for new wuns.

"Why, This Ends the Biznis!"

In breef, they actid about ez mean ez a Northern Dimekrat ever did, and to go lower is unnessary.

This ends the chapter. The confederasy hez at last concentratid its last concentrate. It's dead. It's gathered up its feet, sed its last words, and deceest. And with it the Dimokrasy hez likewise given up the ghost. It may survive this, but I can't see how. We staked our politikle fortune on it; we went our bottom dollar on it; it's gone up, and we ditto. Linkin will serve his term out—the tax on whiskey won't be repealed—our leaders will die off uv chagrin, and delirium tremens, and inability to live so long out uv offis, and the sheep will be scattered. Farewell, vane world. I'll embrace the Catholic faith and be a nun, and in a cloister find that rest that pollytics kin never give.

PETROLEUM V. NASBY,
Lait Paster uv the Church uv the Noo Dispensashun.

12. *The Assassination: "We Wish It to Be Distinkly Understood, We Weep!"*

SAINT'S REST (wich is in the Stait uv Noo Jersey),
April the 20th, 1865.

The nashen mourns! The hand uv the vile assassin hez bin raised agin the Goril—the head uv the nashen, and the people's Father hez fallen beneath the hand uv a patr—vile assassin.

While Aberham Linkin wuz a livin, I need not say that I did not love him. Blessed with a mind uv no ordinary dimensions, endowed with all the goodness uv Washington, I alluz bleeved him to hev bin guilty uv all the crimes uv a Nero.

No man in Noo Jersey laments his untimely death more than the undersined. I commenst weepin perfoosely the minit I diskivered a squad uv returned soljers comin round the corner, who wuz a forcin constooshnel Dimekrats to hang out mournin.

Troo, he didn't agree with me, but I kin overlook that—it wuz his misforchoon. Troo, he hung unoffendin men, in Kentucky, whose only crime wuz in bein loyal to wat *they* deemed *their* guverment, ez tho a man in this free country coodent choose wich guverment he'd live under. Troo, he made cold-blooded war, in the most fiendish manner, on the brave men uv the South, who wuz only assertin the heaven-born rite uv roolin theirselves. Troo, he levied armies, made up uv pimps, whose chiefest delite wuz in ravishin the wives and daughters uv the South, and a miscellaneous burnin their houses. Troo, he kept into offis jist sich men ez wood sekund him in his hell-begotten skeems, and dismist every man who refused to becum ez depraved ez he wuz. Troo, he wood read uv these scenes uv blood and carnage, and in high glee tell filthy anecdotes; likewise wood he ride over the field uv battle, and ez the wheels uv his gorjus carriage crushed into the shuddrin earth the bodies uv the fallen braves, sing Afrikin melodies. Yet I, in common with all troo Dimekrats, weep! We weep! We wish it to be distinkly understood, we weep! Ther wuz that in him that instinktively forces us to weep over his death, and to loathe the foul assassin who so suddenly removed so much loveliness uv character. He hed ended the war uv oppression—he hed subjoogatid a free and brave people, who were strugglin for their rites, and hed em under his feet; but I, in common with all Dimekrats, mourn his death!

Hed it happened in 1862, when it wood hev been uv sum use to us, we wood not be so bowed down with woe and anguish. It wood hev throwd the guverment into confusion, and probably hev sekoored the independence uv the South.

But, alas! the tragedy cum at the wrong time!

Now, we are saddled with the damnin crime, when it will prodoose no results. The war wuz over. The game wuz up when Richmond wuz evacuated. Why kill Linkin then? For revenge? Revenge is a costly luxury—a party so near bankrupt ez the Dimokrasy cannot afford to indulge in it. The wise man hez no sich word ez revenge in his dictionary—the fool barters his hope for it.

Didst think that Linkin's death wood help the South? Linkin's hand wuz velvet—Johnson's may be, to the eye, but to the feel it will be found iron. Where Linkin switched, Johnson will flay. Where Linkin banished, Johnson will hang.

Davis wuz shocked when he heard it—so wuz I, and, in common with all troo Dimekrats, I weep.

PETROLEUM V. NASBY,
Lait Paster uv the Church uv the Noo Dispensashun.

13. De Profundis: "I Used to Bleeve
in Southern Chivelry"

SAINT'S REST (wich is in the Stait uv Noo Jersey),
September the 23d, 1865.

The world is, and alluz hez bin, full uv delusions. A lie,
well started, vigerously stuck to, and energetically pushed, ansers
jest ez well ez the trooth, and will live a long time. I hev lived
in this world uv decepshun long enuff to diskiver that there is a
huge diffrence betwixt the real and the ideal.

For instance. In my youth I wuz given to readin Cooper's
novels, until, becomin infatuated with his descriptions uv the
Injin stile uv livin, and the granjer uv the Injin charakter, I
determined to jine a tribe, and adopt their habits. I imagined
myself a noble red man uv the forest, a chasin the wild deer all
the day thro the leafy wood, and sweetly sleepin at nite in a
leafy bower, never wunst thinkin uv the friteful colds I'd ketch
sleepin out uv doors, and uv the terrible consekences uv a purely
animal diet upon my uneducatid bowils.

Filled with these ijees, I made my way to the nearest reser-
vation, and the first noble red man uv the forest I saw, wuz asleep
under a tree, with a bottle beside him. I awakened him, and addressed him in the language uv the novels, wich I sposed wuz all
he cood understand, thus:—

"Why slumbereth the chief uv the Pocasokes? and why are
not his feet upon the war-path? The skelp uv his father hangs
in the lodge uv Skinewaugh, and his death is unavenged! Awake!"

The noble Injin rolled over lazily on one elbow, took a long
pull at his bottle, ejackulatin,—

"Ugh! go away. White man dam fool—gimme dime—buy
Injin more rum!" and sank back into his inebriated slumber.

Hevin seen the ginuine Injin ez he exists out uv the novels,
I did not jine that tribe.

I used to bleeve in Southern chivelry. Likewise did I bleeve
in Robinson Crusoe, the malstrom, and Jackson's cottonbales;
but, ez I afterwards diskivered, there wuz no reality in these, so
I wuz prepared to bleeve the chivelry uv the South wuz a good
part bottled moonshine.

Wunst, to me, the Southerner wuz a compound uv George
IV., Chevaleer Bayard, Humbolt, and Longfellow, possessin the

deportment uv the fust, the high-grade chivelry and manly physikle perfecshun uv the second, the learnin uv the third, and the deep poetic feelin uv the fourth. I sposed he wood introdoose his knife into the bowels uv his enemy with the fearlessness and dexterity uv Bayard, apologize with the calm grace uv George, and write his obitchuary like Longfellow, in the style uv Hiawatha.

I bleeved his residence wuz a manshun, his common beverage the rosiest kind uv wine, quaffed from the most costly goblets; that money with him wuz a matter uv no account; that his time wuz divided between his country, his books, and manly out-door sports. In war, my notion uv him wuz a cross between Achilles and Wellington, I givin him the credit uv hevin the dash uv the one, the steadiness uv tother, and the heroism uv both. Sich wuz my ijee uv the Southern gentleman.

Wood, O wood that this pleasin delusion hed never bin dissipated! It's the nacher uv the Northern Dimekrat to look up to sumbody, and I didn't like the ijee uv hevin my idol dismountid. I wuz down South doorin the war, hevin served sevral months in the Louisiana Pelicans, a Confedrit regiment, made up uv the fust families uv that State. I found that I hed bin labrin under a delusion all my life. I wuz in Virginia a while, where yoo are supposed to find the highest type uv Southern chivelry. On a average the Virginian is as mizable a cuss ez ther is on earth. His manshun is a shamblin cabin; his rosy wine is a style uv potato whisky, so inexpressibly mean that it wood be rejected with inexpressible scorn by the most reckless and abandoned squaw; his costly goblet is a stun jug with a cob stopper, and his highest ijee uv amoosement is quarter races and poker. Long, lank, lathy, low-browed, peak-nosed, he approaches the appearance uv the Northerner about ez closely ez a ring-tailed baboon resembles Powers' Greek Slave.

In war he haint no better than in peace. He fites well enuff when put to it, but he haint no endurence. Ef he don't win from the start, his game is up. And the less he intends to do, the more he blows afore he commences. His endless blowin about his fitin capacity and resources, afore the war, wuz wat roped us Northern Dimekrats into it, and indoost us to stake our politikle fucher on their success. Alass! we wuz fooled in em, and we go down with em.

I never want to hear a word agin about Southern chivelry. We hev got to git em back agin, for alone we kin do nothin, and I spose when we hev em back, we'll hev to knuckle to em jist ez we did afore the war, for they comprise the heft uv the party; but we'll do it this time for policy, while before we did it from sheer belief in their sooperiority over us. I'd be well satisfied ef we cood git along, ez a party, without em.

PETROLEUM V. NASBY,
Lait Paster uv the Church uv the Noo Dispensashun.

III. The Horrors of Reconstruction

(1865-1870)

NOTE TO THE CHAPTER

Lincoln's assassination broke the deadlock between two Reconstruction policies and tipped the scales in favor of the severe measures of the Radicals, the Wade-Davis bill, which had earlier fallen to the President's pocket veto. Lincoln's own generous plan of reconstruction had been applied in some states but had not become legally effective. Keeping Lincoln's Cabinet, Johnson strove to realize the plan's broad outlines during the first months of his administration. "It is the dooty now uv every Suthern Dimekrat," Nasby counselled, "to take the oath to-wunst, and be metamorphosed into loyalty." The next steps were clear. "Demand," he urged, "that the military be withdrawd, and that yoor representatives be admitted" to Congress. "Then, ef we kin carry enuff deestriks North, yoo have the game in yoor own hand." By early December 1865, the remaking of the former Confederate states was well under way. However, the interval between Johnson's accession and the reconvening of Congress marked not the end of an old struggle, but the beginning of a new one.

The shot in Ford's Theater had thrown the control of the executive department into the hands of a Southerner and a states'-rights Democrat. "Blessed be Booth," Nasby exclaimed, "who give us Androo. . . . Rejoice, O my soul! for yoor good time, wich wuz so long a comin, is come." The Radicals in Congress realized that their plans to shape the re-emerging nation were doomed if Southern states were restored to Federal representation with Johnson's aid. Kentucky's example filled Nasby with glee. "The soldiers voted," he cheered Democratic election victories, "them ez wuz clothed in gray,—and we routed the Abolishnists." The preservation of Republican rule also determined the strategy of the Radicals. They felt that only by manipulating the Negro vote in the Southern states, by enacting new Constitutional limitations on the power of the states, and by curbing the influence of a Democratic president could the disaster be averted which threatened their party.

During the critical year of 1866 the Radicals eliminated step by step any effective presidential opposition to their schemes. Through the use of caucus and party lash they cajoled most moderate Republicans into submission or denounced them as traitors and eliminated their political influence. Nasby shuddered when he counted their "high-handed acts uv usurpashen." The Radicals created the powerful Joint Committee on Reconstruction, denied congressional representation to Southern states, and enacted measures to bring states, army, electoral college, Cabinet and Supreme Court under their control. By one vote they failed to make their rule complete, but the conviction of Johnson was hardly necessary since overriding vetoes had curbed the President's power as an obstacle to Radical legislation.

Lincoln and Johnson, as well as their Democratic opponent, General George B. McClellan, had favored a moderate Reconstruction policy during the campaign of 1864, but victories in the Congressional elections of 1866 gave the Radicals power to put their program into effect, despite Nasby's exhortations to the "Democrats and Conservatives uv the North" not to desert "Androo Johnson, after all the trouble he hez bin to in gettin back to us." The Freedmen's Bureau, originally formed in March 1865, received wide powers by a second act passed over the President's veto in 1866. Operating under the War Department and designed to ease the adjustment of four million liberated slaves to freedom, the Bureau's agents also functioned as virtual deputies of the Republican party on the local scene in the South.

The Thirteenth Amendment had been ratified in December 1865, extinguishing "the last glimerin flicker uv Liberty, by abolishin slavery," Nasby clamored, and completing part of the work of William Lloyd Garrison, Gerrit Smith and Wendell Phillips. The Civil Rights Act became the first Federal statute to define citizenship and safeguard civil rights within the states. It nullified the Black Codes of 1865-1866, which Northerners felt the ex-Confederate states had passed as a guise to revive slavery, but which Southerners insisted served to curb the chaos resulting from the destruction of a social system based on slavery. The two-thirds majority in Congress which overrode Johnson's veto to the Civil Rights Act put the Radicals in full control of Reconstruction.

The Civil Rights bill was later incorporated into the resolution framing the Fourteenth Amendment. The Radicals made its adoption the price of readmitting rebel states into the Union. The Fifteenth Amendment, proclaimed March 30, 1870, aimed at further guarding Negro suffrage which the Radicals had failed to secure in a more drastic amendment since Northern states objected to Federal interference with suffrage laws. "I never saw sich enthoosiasm, or more cheerin indicashuns uv the pride uv race," Nasby gaily reported to his friends in Kentucky after he had helped the voters of Ohio defeat the amendment which would have removed the word "white" from their state constitution.

The manipulation of the bulk of newly enfranchised Negro voters became one of the great tasks facing all political factions in the Reconstruction period. In the North, Nasby diligently sought to keep

Negroes out of the Republican party, operating from such rallying grounds of Democracy as the post office at Confedrit X Roads and the Harp uv Erin S'loon in New York City's nefarious Sixth Ward. He linked Fernando Wood, the Democratic politician and anti-Abolitionist, and Frederick Douglass, the fugitive from slavery and Abolitionist lecturer, as running mates for the White House. In the comment of the Democratic New York World that "the Nigger vote must come to us, becoz the Dimocrisy hed alluz hed success in managin the ignerant and degradid classes," he found the inspiration for his difficult job. In the South the Radical Republicans invaded the bastions of the Democratic party with their legions of Reconstruction officials, from major generals to schoolmasters, acting as the party's emissaries and organizers of Loyal Leagues which attempted to bring the Negro voters and the white Unionists harmoniously together in the Republican party.

Some Southerners acquiesced in the schemes, some blocked efforts to mobilize the Negro with subtle means of intimidation, and some worked through party conventions to increase conservative influence. The rougher elements struck back by the violent methods of the Ku Klux Klan, which, until its suppression in 1871, aimed at the establishment of white control. Nasby felt that by destroying schools "the Ethiopian wuz taught that to him, at least, the spelling book is a sealed volume, and that the gospel is not for him, save ez he gits it filtered through a sound, constooshnel, Dimekratic preacher." Yet riots in Memphis and New Orleans were paralleled in the outbursts of Northern workingmen against Negro laborers. Nasby the racist hastened to encourage the white laborers' refusal "to compermise their dignity by lowering themselves to the level of the greasy Afriken"; Nasby the politico admonished the workingman to rise to the level of Tim McGuire, whose "nateral instinks compelled him to drop that shillala on their heads ez usual, but the politikle considerashens restraned him."

The issues of Southern Reconstruction and the redemption of Civil War bonds with greenbacks dominated the public debate during the presidential campaign of 1868. Grant's immense popularity minimized their actual importance at the polls. Nasby's "matoor considerashon" threw light on the difficulties which the Democrats faced in finding an equally ideal candidate for the White House. Andrew Johnson, though not unwilling to make a stand, was out of the question. Winfield Scott Hancock's war record recommended the general, but other Democrats found him unacceptable for exactly that reason. As a Greenbacker, George H. Pendleton's views were well liked in the West but anathema to Eastern Democrats who feared paper money. Even his beautiful, unscrupulous and devoted daughter Kate was unable to sell Chief Justice Salmon P. Chase to the New York convention, which picked its presiding officer, Horatio Seymour, as the compromise candidate of Eastern Democrats, who would not stomach Pendleton, and Western Democrats, who would not have Thomas A. Hendricks of Indiana.

Radical Reconstruction was fastened on the South in 1868 and 1870, when officials who gave equal rights to the Negro assumed the government of the states. The constructive reforms which they accomplished were overshadowed by their incompetence and corruption, symbolized by carpetbaggers and scalawags. Yet in a period plagued with political scandals in all parts of the country, their aberrations merely emphasized problems the entire nation produced and endured. About one million newly enfranchised freedmen provided the mainstay of the regimes. "It's my candid convicshun," Nasby grumbled, that "the grovelin cusses work and earn money jest to spite us." The freedmen strove to secure land, education and even some social equality, and "assoomed," to the horror of Nasby, "so much uv the style ov people that ef it hadn't bin for their black faces, they would have passed for folks."

1. Address to the South: "The War Hez Hed Its Uses"

SAINT'S REST (wich is in the Stait uv Noo Jersey),
July the 21st, 1865.

TO THE DIMOKRASY UV THE SUTHERN STAITS:

Dearly beloved, I saloot yoo!

The events uv the past four years hev bin momenchus. The war hez ended—to a sooperfishel observer it wood seem disastrusly to yoo and us, but to him whose eagle eye kin pierce the misty fucher, gloriously.

Troo, we lost the orfises, and hev bin for four long and weary years on steril ground, whose fruits wuz wormy and whose water wuz bitter. So the childern uv Israel wandered forty years in the wildernis, but they finally found a Canan, full uv fatnis, runnin with milk and honey, and sich. So shel we emerge into *our* Canan ere long.

The war hez hed its uses. We hev diskivered that the Suthern Dimekrat cood be depended on to fite; yoo hev diskivered that the Northern Dimekrat cood be depended on to do yoor dirty work, thro thick or thin, and we hev both diskivered that the Ablishnist is no coward, and will really make sacrifices for principle. Knowin all this, we kin work intelligently in the fucher.

It is the dooty now uv every Suthern Dimekrat to take the oath to-wunst, and be metamorphosed into loyalty. Then we've got em. Demand, ez only a Sutherner kin demand, that the military be withdrawd, and that yoor representatives be admitted. Then, ef we kin carry enuff deestriks North, yoo hev the game in yoor own hand. But to accomplish this last feat, yoo must aid us.

We hev bin unforchnit in our politikle venchers, and at least wun uv our prophecies must cum troo, otherwise how kin we go afore the people? The nigger is all we've left, and the variety we hev up here is uv no yoose to us, for they are all earnin their own livin, and ain't crowdin white folks out uv poor-houses, at all. It's my candid convicshun that the grovelin cusses work and earn money jest to spite us. In some localities, our sagashus managers hev indoost sum uv em to drink with em, and in a few months got em into delirium tremens, and their families into the poor-houses. To their untutored bowels our likker is litenin. But this can't be dun ginrally, becoz it's all our leaders kin do to keep their own skins full. To yoo we look for aid.

A enterprisin Yankee (cusses on the race!) wuz wunst askt wat biznis he followd to make so much money. He replied that he hed the itch, and he traveled ahead, givin it to people, his brother comin immejitly after, sellin a cure. Let us imitate their wisdom. Promptly ship to each Northern stait 200,000 old niggers who can't work, and to make asshoorence doubly shoor, starve em awhile, and run the measles and smallpox thro em. Mix with em a few thousand black wimmen with mulatto childern, to show the horrors uv amalgamashun. Then we'd hev suthin to go on! Ez we carted em into the poor-houses, and levid taxes to support em, how our speakers wood gush! how our papers wood howl! After four years uv failyoor in the prophecy biznis, the ijee uv hevin wun cum troo, sets me into a delirium tremens uv joy.

Then, immejitly, yoor legislachers must pass stringent laws agin a nigger leavin his respective county, and then pass another law not allowin any man to give able-bodied wuns to exceed $5 a month. This dun, I hev faith to bleeve thousands uv em will beg to be agin enslaved, about mid winter. Ef they will persist in dyin in freedom, we kin, at least, pint to ther bodies, and say in a sepulkral tone: "Wen niggers wuz wuth $1500, they wuz not allowd to die thus—behold the froots uv Ablishn philanthropy!" Either way, it's cappital for us.

"At Last! The Deed Is Done!"

Yoo must inkulkate the doctrin uv State Rites zealuser than ever, and while yoo are gittin yoor people tuned up on that, we'll hammer away at debt and corrupshun, and sich deliteful themes, and wunst more we'll git the Ablishnist under our feet.

I hev indicatid briefly the ginral outlines uv the policy we must pursoo ef we wood succeed. Uther ijees will sejest themselves to yoo—let us hev em, and we'll act on em.

In conclooshun. Be wary and untirin. Remember, on yoo depends the politikle fortunes uv the thousands who wunst held offis, but who hev bin to grass for four long weery years. We must succeed now or never.

PETROLEUM V. NASBY,
Lait Paster uv the Church uv the Noo Dispensashun.

2. Slavery Finished: "At Last! The Deed Is Done!"

CONFEDRIT X ROADS (wich is in the Stait uv Kentucky),
December 20, 1865.

At last! The deed is done! The tyranikle government which hez sway at Washington hez finally extinguished the last glimerin flicker uv Liberty, by abolishin slavery! The sun didn't go down in gloom that nite—the stars didn't fade into a sickly yeller, at wich obstinacy uv nachur I wuz considably astonished.

I got the news at the Post Offis, near wich I am at present stayin, at the house uv a venerable old planter, who accepts my improvin conversation and a occasional promise, wich is cheap, ez equivalent for board. Sadly I wendid my way to his peaceful home, dreadin to fling over that house the pall uv despair. After supper I broke to em ez gently ez I cood the intelligence that three fourths uv the States hed ratified the constooshnel amendment—that Seward had ishued his proclamation, and that all the Niggers wuz free!

Never did I see sich sorrer depicted on human countenance —never wuz there despair uv sich depth. All nite long the bereaved inmates uv that wunst happy but now distracted home wept and waled in agony wich wuz perfectly heart rendin.

"Wo is me," sobbed the old man, wringin his hands.

"John Brown's karkis hangs a danglin in the air, but his sole is marchin on.

"It took posseshun uv Seward, and through his ugly mouth

it spoke the words 'the nigger is free,' and there is no more a slave in all the land.

"Wunst I hed a hundred niggers, and the men were fat and healthy, and the wenches wuz strong, and sum uv em was fair to look upon.

"They worked in my house, and my fields, from the risin uv the sun to the goin down uv the same.

"Wuz they lazy? I catted them till they wuz cured thereof; for lo! they wuz ez a child under my care.

"Did they run away? From Kentucky they run North, and lo! the Locofoco Marshals caught them for me, and brought them back, and delivered them into my hand, without cost, sayin, lo! here is thy nigger—do with him ez thou wilt (wich I alluz did), wich wuz cheeper than keepin dogs, and jest ez good.

"Solomon wuz wise, for he hed uv concubines a suffishensy, but we wuz wiser in our day than him.

"For he hed to feed his children, and it kost him shekels uv gold and shekels uv silver, and much corn and oil.

"We hed our concubines with ez great a muchness ez Solomon, but we sold their children for silver, and gold, and red-dog paper."

And all nite long the bereaved old patriarch, who hed alluz bin a father to his servants (and a grandfather to many uv em) poured out his lamentations.

In the mornin the niggers wuz called up; and ez they all hed their coats on, and hed bundles, I spect they must hev heard the news. The old gentleman explained the situation to em.

"Yoo will," sed he, "stay in yoor happy homes—yoo will alluz continue to live here, and work here, ez yoo hev alluz dun?"

The niggers, all in korous, with a remarkable unanimity, remarkt that ef they hed ever bin introdoost to theirselves, they thought they woodent. In fact, they hed congregated at that time for the purpose uv startin life on their own hook.

A paroxysm uv pain and anguish shot over the old man's face. Nearest to him stood a octoroon, who, hed she not bin tainted with the accurst blood uv Ham, wood hev bin considered beautiful. Fallin on her neck, the old patriarch, with teers a streamin down his furrowd cheeks, ejackilated,—

"Farewell, Looizer, my daughter, farewell! I loved yoor mother ez never man loved nigger. She wuz the solace uv my leisure hours—the companion uv my yooth. She I sold to pay off a mortgage on the place—she and yoor older sisters. Farewell!

I hed hoped to hev sold yoo this winter (for yoo are still young), and bought out Jinkins; but wo is me! Curses on the tyrent who thus severs all the tender ties uv nachur. O! it is hard for father to part with child, even when the market's high; but, O God! to part thus—"

And the old gentleman, in a excess uv greef, swoonded away genteelly.

His son Tom hed bin caressin her two little children, who wuz half whiter than she wuz. Unable to restrain hisself, he fell on her neck, and bemoaned his fate with tetchin pathos.

"Farewell, farewell, mother uv my children! Farewell, faro, and hosses, and champane—a long farewell! Your increase wuz my perquisites, and I sold em to supply my needs. Hed yoo died, I cood hev bin resigned; for when dead you ain't wuth a copper; but to see yoo torn away livin, and wuth $2000 in any market—it's too much, it's too much!"

And he fainted, fallin across the old man.

"Who'll do the work about the house?" shreekt the old lady, faintin and fallin across Tom.

"Who'll dress us, and wash us, and wait on us?" shreekt the three daughters, swoonin away, and fallin across the old woman.

My first impulse wuz to faint away myself, and fall across the three daughters; but I restrained myself, and wuz contented with strikin a attitood and organizin a tablo. Hustlin the niggers away with a burnin cuss for their ingratitood, I spent the balance uv the forenoon in bringin on em too. Wun by wun they became conshus; but they wuz not theirselves. Their minds wuz evidently shattered; they wuz carryin a heavy heart in their buzzums.

Wood, O! wood that Seward cood hev seen that groop! Sich misery does Ablishnism bring in its train—sich horrers follers a departure from Dimikratik teechins. When will reason return to the people? Eko answers, When?

PETROLEUM V. NASBY,
Lait Paster uv the Church uv the Noo Dispensashun.

3. Veto of the Civil Rights Bill: "Sing, O My Soul!"

CONFEDRIT × ROADS (wich is in the Stait uv Kentucky),
April 7, 1866.

I am a canary, a nightengale. A lark, am I.

I raise my voice in song. I pour forth melojus notes.

I am a lamb, wich frisketh, and waggeth his tale, and leapeth, ez he nippeth the tender grass. I am a colt, wich kicketh up its heels exuberantly.

I am a bridegroom, wich cometh from his bride in the mornin feelin releeved in the knowledge that she wore not palpitators, nor false calves, nor nothin false, afore she wuz hizn.

I am a steamboat captin with a full load, a doggry keeper on a Saturday nite, a sportin man with four aces in his hand.

All these am I, and more.

For we sought to establish ourselves upon a rock, but found that the underpinnin wuz gone out uv it.

Even slavery wuz our strong place, and our hope; but the corners hed bin knocked out uv it.

The sons uv Belial hed gone forth agin it; Massachoosetts hed assailed it, and the North West hed drawd its bow agin it.

Wendell Phillips hed pecked out wun stun, Garret Smith another; and the soldiers hed completed what they hed begun.

And Congris, even the Rump, hed decreed its death, and hed held forth its hand to Ethiopia.

It passed a bill givin the Niggers their rites, and takin away from us our rites:

Sayin, that no more shel we sell em in the market place,

Or take their wives from em,

Or be father to their children,

Or make uv em conkebines aginst their will,

Or force em to toil without hire,

Or shoot em, ez we wuz wont to do under the old dispensashun,

Or make laws for em wich didn't bind us as well.

And our hearts wuz sad in our buzzums; for we said, Lo! the nigger is our ekal; and we mourned ez them hevin no hope.

But the President, even Androo, the choice uv Booth, said, Nay.

And the bill wuz vetoed, and is no law; and our hearts is made glad.

And from the Ohio to the Gulf shel go up the song uv gladness and the sounds uv mirth.

The nigger will we slay, for he elevated his horn agin us.

We will make one law for him and another for us, and he will sigh for the good old times when he wuz a slave in earnest.

His wife shel be our conkebine, ef she is fair to look upon; and ef he murmurs, we'll bust his head.

His daughters shel our sons possess; and their inkrease will we sell, and live upon the price they bring.

In our fields they shel labor; but the price uv their toil shel make us fat.

Sing, O my soul!

The nigger hed become sassy and impudent, and denied that he wuz a servant unto his brethren.

He sheltered hisself behind the Freedman's Burow, and the Civil Rights Bill, and the soldiery, and he wagged his lip at us, and made mouths at us.

And we longed to git at him, but because of these we durst not.

But now who shel succor him?

We will smite him hip and thigh, onless he consents to be normal.

Our time uv rejoicin is come.

In Kentucky, the soldiers voted,—them ez wuz clothed in gray,—and we routed the Abolishnists.

Three great capchers hev we made: New Orleens we capcherd, Kentucky we capcherd, and the President—him who aforetime strayed from us—we capcherd.

Rejoice, O my soul! for yoor good time, wich wuz so long a comin, is come.

We shel hev Post Offisis, and Collectorships, and Assessorships, and Furrin Mishns, and Route Agencies, and sich; and on the proceeds thereof will we eat, drink, and be merry.

The great rivers shel be whisky, the islands therein sugar, the streams tributary lemon joose and bitters, and the faithful shel drink.

Whisky shel be cheap; for we shel hold the offises, and kin pay; and the heart uv the barkeeper shel be glad.

The Ablishnist shel hang his hed; and we will jeer him, and

flout him, and say unto him, "Go up, bald head!" and no bears
shel bite us; for, lo! the President is our rock, and in him we
abide.

Blessed be Booth, who give us Androo.

Blessed be the veto, wich makes the deed uv Booth uv sum
account to us.

Blessed be Moses, who is a leadin us out uv the wilderness,
into the Canaan flowin with milk and honey.

PETROLEUM V. NASBY,
Lait Paster uv the Church uv the Noo Dispensashun.

4. Good Tidings from Memphis: "I Warmed upon This Elokently"

CONFEDRIT × ROADS (wich is in the Stait uv Kentucky),
May 12, 1866.

The news from Memphis filled the soles uv the Dimocrisy
uv Kentucky with undilooted joy. There, at last, the Ethiopian
wuz taught that to him, at least, the spelling book is a sealed
volume, and that the gospel is not for him, save ez he gits it filtered through a sound, constooshnel, Dimekratic preacher. We
met at the Corners last nite to jollify over the brave acts uv our
Memphis frends, and I wuz the speeker. I addressed them on
the subjick uv the nigger,—his wants, needs, and capacities,—a
subjick, permit me to state, I flatter myself I understand. Probably no man in the United States hez given the nigger more
study, or devoted more time to a pashent investigashen uv this
species uv the brute creashen, than the undersigned. I have con-
templated him sittin and standin, sleepin and wakin, at labor
and in idleness,—in every shape, in fact, ceptin ez a free man,
wich situashen is too disgustin for a proud Caucashen to contemplate him; and when he ariz before my mind's eye in that shape,
I alluz turned shudderin away.

I hed proceeded in my discourse with a flowin sale. It's easy
demonstratin anythin yoor awjence wants to bleeve, and wich
their interest lies in. For instants, I hev notist wicked men, who
wuz somewhat wedded to sin, generally lean toward Universal-
ism; men heavily developed in the back uv the neck are easily
convinst uv the grand trooths uv free love; and them ez is too
fond uv makin money to rest on the seventh day, hev serious

doubts ez to whether the observance uv the Sabbath is bindin onto em. I, not likin to work at all, am a firm beleever in slavery, and wood be firmer ef I cood get start enuff to own a nigger.

I hed gone on and proved concloosively, from a comparison uv the fizzikle structer uv the Afrikin and the Caucashen, that the nigger wuz a beast, and not a human bein; and that, consekently, we hed a perfeck rite to catch him, and tame him, and use him ez we do other wild animals. Finishin this hed uv my discourse, I glode easily into a history uv the flood; explained how Noah got tite and cust Ham, condemnin him and his posterity to serve his brethren forever, wich I insisted give us an indubitable warranty deed to all uv em for all time.

I warmed upon this elokently. "Behold, my brethren, the beginnin uv Dimocrasy," I sed. "Fust, the wine (which wuz the antetype of our whisky) wuz the beginnin. Wine (or whisky) wuz necessary to the foundation uv the party, and it wuz forthcomin. But the thing wuz not complete. It did its work on Noah, but yet there wuz a achin void. There wuz no *Nigger* in the world, and without nigger there cood be no Dimocrasy. Ham, my friends, wuz born a brother uv Japhet, and wuz like unto him, and, uv course, could not be a slave. Whisky wuz the instrument to bring him down; and it fetched him. Ham looked upon his father, and wuz cust; and the void wuz filled. THERE WUZ NIGGER AND WHISKY, and upon them the foundashuns uv the party wuz laid, broad and deep. Methinks, my brethren, when Ham went out from the presence uv his father, black in the face ez the ace uv spades (ef I may be allowed to use the expression), bowin his back to the burdens Shem and Japhet piled onto him with alacrity, that Democracy, then in the womb uv the future, kicked lively, and clapped its hands. There wuz a nigger to enslave, and whisky to bring men down to the pint uv enslavin him. There wuz whisky to make men incapable uv labor; whisky to accompany horse racin, and poker playin, and sich rational amusements, and a nigger cust specially that he mite sweat to furnish the means. Observe the fitness uv things. Bless the Lord, my brethren, for whisky and the nigger; for, without em, there could be no Dimocrisy, and yoor beloved speaker mite hev owned a farm in Noo Jersey, and bin a votin the whig ticket to-day."

At this pint, a venerable old freedman, who wuz a sittin quietly in the meetin, ariz, and asked ef he mite ask a question. Thinkin what a splendid opportunity there wood be uv demonstratin the sooperiority uv the Caucashen over the Afrikin race, I answered, "Yes," gladly.

"Well, Mas'r," sed the old imbecile, "is I a beast?"

"My venerable friend, there ain't nary doubt uv it."

"Is my old woman a old beastesses, too?"

"Indubitably," replied I.

"And my children—is they little beasts and beastesses?"

"Onquestionably."

"Den a yaller feller ain't but half a beast, is he?"

"My friend," sed I, "that question is—"

"Hold on," sed he; "wat I wanted to git at is dis: dere's a heap uv yaller fellers in dis section, whose fadders must hev bin white men; and, ez der mudders wuz all beastesses, I want to know whedder dar ain't no law in Kentucky agin—"

"Put him out!" "Kill the black wretch!" shouted a majority uv them who hed bin the heaviest slave owners under the good old patriarkle system, and they went for the old reprobate. At this pint, a officer uv the Freedmen's Bureau, who we hadn't observed, riz, and bustin with laughter, remarked that his venerable friend shood have a chance to be heerd. We respeck that Burow, partikelerly ez the officers generally hev a hundred or two bayonets within reech, and, chokin our wrath, permitted ourselves to be further insulted by the cussed nigger, who, grinnin from ear to ear, riz and perceeded.

"My white friends," sed he, "dar pears to be an objection to my reference to de subjeck uv dis mixin with beasts, so I won't press de matter. But I ask yoo, did Noah hev three sons?"

"He did," sed I.

"Berry good. Wuz they all brudders?"

"Uv course."

"Ham come from the same fadder and mudder as the odder two?"

"C-e-r-t-i-n-l-y."

"Well, den, it seems to me—not fully understandin the skripters—dat if we is beasts and beastesses, dat you is beasts and beastesses also, and dat, after all, we is brudders." And the disgustin old wretch threw his arms around my neck, and kissed me, callin me his "long lost brudder."

The officer uv the Freedmen's Bureau laft vosiferously, and so did a dozen or two soldiers in the crowd likewise; and the awjence slunk out without adjournin the meetin, one uv em remarkin, audibly, that he had noticed one thing, that Dimocrisy

wuz extremely weak whenever it undertook to defend itself with
fax or revelashun. For his part, he'd done with argyment. He
wanted niggers, because he cood wallop em, and make em do his
work without payin em, wich he coodent do with white men.

I left the meetin house convinst that the South, who worked
the niggers, leavin us Northern Dimokrats to defend the system,
hed the best end uv the bargain.

PETROLEUM V. NASBY,
Lait Paster uv the Church uv the Noo Dispensashun.

5. *Presumptuous Freedmen: "Ef It Hadn't Bin for Their Black Faces, They Wood Have Passed for Folks"*

POST OFFIS, CONFEDRIT × ROADS
(wich is in the Stait uv Kentucky),
September 16, 1866.

I found my flock in a terrible state uv depression, at which,
when I was told the cause, I didn't wonder at. There wuz, back
uv the Corners, over towards Garrettstown, about three quarters
uv a mile this side of Abbott's grocery (we estimate distance here
from one grocery to another), five or six families uv niggers. The
males of this settlement had all been in the Federal army ez
soljers, and hed saved their pay, and bounty, and sich, and hed
bought uv a disgustid Confederate, who proposed to find in Mexico that freedom which was denied him here, and who, bein determined to leave the country, didn't care who he sold his plan-
tashen to, so ez he got greenbax, three hundred acres, wich they
hed divided up, and built cabins onto em, and wuz a cultivatin
it. There wuz a storekeeper at the Corners who come here from
Illinoy, and who hed been so greedy uv gain and so graspin ez
to buy their prodoose uv em, and sell em sich supplies ez they
needed. These accursed sons and daughters uv Ham wuz a livin
there in comfort. The thing wuz a gittin unendoorable. They
come to the Corners dressed in clothes without patches, and
white shirts, and hats on; and the females in dresses, and hoops
under em; in short, these apes hed assoomed so much uv the
style uv people that ef it hadn't bin for their black faces, they
wood have passed for folks.

Our people become indignant, and ez soon ez I returned, I

was requested to call a meetin to consider the matter, which I uv course did.

The horn wuz tootid, and the entire Corners wuz assembled, excepting the Illinoy store-keeper, who didn't attend to us much. I stated briefly and elokently (I hev improved in public speakin sense I heered His Serene Highness, Androo the I., all the way from Washinton to Looisville), and asked the brethren to ease their mind.

Squire Gavitt hed observed the progress uv them niggers with the most profoundest alarm. He hed noticed em coming to the Corners, dressed better than his family dressed, and sellin the produx uv their land to that wretch—

At this point the Illinoy store-keeper come in, and the Squire proceeded.

—he shood say Mr. Pollock, and he hed made inquiries, and found that one family hed sold three hundred and seventy-five dollars worth uv truck, this season, uv which they hed laid out for clothes and books two hundred dollars, leavin em one hundred and seventy-five dollars in cash, which was more money than he had made sense the accursed Linkin passed the emancipashen proclamation. And what hed driv the iron into his soul wuz the fact that wun uv them niggers wuz *his* nigger. "The money they hev," pursood the Squire, "is MY MONEY; that man worth $1500 is my man; his wife is my woman; her children my children—"

"That's a literal fact!" shouted Joe Bigler, a drunken, returned Confederate sojer; "they hev yoor nose exactly, and they're the meanest yaller brats in the settlement."

This unhappy remark endid in a slite unpleasantness, wich resulted in the Squire's bein carried out, minus one ear, and his nose smashed. Joseph remarked that he'd wantid to git at him ever sense he woodn't lend him a half dollar two months ago. He was now satisfied, and hoped this little episode woodn't mar the harmony uv the meetin.

Elder Smathers observed that he hed noticed with pain that them niggers alluz hed money, and wuz alluz dresst well, while we, their sooperiors, hed no money, and nothin to boast uv in the way uv close. He wood say—

Pollock, the Illinoy store-keeper, put in. Ef the Elder wood work ez them niggers wuz workin, and not loaf over half the time at Bascom's grocery, he mite possibly hev a hull soot uv close, and now and then a dollar in money. It wuz here, ez it wuz in all strikly Dimekratic communities, the grocery keepers absorb all the floatin capital, and—

He wuz not allowed to proceed. Bascom flung a chair at him, and four or five uv his constitooents fell on him. He wuz carried out for dead. Bascom remarked that he wuz for the utmost freedom uv speech, but in the discussion uv a great Constooshnel question, no Illinoy Ablishnist shood put in his yawp. The patriotic remark wuz cheered, but when Bascom ask't the whole meetin out to drink, the applause wuz uproarious. Bascom alluz gets applause; he knows how to move an audience.

Deekin Pogram sed he'd bore with them niggers till his patience wuz gin out. He endoored it till last Sunday. After service he felt pensive, ruther, and walked out towards Garrettstown, meditatin, as he went, on the sermon he hed listened to that mornin on the necessity uv the spread of the Gospil. Mournin in sperit over the condition of the heathen, he didn't notis where he wuz till he found hisself in the nigger settlement, and in front uv one uv their houses. There he saw a site wich paralyzed him. There wuz a nigger, wich wuz wunst his nigger,—wich Linkin deprived him uv,—settin under his porch, and a profanin the Holy Bible by teachin his child to read it! "Kin this be endoored?" the Deekin asked.

Deekin Parkins sed he must bear his unworthy testimony agin these disturbers. They hed—he knowd whereof he spoke— hired a female woman from Massachusetts to teach their children! He hed bin in their skool-room, and with his own eyes witnest it.

Bascom, the grocery keeper, hed bin shocked at their conduct. He wuz convinct that a nigger wuz a beast. They come to the Corners to sell the produx of their lands; do they leave their money at his bar? Nary! They spend sum uv it at the store uv a disorganizer from Illinoy, who is here interferin with the biznis uv troo Southern men, but he hed never seed one uv em inside his door. He hed no pashence with em, and believed suthin shood be done to rid the community uv sich yooseless inhabitance. Ef they ever git votes they'r agin us. No man who dodges my bar ever votes straight Dimocrisy.

Ginral Punt moved that this meetin do to-wunst proceed to the settlement, and clean em out. They wuz a reproach to Kentucky. Of course, ez they were heathens and savages, sich goods ez they hed wood fall to the righteous, uv whom we wuz which, and he insisted upon a fair divide. All he wanted wuz a bureau and a set uv chairs he hed seen.

The motion wuz amendid to inclood Pollock, the Illinoy storekeeper, and it wuz to-wunst acted upon.

Pollock wuz reconstructed first. Filled with zeal for the right, his door wuz bustid in, and in a jiffy the goods wich he wuz a contaminatin our people with wuz distributed among the people, each takin sich ez sooted em. Wun man sejested that ez they wuz made by Yankees, and brought South by Yankees, there wuz contaminashen in the touch uv em, and that they be burned, but he wuz hooted down, our people seein a distinction. The contaminashen wuz in payin for em; gittin em gratooitusly took the cuss off.

Elated, the crowd started for the settlement. I never saw more zeal manifested. A half hour brought us there, and then a scene ensood wich filled me with joy onspeekable. The niggers wuz routed out, and their goods wuz bundled after em. The Bibles and skool books wuz destroyed first, coz we hed no use for em; their chairs, tables, and bureaus, clothin and beddin, wuz distributed. A woman hed the impudence to beg for suthin she fancied, when the righteous zeal uv my next door neighbor, Pettus, biled over, and he struck her. Her husband, forgettin his color, struck Pettus, and the outrage wuz completed. *A nigger hed raised his hand agin a white man!*

The insulted Caucashen blood riz, and in less than a minnit the bodies uv six male Ethiopians wuz a danglin in the air, and the bodies uv six Ethiopian wimin wuz layin prostrate on the earth. The children wuz spared, for they wuz still young, and not hevin bin taught to read so far that they cood not forgit it, ef kept carefully from books, they kin be brought up in their proper speer, ez servance to their brethern. (By the way, the inspired writer must hev yoosed this word "brethern," in this connection, figeratively. The nigger, bein a beast, cannot be our brother.) Some may censure us for too much zeal in this matter, but what else cood we hev done? We are high toned, and can't stand everything. These niggers hed no rite to irritate us by their presence. They knowd our feelins on the subjick, and by buyin land and remainin in the vicinity, they kindled the flame wich resulted ez it did. Ez they did in Memphis and Noo Orleans, they brought their fate onto their own heads.

Pollock recovered, and with the Yankee school marm who wuz a teechin the niggers, left for the North yisterday.

It speeks well for the forbearance uv our people that they wuz permitted to depart at all.

Petroleum V. Nasby, P. M.
(wich is Postmaster),
and likewise late Chaplin to the expedishn.

6. The 1866 Elections: "The Signs uv the Times Is Ominus"

Post Offis, Confedrit × Roads,
(wich is in the Stait uv Kentucky),
October 1, 1866.

President Johnson, who hez bin likened to Androo Jaxson, and wich, since my appintment I conseed him to be, in many partikelers, his sooperior, requested me and William H. Seward (his secretary and chaplin) to draw up and publish to the Democracy of the various States holdin elecshuns this fall an address, or ruther an appeal, firmly beleevin that hed he extendid his tour to Maine, and isshood an address to em, that that State wood not hev gone ez it did. William refoozed to take part in the appeal, sayin that it warnt uv no use, and so the dooty devolved upon me.

Democrats and Conservatives uv the North:
Appresheatin the gravity uv the isshoo, I address yoo. The signs uv the times is ominus. A Radikle Congress, electid durin the time when the Southin States, wich comprises reely all the intellek uv this people, didn't take no part in the elekshen, bein too bizzy gettin out uv Sherman's way to open polls,—a Congress, I repeat, in which there ain't no Southern man, and wich consekently kant, by any stretch uv the human imaginashen, be considered Constitooshnel, hez dared to thwart the President uv the United States, and set up its will agin hisn! I need skarcely recount its high-handed acts uv usurpashen. It passed a bill givin rites to niggers, wich, accordin to Scripter (see Onesimus, Ham, and Hagar, the only three texts in Scripter uv any partikeler account) and the usages uv the Democrisy, ain't got no

rites; and the President, exercisin the high prerogatives put into his hands by the Constitooshen, vetoed it. Here the matter shood hev endid. He hed expressed, in a manner strikly Constitoo-shenel, his objecshens to the measure; and a proper regard for his feelins, and just deference for his opinions, ought to hev indicated the right course. Here wuz peace offered this Congress. Here wuz the tender uv a olive branch. The President didn't want a quarrel with Congres; he didn't desire a continuance uv the agitation wich hed shook the country like a Illinois ager; but he desired Peece. Congres cood hev hed it hed they only with-drawed their crood noshens uv what wuz rite and what wuz wrong; ratified, ez they shood hev done, sich laws ez the President saw fit to make: in short, hed they followed the correct rool when we hev a Demokratic President, and put the Govern-ment in his hands, with an abidin trust in his rectitood and wis-dom, we mite hev avoided this struggle, and thus wood hev bin peaceful. But this reckless Congris, bent upon concentrating power in its hands instid uv dividin it between him and Seward, passed the bill over his head, regardlis uv his feelins! The re-sponsibility for the dissension rests, therefore, with Congres.

But these questions are altogether too hefty for the Demo-kratic intellek, and I fling em out for the considerashen uv the few Post Masters we got from the Union ranks. To the Dimocrisy I address myself more partickerlerly.

DO YOU WANT TO MARRY A NIGGER? This ishoo is agin be-fore yoo. Are you in favor uv elevatin the Afrikin to a posishen where he kin be yoor ekal, or perhaps yoor sooperior? That ishoo is agin before yoo for yoor decision, only the danger to yoo is increased. The matter has become threatening; for, disgise it ez we may, thousands uv em kin read, and they are accumulatin property, and wearin good clothes to a extent trooly alarmin to the Dimokratic mind. We hev alluz consoled ourselves with the soothin reflection that there wuz a race lower down in the scale uv humanity than us uns. Shall we continue to enjoy that com-fort? That's the question for every Dimokrat to consider when he votes this fall. Remove the weight uv legal disability, and ten to one ef they don't outstrip US even, and then where are we goin to look for a race to look down upon? It's a close thing atween us now; and ez we uv this generation can't elevate our-selves, why, for our own peace uv mind, we must,—I repeet it,— MUST pull them down.

Agin then I repeet, DO YOU WANT TO MARRY A NIGGER?

Yoor daughters wunst carried banners onto wich wuz inskribed that trooly Dimokratic motto, "White husbands or none!" and in consequence they've bin mostly livin in the enjoyment uv none. Are they to go back on that holy determinashen to preserve the Anglo Sackson race on this continent in its purity? Do yoo want the nigger—the big buck nigger—the flat-footed nigger—the woolly-headed nigger—the long-heeled nigger—the bow-legged nigger—the NIGGER—to step up aside uv yoo, and exercise the prerogatives uv freemen in this country? Do you want the nigger aforesed to be mayors uv your towns, with all the hatred they hev towards us? Wat chance, O Dimokratic dweller in cities! think yoo yoo'd hev if hauled up afore a nigger mayor on a charge uv disorderly conduct? Wat chance wood yoor children hev in a skool uv wich all the teechers wuz niggers? Wat chance wood yoo hev wen arrestid for small misdemeanors, afore nigger judges? How, let me ask, in the name uv High Heaven, wood yoo like to be tried for hoss stealin afore a nigger jury?

"But," say some uv yoo, who, set ravin by drums, and flags, and sich, went off violently into the war, and wuz, perhaps, saved from starvin by niggers, "these niggers wuz our friends in the late war—they fought agin the South!"

O, wat a deloosion! O, wat blindnis! Troo, they did; and that shows the danger that's afore us; that lifts the fog from the precipice onto wich we are standin, and shows us our danger. Wat does this fact prove? It proves the onreasonablenis uv the Nigger—his discontentednis with the posishen to wich nacher assigned him, and his cussid disposition to upset the normel condition. The Bible makes him a servant unto his brethren (see Ham, Hagar, and Onesimus, three blessed texts). Science proves him to be, not a man, but a beast; and so, take him ez we may, either ez our brother or ez a beast,—and Dimocrisy, with that liberality wich hez always distinguished it, gives every man his choice wich theory to take,—his condition is servitood. But he, with a cussidness, a perversity wich I never cood understand, flies into the face uv the Divine decree, flies into the face uv science, and asserts his independence! He turned agin them ez hed fostered him; turned agin, in many instances, his own parents (in these instances, for convenience, the parents adopted the brethren theory), and for an abstract idea fought agin em. That restlessness under bonds alarmed the Dimocratic mind. We who owned em under the Skripter (see Onesimus, Hagar, and Ham),

and under the eternal laws uv scientific trooth, wuz content
with the arrangement, and why shood they not hev bin? Things
wuz normal. They worked, and we eat; and ef they hed bin content with this ekitable division uv the labor uv life, all wood hev
bin smooth to-day.

Their takin part agin us at the South, and in favor uv the
Federals, is, instead uv a coz uv feelin good toward em, a source
uv oneasiness; instid uv bein a reason for elevatin uv em, it's my
principal reason for depressin uv em. Sich onsettled minds shood
be quieted; this itchin to raise theirselves shood be crushed out
uv em, that Science and Holy Writ (see Onesimus, Hagar, and
Ham) may be vindicated.

Shel we desert Androo Johnson, after all the trouble he hez
bin to in gettin back to us? Shel we elect a Congres this fall so
soaked in Ablishin—so filled with objeckshuns to our Southern
brethren, ez to refooze to receive em back into the seats which
they vacated? Consider! The Southern Dimokracy hevn't,
and don't, lay up nothin agin yoo. They are willin to forgive
and forget. They failed, but they are willin to forgiv the cause uv
the failyoor. They hevn't got the government they wanted, but
they find no fault with that, but are willin to take charge of the
wun they hev bin compelled to live under. Kin they offer fairer?
The fate uv war wuz agin em. Buryin all hard feelins, they extend to us Chrischen charity, and say, Here we are—take us—
give us our old places. They hev bin chastened. Their household
gods hev bin destroyed, and their temples torn down. Wun neighbor uv mine lost two sons in the Confedrit army; another son,
which he hed refoosed $1500 for in 1860, he wuz compelled to
shoot, coz he wuz bound to run away into the Federal army; and
two octoroons, which he hed a dozen times refoosed $2500 for,
each, in Noo Orleans, he saw layin dead on the steps uv a skool
house in Memphis. Hez he suffered nothin? And yet he is willin
to take a seat in Congress—forgettin all he hez suffered, and for-
givin the cause thereof. What wickedness it is wich would
further bruise sich a broken reed!

Therefore, ez yoo love yourselves and hate the nigger, I implore yoo to act. Take yoor choice uv the platforms uv the different States—vote ez a Johnson Unionist, or ez a Democratic John-
sonian—but vote.

Kentucky holds out her hands appealingly! Kentucky im-
plores yoo to build up a bulwark North uv the Ohio River to
save what little is left uv pure Dimokracy there! Kentucky will

back yoo in yoor endeavors. Will you heed her cry? Shel she appeel in vain? Forbid it, Hevin!

PETROLEUM V. NASBY, P. M.

(wich is Postmaster).

7. *"Consiliashen Is Our Best Holt": A Switch in Tactics*

POST OFFIS, CONFEDRIT × ROADS
(wich is in the Stait uv Kentucky),
March 28, 1867.

I hev made many sudden and rather 'strordinary changes in politix—some so very sudden that the movement perdoost conjestion uv the conshence. I rekollect wunst uv advokatin free trade and high protective tariff, all within twelve hours (I made a speech in a agricultooral deestrik uv Noo York in the forenoon, at 10 A. M., and in a manufacturin town in Pennsylvany in the evenin, our platform bein so construktid that both sides cood find a endorsement in it), and hev performed many other feats uv moral gymnastiks; but this last change I hev bin called upon to make is probably the suddenest. Last week Toosday, Deekin Pogram, Captain McPelter, and I, wuz engaged in riddin the Corners uv niggers. We hed endoord em ez long ez we thot possible, and determined on standin it no longer. Selectin three, wich we wuz satisfied hed too much spellin-book into em to be enslaved agin, we wuz preparin notises to be served onto em, orderin em to leave in twenty-four hours, when I reseeved in the northern mail a letter marked "Free—Alex. W. Randell, P. M. G." I knowd it wuz offishel to-wunst—that blessid signatoor is on my commisshun, and I've contemplatid it too often to be mistaken in it. Its contents wuz brief, and run thus:—

"To all Postmasters in the Southern States: The niggers hev votes—consiliashen is our best holt. See to it."

This breef, tho not hard to be understood order, wuz sealed with the offishel seal uv the Post Offis Department, stampt into putty instid uv wax, to wit: a loaf of bread, under a roll uv butter, with ten hands a grabbin at it. I comprehended the situation at site, and set about doin my dooty with Spartan firmness. "Deekin," sez I, tearin up the notises, "these niggers we hev misunderstood. They are not a inferior race—they are not descendants uv Ham and Hager—it wuzn't Paul's idea in sendin back Onesimus to condemn him to servitood—we hev misunderstood the situation, and must make amends. The nigger is devoid uv smell, and is trooly a man and a brother!"

"Wat?" said the Deekin, tippin back in amazement.

"Jest wat I say," sez I. "Read that," and I flung him the letter.

The upshot uv the conference wich follered wuz the callin uv a meetin the next nite, at wich all the Ethiopians uv the Corners wuz invited and urged to be present.

The trouble wuz to git the niggers to attend the meetin. The fust one I spoke to lafft in my face, and askt me how long it wuz sence I hed helped hang a couple uv niggers, by way uv finishin off a celebrashen. Pollock, the Illinois storekeeper, got hold uv it, and told Joe Bigler, and Joe swore that ef the niggers hedn't any more sense than we give em credit for, in sposin we cood bamboozle em so cheep, he shood go back to the old beleef, to wit: that they wuz only a sooperior race uv monkeys, after all; and by nite every nigger in the visinity wuz postid thoroughly, and out uv all uv em I cood only git four who would promise to attend, and them the Deekin hed to pay $2 apiece to. To give it eclaw I promised one uv em $5 (to be paid at the close uv the meetin) to sit on the stand with me, wich, bein a very poor man, and hevin a sick wife in a shanty near by, who wuz suffering for medicine (wich he coodent git without money), he accepted.

At this pint an idee struck me. I remembered Philadelfy, and determined to hev a scene rivalin the Couch and Orr biznis. "Another thing, Cuff. Understand that it's a part uv the bargain that when in my speech I turn to yoo and stomp, yoo must rise and embrace me."

"Wat?" sez he.

"Fall into my arms, lovin-like—yoo understand—jest as tho we wuz long-lost brothers!"

"Scuse me!" sed he. "I'se a mity low nigger, and wants to buy de old woman some quinine, and wood do most anything foah dat; but, golly, dat's too much!"

"Not a cent," sed I, sternly, assoomin my most piercinist gaze; "onless this is included!"

"Well," returned he, sulkily, "ef I must, I speck I must; but, golly—"

The nite arrived, and the meetin-house wuz full. We thot fust uv holding it in the chapel uv the College, but give up the

idea ez impracticable, ez, owin to the dillytorinis uv our Northern friends in forwardin sich subscripshens ez they hev raised,
we hevent got no further with the bildin than layin the corner-
stun. In the front wuz the four niggers, all in clean shirts, and
on the stand wuz the nigger I hed engaged. Over the platform,
wuz the follerin mottoes:—

"In Yoonion ther is strength— For President in 1868, Fernando Wood. For Vice President, Frederick Duglis."

"In the nigger, strength— In the Caucashen, beauty— In
the mulatter, who is trooly the noblest uv the human species—
both."

In addishen to these, we dug up all the old mottoes wich
Jefferson writ, about yooniversal liberty and sich, wich hedn't bin
quoted in Kentucky for twenty years, and postid em up; in brief,
hed Wendell Phillips' blessed sperit bin a hoverin over that
meetin-house, it wood hev smiled approvinly.

I spoke to em elokently on the yooniversal brotherhood uv
mankind, holdin that whatever else cood be sed, Adam wuz the
father uv all mankind, and that the only difference between a
white man and a nigger wuz, the nigger wuz sun-burnt. The nigger, I remarkt, wuz ondoubtedly, origenally white; but hevin
bin, sence his arrival in this country, addicted to agricultooral
persoots, he hed become tanned to a degree wich, tho it marred
his physikle beauty, did not interfere with his sterlin goodnis uv
heart. Ther hed bin differences between the races—at times
ther hed bin onpleasantnises wich no one regretted more than I.
The whites uv the Corners hed not alluz bin ez considrit ez I
cood hev wished. They hed flogd sevral uv em, and hung many
more, and in times past hed held em in slavery and sich; but that
shood not be thot uv at this happy time. It wuz constooshnel to
do these things then, and Kentucky wuz eminently a law-abidin
State. "Here," sez I, "on this platform, with the flag uv our common country over me, I declare eternal friendship to the colored
man, and to seel the declarashen I thus embrace—"

The obstinit nigger didn't stir a step.

"Come up and fling yoor arms around me, you black cuss,"
sed I, in a stage whisper. "Come up!"

"No yoo don't, boss!" sed the nigger, in a loud voice, wich
wuz audible all over the church, and holdin out his hand. "I can't
trust yoo a bressid minit. Gib me de $5 fust. Yoo owe dis chile
foah dollars now fo' sawin wood fo' yoah post offis, and ef we's a
gwine to hab our rites de fus yoose I shel put mine to will be the

gittin dat money. Pay up fus, and de 'brace afterward. I can't do sich a disagreeable ting widout de cash in advance."

This ruther destroyed the effect. The unities wuzn't preserved. The niggers in front bust out in a torturing laff, and Pollock and Bigler rolld in convulsions uv lafture, in wich half uv our people joined. Me a standin petrified, in the attitood of embracin, and that cussed nigger standin with his hand extended for the money, with the Deekin and Bascom horrorstruck jist behind, formed a tabloo wich wuz more strikin than pleasant.

The meetin wuz to-wunst adjourned, for it wuz evident to the dullest comprehenshen that nothin more coodent be done that nite. Es yoosual I failed for want uv capital. Hed I bin possesst uv the paltry sum uv five dollars, how diffrent wood hev bin the result! Perchance we may, thro that defishency, lose Kentucky. It must never occur agin—my salary must be raised. I can't make brix without straw.

Joe Bigler met me next mornin, and remarkt that he regrettid the occurrence, ez he ardently desired to see the two races a pullin together. "The fault, Perfessor," sed he, "wuz in not managin properly. The next time yoo want a 'spectable nigger to sit on the platform with yoo and the Deekin, or kiss or embrace yoo—git him drunk. He'll do it then, probably—I know he will. Ef he's drunk enuff, he'll hurrah for Johnson, and it's possible to git em down to the pint uv votin with yoo. Lord! how whiskey drags a man down. See wat it's brot yoo to!" and the insultin wretch rolled off, laffin boisterously. "Git em drunk, Perfesser!" he yelled ez long ez he cood see me.

We don't intend to give it up. Bigler's advice wuz given in jest; but, nevertheless, I shel act upon it. Whiskey is wat brings white men to us; and ef a white man kin be thus capchered, why not a nigger? The Afrikin hezn't got ez far to fall to git down to our level, and it'll take less to bring him. Bascom ordered five barrels to-day, wich I spose the Administrashen will pay for. We hev yet the Noo York Custom House, and more uv the perkesits must be yoosed for politikle purposes.

PETROLEUM V. NASBY, P. M.

(wich is Postmaster), and likewise Professor.

8. *"Cheerin Indicashuns uv the Pride uv Race":*
Ohio Offers a Ray of Hope

POST OFFIS, CONFEDRIT × ROADS
(wich is in the Stait uv Kentucky),
October 12, 1867.

Feelin that the time hed arrived which wuz to decide whether 7,000 degradid niggers wuz to grind 500,000 proud Caucashens into the dust, I felt that ef I shood fail in my dooty now, I shood be forever disgraced. Accordingly, I put in the eleckshun day at a Dimocratic town in Ohio—the battle-field—the identikle place into wich I made a speech doorin the campane.

I arrived ther on the mornin uv the elekshun, and found that comperhensive arrangements hed bin made for defeatin this most nefarus and dangerous proposishen. Paradin the streets ez early ez 7 A. M. wuz a wagon containin 25 virgins, runnin from 27 to 39, the most uv em ruther wiry in texture, and over their heads wuz banners, with the followin techin inscriptions: "Fathers, save us from Nigger Ekality!" "White Husbans or none!" It wood hev bin better, I thot, hed they bin somewhat younger. Ther wuz suthin preposterous in the ijee uv females uv that age callin upon fathers to save em from anythin, when in the course of nacher their fathers must hev bin a lyin in the silent tomb for several consecutive years, onless, indeed, they marrid young. Ef still livin (I judged from the aged appearance uv the damsels), their parents must be too far advanced in yeers to take an activ part in biznis. In another wagon wuz a collekshun uv men wich hed bin hired from the railrode, twelve miles distant, whose banners read, "Shel ignerent Niggers vote beside intelligint Wite men?" Hangin over the polls wuz a broad piece uv white muslin, onto wich was painted, in large letters, "Caucashuns, Respeck yer Noses—the nigger stinks!" Then I knowed it wuz safe. That odor hez never yet bin resisted by the Democrasy, and it hez its inflooence over Republikins.

I never saw sich enthoosiasm, or more cheerin indicashuns uv the pride uv race. Ez evidence uv the deep feeling that pervaded that community, I state that nine paupers in the poorhouse demanded to be taken to the polls, that they might enter their protest agin bringin the nigger up to a ekality with em, wich wuz nine gain with no offsets, ez ther wuzn't an Ablishnist

in the institooshun. Two men, in the county jale for petty lar-
ceny, wuz, at their own rekest, taken out of doorence vile by the
Sheriff uv the county, that they mite, by the ballot, protest agin
bein degraded by bein compelled, when their time wuz out, to
acknowledge the nigger ez their ekal. One enthoosiastic Dimekrat, who cost us $5, hed to be carried to the polls. He hed com-
menced early at one uv the groseries, and hed succumbed afore
votin. We found him sleepin peacefully in a barn. We lifted the
patriotic man, and in percession marched to the polls. We stood
him on his feet, two men supportin him—one on either side. I
put a straight ticket into his fingers, and takin his wrist with one
hand, held his fingers together with tother, and guided his hand
to the box. Ez it neared the winder, he started ez ef a elec-
tric shock hed struck him, and, straightenin up, asked, "Is it the
sthrate ticket? Is Constooshnel Amindmint No! onto it?"

Ashoorin him that it wuz all rite, he suffered me to hold his
hand out to the Judge uv Eleckshun, who took the ballot and
deposited it in the box. "Thank Hivin!" sed he, "the nagur is not
yet my ayquil!" and doublin up at the thigh and kneejoints, he
sank, limber-like, and gently, onto the ground. Ez he hed discharged the dooty uv an Amerikin freeman, we rolled him out
to one side uv the house, wher the drippin uv rain from the roof
wood do suthin toward soberin him off, and left him alone in
his glory.

The amendment got but a very few votes in that locality.
The Republikins jined us in repudiatin it, mostly upon
ethnologikle grounds. One asserted that he hed bin in favor uv
emancipashen in time uv war, becoz the Afrikin cood thereby be
indoost to fite agin their Southern masters, and it wood hev the
effeck uv makin the drafts come lighter in his township. He wuz
a humanitarian likewise. He opposed crooelty toward em. He
wept when he heerd uv the massacre at Fort Piller, becoz in the
army the nigger wuz ez much a man ez anybody, and sich wholesale slaughters tendid to make calls for "500,000 more" more frekent. But when it come to givin uv em the privilege uv votin beside him, it coodent be thot uv. He cood never consent that a race
whose heels wuz longer than hizzen shood rool Ameriky. "My
God!" sed this ardent Republikin, "ef you give em the ballot, wat
kin prevent em from bein Congrismen, Senators, Vice-Presidents,
and even Presidents? I shudder when I think uv it;" and he hurried in his vote.

I didn't quite see the force uv his objecshen, for it never ok-

kurred to me that bein sent to Congris wuz the nateral consekence uv votin. I hev voted for thirty years, at many elections
four or five times, but I hev never bin to Congris. Wher is the
constituency wich wood elect me? But it wuzn't my bizniss to con-
trovert his posishen. It made no difference to me wat his reason
wuz for votin ez I desired him to vote.

The nigger-lovers beat up one man to vote for the Amendment, wich, I saw by his dissatisfied look, hed bin over-
perswadid. "Sir!" sed I, "do yoo consider a Afrikin suffishently
intelligent to be trustid with so potent a weapon ez the ballot?"

Bustin away from them wich hed him in charge, he exclaimed, "No, I don't! I can't vote for it. They ain't intelligent
enuff. Sir, scratch off the 'Yes' from my ballot, and put onto it
'No!'"

"Here is a pensil," sed I.

"Do it yerself," sed he; "I can't write."

And I did it. Sich is the effeck uv a word in season. Words
fitly spoken is apples uv gold, set in picters uv silver.

One man woodent listen to me, but votid the Amendment.
He hed bin a soljer, and for eleven months pertook uv the hospitality uv the Confedrits at Andersonville. Escapin, he wuz
helped to the Fedral lines by a nigger, who wuz flogged almost
to death, in his site, for not betrayin wher he wuz hid. I mite ez
well hev talked to a lamp-post, or whispered Gray's Elegy into
the ears uv a dead mule, wich is the deadest thing I ever see. Ez
he shoved in his ballot, he remarkt suthin about he'd ruther see
a nigger vote than a d—d rebel, any time. From the direckshun
uv his eye-site, I persoom he referred to me.

I left for home ez soon ez the votes wuz counted, and the result wuz made known, only waitin till the poll-books wuz made
out, and the judges uv eleckshun hed got ther names written by
the clerks, and hed made their marks to em. On my way
home I wuz gratified to see how the nateral antipathy to the nigger hed revived. At Cincinati, the nite uv the eleckshn, they
wuz bangin uv em about, the patriotic Democrisy goin for em
wherever they cood find em, and the next day, ez I saw em at the
ralerode stashens, they hed, generally speekin, ther heds ban-
daged. It wuz cheerin to me, and I gloated over it.

Full uv gladnis, I entered Kentucky, and joyfully I wendid
my way to the Corners. I wuz the bearer uv tidins uv great joy,
and my feet wuz pleasant onto the mountins. Ez I walked into
Bascom's, they all saw in my face suthin uv importance.

"Wat is it?" sed Deekin Pogram. "Is it weal or woe?"

"Is the proud Caucashen still in the ascendant in Ohio, or hez the grovelin Afrikin ground him into the dust?" askt Issaker Gavitt.

"My friend," sed I, takin up the Deekin's whisky, wich, in the eggscitement uv the moment, he didn't observe, "the Constitooshnel Amendment, givin the nigger ekal rites, hez bin votid down by the liberty-lovin freemen uv Ohio. Three cheers for Ohio."

They wuz given with a will. The wildest enthoosiasm wuz awakened. Bascom put a spigot in a fresh barl, and the church bells wuz set a ringin. The niggers wore a dismayed look, and got out uv the way ez soon ez possible. A meetin wuz to-wunst organized. Deekin Pogram felt that this wuz a proud day. Light wuz breakin. The dark clouds uv fanaticism wuz breakin away. We hed now the Afrikin in his normal posishen in Ohio, and we will soon hev him likewise in Kentucky. He moved the adopshen uv the follerin resolooshens:—

"WAREAS, Noer cust Canan, and condemned him to be a servant onto his brethren, thereby cleerly indikatin the status uv the race for all time to be one uv inferiority; and,

"WAREAS, To further show to the eyes uv the most obtoose that a difference wuz intended, the Almighty gave the nigger a different anatomicle struckter, for full partikelars uv wich see the speeches uv the Demokratic stumpers doorin the late campaign; and,

"WAREAS, The attempt to place the nigger on an ekality with the white in votin ez well ez taxashun, we consider the sappin uv the very foundashun uv civil liberty, ez well ez uv the Crischen religion; therefore,

"*Resolved,* That the Constooshnel and Biblikle Democracy uv Kentucky send greetin to their brethren uv Ohio, with thanks for their effectooal squelchin uv nigger superiority.

"*Resolved,* That to the Republikins uv Ohio, who voted agin suffrage, our thanks is due, and we congratulate em that now they, ez well ez us, are saved from the danger uv marryin niggers; and likewise, do we asshoor em, that in a spirit uv mutual forbearance, we care not wat particular creed they perfess, so long ez they vote our principles.

"*Resolved,* That the will uv the people havin bin cleerly indikated, we demand the insershun uv the word 'white' in the Constitooshun uv the Yoonited States.

"*Resolved,* That we ask the colored voters uv Tennessee, and other States where colored men hev votes, to observe how they are treated in Ohio, where the Ablishnists don't need em. In them States we extend to em a corjel invitashun to act with us."

The fakulty uv the Institoot met next mornin, for the purpus uv revisin the Scripters. It wuz decided that the word "white" should be insertid wherever necessary, and that that edishen only be yoosed by the Dimocracy and Conservativ Republikins. We made progress, the follerin bein a few uv the changes:—

" 'So God created a *white* man in his own image.'
" 'Whosoever, therefore, shall confess me before *white* men,' &c.
" 'Suffer little *white* children to come unto me, for uv sich is the kingdom uv Heaven.' "

Wich last is comfortin, ez it shows that the distincshen is kept up through all eternity. I give these merely ez samples. We shel hev it finisht in a few days, and, ef funds kin be raised, shel publish it. Such a vershun uv the Skripters is needid.

PETROLEUM V. NASBY, P. M.
(wich is Postmaster).

9. *The Ideal Presidential Candidate:* *"All the Elements uv Popularity"*

POST OFFIS, CONFEDRIT × ROADS
(wich is in the Stait uv Kentucky),
June 1, 1868.

The matter uv a Presidenshl candidate hez opprest me, and hez also exercised the gigantic intellex who congregate at the Corners. We hev desided that Cheef Justis Chase won't do. We kin support him cheerfully, for his method uv conduktin the impeachment trial hez satisfied us uv his hankerin for a standin in our party. Besides this, havin made a start, we consider him safe anyhow. The man wich kin take a nominashen at our hands, or identify hisself with us, may alluz be countid onto. The Ablishnists never forgive sich, and ther ain't no other place to go.

When Johnson and Doolittle and that crowd left the Ablish-nists, I knew where they would land better than they did. *Facilis descensus averni,* wich bein translated into the vulgar tongue, means, the road to hell is macadamized. Hancock won't do, be-coz our Southern brethren hev a prejoodis agin the flag he drawd his sword under. Pendleton wood anser the West, but the East is opposed to him. I therefore, after givin the matter matoor considerashen, hev desided to propose for the posishen the name uv Jethro L. Kippins, uv Alexander county, Illinoy.

I hev the follerin reasons for insistin on his nominashen:—

1. He's geographically level. By lookin on the map, it will be seen that that county in Illinoy is the extreme south-westerly part uv the State. It is a Northern county with Southern ideas. Across the river is Kentucky, west is south-eastern Missoury, and east is lower Injeany. They grow tobacco there, and yearn after slave labor ez intensly ez we do across the river.

2. Nobody knows him. The name uv Jethro L. Kippins, hez never filled the soundin trump uv fame. With him on our tikkit several pints wood be gained. On all the questions on wich there is a doubt in the minds uv the Democracy, Jethro L. Kippens is uncommitted. He is unembarrassed with views, and on trouble-some questions hez nary an opinyun. The trouble Pendleton hez with the greenbax wood not affect him, neither wood any uv them other questions wich are ruther embarrassin than other-wise. He hez but one political principle, wich he holds is enuff for any one man, and that is Democracy, ez it hez bin, ez it is, and ez it may be. He beleeves firmly in the cuss uv Canaan, he holds close to Onesimus and Hagar, and hez sworn a solemn oath that no nigger shel ever marry a daughter uv hizzen. This noble sentiment, wich alluz strikes a responsive cord in every buzzum, wood be emblazoned on the Kippins banner.

3. Jethro L. Kippinses posishen on the war question is happy. He opposed all the steps wich led to it, and when it finally broke out, he proposed the only troo Demokratic way uv stop-pin it. It wuz his opinyun that we hed no rite to coerce the South —that there wuz no warrant in the Constitooshen for any sich perceedin. "Ef Boregard fires onto Major Anderson," sed he, "let Major Anderson go afore the nearest Justice uv the Peece and hev him bound over to keep the peece, and ef the Justis can't enforce his warrant, why that ends it. We can't go beyond the Constitooshn." After hostilities actooally begun, his posishen wuz eminently satisfactory to both sides. He wuz in favor uv the

war, but opposed to its prosecooshen. He remarkt that the South hed committed a indiscreshen, but were he in Congris he shoodn't vote for nary man nor dollar for carryin on a war agin em. His two sons served in the war, one in the Confedrit servis and one in the Fedral—both ez sutlers. The war bore heavy on him—he made great sacrifices. Three other sons he supported in Canada doorin the continyooance uv the unnachrel strife.

4. Jethro L. Kippins hez all the elements uv popularity. He wuz born in a log cabin; he studied Daboll's Arithmetic by the lite uv a pine knot, held for the purpose by his mother; he drove hoss on the canal, wuz a salt boiler in Southern Ohio, a wagon boy on the Nashnel Road, wuz left an orphan when six weeks old, swept a store in his early yooth, went down the Mississippi on a flat boat, wuz in the Mexikin war, and hez a consoomin pashen for horses. He hez, in this, the advantage of Grant, ez his pashen wuz so consoomin that it got him into a temporary difficulty, wich required 12 men, a Judge, and two lawyers to settle, one uv the lawyers bein the State's Attorney uv the county. These facts in his biography I got from his own lips. Ef there's any discrepancies, uv course the committee on biography will reconcile em. It may be that he may hev done too much—wich is to say, ef all he sez is troo, he wood be two or three hundred years old. Ef so, it will hev to be pared down. He hez bin justis uv the peece ten years in his native township, wich gives him a splendid knowledge uv constooshnel law.

5. He's trooly nashnel in his views. He knows no North, no South, no East, no West, no nothin. That last qualificashen mite prejudis some agin him, but to me its his chief holt. For with sich a man in the Presidenshel chair I wood be safe. We hev an abundance uv sich men ez Wood, Seymour, Vallandygum, et settry, who kin manage a President, but who are too odorous to be electid very much to that posishen themselves. Therefore, it's necessary that precisely sich a man ez I hev described be electid; and the fact that Chase knows too much, is the objection I hev to him. Polk wuz manageable, Pierce eminently so, and poor old Bookannon was wonderfully pliable.

Sich is the candidate wich I present. There are many pints in his favor. Our people wood to-wunst exclaim, "Who'n thunder is Kippins?" and before they cood find out, the day uv election wood be on em, and they'd vote him. His hevin no record is also in his favor. Wat wood Pendleton, Vallandygum, Seymour, and Wood give ef they hed no record? A record is like a

tin kittle to a dog's tale—it's a noisy appendage, wich makes the
dog conspicuous, and invites everybody to shy a brick at him.

I hevent menshund in this, nor shel I, who would be a
proper man for the seckund place on the ticket. I hev my opinion. Kentucky is deservin uv recognishun—that's all I shel say.
The modesty wich is characteristic uv me prevents me from segestin the partickeler citizen uv Kentucky who ought to be thus honored. We shal see whether or not republics is ongrateful.

PETROLEUM V. NASBY, P. M.
(wich is Postmaster).

P. S. The fact that Jethro L. Kippins holds my note
for $18.63, with interest for two yeers, hez no inflooence in my
segestin his name. I am inflooenced by no mercenary consider-
ashuns.

10. Crisis at the Corners: "The Last Outrage Wich a Chivalrous People Has Been Compelled to Bear"

POST OFFIS, CONFEDRIT X ROADS
(wich is in the Stait uv Kentucky),
April 9, 1869.

Ef the Dimocrisy uv the North arn't satisfied by this time
that the ultimate intenshen uv the Ablishnists is to subjoogate
em and redoose em to the level uv the nigger, the voice uv one
risin from the dead woodn't avail nothin. Yesterday the last outrage wich a chivalrous people has been compelled to bear was
perpetrated onto a citizen of the Corners. A NIGGER IS NOW AN
OFFIS-HOLDER AT THE CORNERS! I shel state the case calmly.

The posishen uv Assessor uv Internal Revenoo for the Deestrick uv wich the Corners is the centre, hez bin held by Captain
Hugh McPelter, late uv Morgan's cavalry, C. S. A. That he hez
filled the posishen to the satisfaction uv the citizens uv the Corners, no one denies. He is a distiller—in fact he and Elder Pennibacker run the two distilleries in the town, and they hev did a
thrivin biznis. McPelter wuz Assessor, and Pennibacker Collector,
and ez a consekence none uv the capital uv the Corners hez bin
substracted and carried to Washington to feed the Ablishen
theeves there. Ez no tax hez ever bin paid on the whiskey at this

place, Bascom hez bin enabled to continyoo to sell it at five cents per drink, while everywhere else the regler price is ten and fifteen. There wuz other advantages in havin the Assessorship and Collectorship in their hands. By simply hintin to em that it wuz my dooty ez a Fedril offis-holder to investigate their modes uv doin the government biznis, I hev not only bin the happy recipient uv scores uv two gallon jugs, but I hev bin enabled at divers and sundry times to prokoor loans uv em uv various amounts, the lowest bein $1.75, and the highest reachin $20.

This happy condishun uv affairs is bustid. Gabrel Babcock, a nigger—that is, a half nigger—formerly the property uv Deekin Pogram, and who looks enuff like the Deekin's oldest son, Jehiel, to be his half-brother, wuz last week appinted and confirmed Assessor in the place uv Captain McPelter, and immejitely he entered onto the discharge uv his dooties.

There are many feechers pekoolyerly aggravatin in the appintment. To begin with, this Babcock wuz notoriously obnoxyus to the Corners doorin the late onpleasantnis. At the beginnin thereof he run away from Deekin Pogram and entered the Fedral servis. He wuz partikerly activ and cussid. His knowledge uv the country made him yooseful to the Fedral offisers ez a guide and scout, and at least one Fedral victory is chargeable direct to the information he brot. Then his wife wuz knowd to hev hid five Fedral soljers who hed escaped from Andersonville. When he finally fell into the hands uv Captain McPelter at Fort Pillow kin it be wondered at that he wuz left for dead? or kin it be wondered at that the people uv the Corners wuz surprized when he appeared among em at the close uv the war with one leg off and one arm stiff? Not much. Captain McPelter wuzn't in the habit uv half doin his work, and the appearance uv this nigger who hed passed through his hands ruther astonished the captin.

Doorin his absence he hed learned to read and write, and he wuz made a teecher in the Freedmen's Skool wich wuz establisht in this place, and now he's Assessor, with Pollock on his bond.

Ez a matter uv course we despair uv the republic. Wat freedom kin there be for us with a nigger in offishel posishen to tyranize over us? Wat man uv culcher, uv ejucashen, uv refinement, kin afford to live in a community where a disgustin mulatto is made not only our ekal but our sooperior?

Deekin Pogram said this indignantly to Joe Bigler, who immejitly askt the Deekin whether or not he didn't count Babcock's mother his ekal thirty years ago? Wich question, wich was askt in the presence uv the Deekin's wife, who hez a temper, wuz the occasion uv severe remarks between the worthy pair. Joe Bigler delites in openin old sores.

The first act uv this Babcock in his offishl capassity wuz the shuttin up uv McPelter's and Pennibacker's distilleries, and Bascom's bar, on the skore that none uv em hed ever taken out licenses, or even paid any taxes. There wuz the most terrific ebulishn uv feelin at this act of tyranny that it hez ever bin my lot to witness.

"Kill the d—d nigger!"

"Hang the black cuss!"

"Down with the Afrikin despot!"

Shoutid the infuriated citizins. With a refinement uv crooelty wich cood only be the offspring uv a most depraved and vishus mind, he shut up these places at seven o'clock in the mornin, before one uv the citizens hed hed his mornin bitters! Hed he postponed it an hour we might hev fought it out, for some one else would hev prokoored a supply before noon, and things would hev gone on normal. But here wuz the entire populashen uv the Corners at 7 A. M., with throats like limekilns, and nary a drop to be hed for love or money. The skeem wuz well considered and successful. The citizens cood hold out but fifteen minits, and they surrendered. They gave bonds, to wich they all appended their marks, to indemnify the government for back taxes, and compelled Bascom to take out license. This done, the nigger, who wuz backt up by Bigler and Pollock, opened his doors, and the multitood surged in and wuz satisfied. To think uv a nigger holdin the destinies uv the Corners in his hands!

Ez a matter uv course, Elder Pennibacker will follow next; "indeed he wants to resign now, for, sez he, with the Assessorship in hostile hands uv wat avail is it to be Collector?" And then, how long will my head stay on my shoulders? Is a nigger to take my place! Already Bascom hez raised his price to 10 cts. per drink, and notified me that likker from this time out is cash, and already hez Pennibacker and McPelter refoozed to lend me a cent! My kingdom is crumblin. The eleckshen uv Grant wuz the wedge wich is rivin me from stem to stern. I shel be compelled to go hentz a broken man. Good Hevings, why coodn't I hev died while Johnson wuz still President!

The blindness uv this present Administrashen is trooly astonishen. Things wuz settlin rapidly at the Corners. McPelter wuz becomin pacified, and Deekin Pennibacker likewise. They wuz not satisfied with the Government, nor did they approve uv anything it did, but they were passive. Now the old sores is opened. Now McPelter is breathin slaughter, and is for lettin slip the dorgs uv war. And wat hez Grant got in return? Why, a nigger who wuz already hizzen, and the two whites at the Corners who voted for him last fall, and will agin, anyhow. General Grant evidently don't mean to pacify us—he ain't on the soothe, nor hez he a clear idea uv wat is needed to conciliate. I shel go next. There is to be a meetin held next week to protest agin these changes, but it won't avail nothin. We are all marked.

PETROLEUM V. NASBY, P. M.
(wich means Postmaster).

11. Emancipation and the Labor Movement: "Mechanics of the Hawty Caucashen Race"

POST OFFIS, CONFEDRIT × ROADS
(wich is in the Stait uv Kentucky),
May 28, 1869.

The agitashen uv the question uv niggers labrin with white men in Washington reached the Corners four weeks ago, and perdoost, ez mite hev bin expectid, most profound feelin. Our white artisans assembled to-wunst and passed resolooshens in sympathy with their brethren in Washington, and urgin uv em to hold out to the bitter end rather than compermise their dignity by lowerin themselves to the level uv the greasy Afriken. The meetin wuznt a large one, for we hev only five mechanics uv the hawty Caucashen race at the Corners, but it wuz enthoosiastic. Three uv the five hed bin at Bascom's four days, hevin bin jist paid off by a new-comer, for a house they hed repaired for him, and they wuz in a frame uv mind for most anything that wuz eggscitin.

I directed the attenshun uv these men to the fact that a nigger plasterer wuz even at that time employed in plasterin a house between the Corners and Garrettstown, and I askt em ef they wuz content to lay still and see an inferior race take the bread out uv their mouths in that way? I implored em, ez labrin men, to preserve the dignity uv labor. Shel niggers invade yoor okkepashens?

They wuznt none uv em plasterers, but they replied, "Never! Never!" and demanded, with the utmost promptitood, to be showd the wretch, that they mite go for him. But I restraned em till I hed organized em into a Free Labor Unyun, which perhibited anybody from workin at anythin which didn't jine it, and wich perhibitid niggers from jinin it. This preliminary work accomplished, I remarkt, "Follow me!" They did it with alacrity.

On reachin the house we halted, and there our eyes rested onto a site wich blarsted em. There wuz a nigger, a full-blooded nigger, with a cap onto him, and overalls, plasterin away, whistlin and singin (sometimes one, sometimes another, and then agin both to-wunst) Methodist hymns. And ever and anon the unthinkin man of inferiority wood stop and execoot a break-down, and laff to hisself, so that he could be heard a mile. The disgustin wretch displayed his grovelin nacher by drinkin water out uv a bucket wich he hed handy by him.

We made short work uv it. We informed him that the la-borers uv the Corners hed organized a Union, and that no one cood be permitted to work within its boundaries ceptin members thereof.

"Berry well!" remarkt the Afrikin cuss, calmly puttin on a dab uv mortar and smoothin it, "berry well! I'll jine the Yoon-yun."

"But you can't. No nigger can be admitted."

"Den I specks I shel hev to go on and work widout bein a member. De ole woman and de babies must hab dar bread, yoo know."

Sich insolence cood not, uv course, be tolerated. We hed stated the case to him calmly and dispassionately. We hed in-formed him uv the laws we hed made, and this wretch deliber-ately defied us, by insistin that he shood go on with his work! Ther wuz but one course to take, and we took it. We snaked the platform out from under him; we tore up his mortar bed; we broke his trowel and other tools, and notified him offishelly that any attempt at resoomin work would result in lynchin uv him.

The next day we found that the nigger hed in trooth quit plasterin, but hed found employment ez a striker in a black-smith shop. Uv course sich an outrage on the pure Caucashen employed in that shop, wich his name wuz O'Toole, cood not be permitted, and ez O'Toole refoosed to work with him, he wuz discharged. The next day I notist him on the streets, rather pale and haggard than otherwise, carryin home a shin bone uv beef wich he hed bought. The next day after I observed that he lookt better, and I diskivered that he hed found employment at last on a turnpike road wich is bein built east uv the town. Issaker Gavitt and me, the two champions uv labor for this seck-shun (ez we don't work we hev time to attend to it), sejested to the noble Celts employed on the job the hidjusnis uv compellin em to work on an ekality with a nigger, and they struck agin it with the yoosual result. The nigger wuz discharged. He made but one or two more efforts. He undertook to git work at various places, but by this time it wuz well enuff knowd that the citizens uv the Corners wuz inflexibly opposed to the recognisin uv em in any capassity, and he yeelded. He got very thin, and pale, and haggard, and his large family likewise. It wuz evident that they wuznt feelin very well at home. Notis the nateral result of free-dom! He ABSLOOTTELY BEGGED! But uv course the Corners wood give nothin to a nigger. Then the instinktiv nateral cussidness uv the nigger—the infernal depravity wich is inherent into all uv em—began to display itself. He demoralized rapidly, and in a week became a most disgustin objick. He stole chickens uv Dee-kin Pogram, leastways Deekin Pogram's chickens wuz missin, and who should hev stole em but this nigger? He stole corn uv Elder Pennebacker, and wuz finally detected takin a ham from Bas-com's smoke-house. There wuz no doubt ez to his guilt; he wuz taken in the act, with the fatal ham in his possession. He hed taken it home, and his wife wuz fryin large slices uv it.

There cood be but one endin to *sich* a succession uv crimes. The citizens were too much incensed to await the uncer-tain ackshen uv the law, and they hung him at site. The Corners will never tolerate a nigger theef in their midst, no how.

Uv course I improved the occasion. Ez his body wuz a swingin in the air, I askt our people to behold the fruits of Radicalism and Fanatycism. That nigger wuz wunst the happy slave uv a happy owner; there wuz atween em a nateral relashen. The nigger workt, and his owner eat, and thus wuz fulfilled the entire dooties uv life. He wuz not hung then, for he wuz worth too much money to hang. How hed it bin with him sense? He de-manded to be made a free man; he wuz made a free man, and here he is. I told em that there wuz no need uv sayin more; that body a danglin in the air, wich its sole wuz a marchin on, wuz the most elokent sermon wich cood be preacht.

The man whose house the nigger wuz a plasterin wuz in town yesterday, tryin to get Caucashin plasterers to finish the job; but ez ther ain't none uv em here, he isn't succeedin very well. He probably won't get into his new quarters this fall.

I am not certain wot become uv his family. There wuz a nigger woman's body pulled out uv the dam a day or two afterwards, wich somebody remarkt wuz the wife uv the deceast, and Captain McPelter remarkt that when he went to the cabin uv the deceest nigger to secoor his share of the furnitoor, that two leadin niggers from Garrettstown were notist makin off with the children. But there's no tellin whether there's any trooth in these rumors or not. I think I shel go to Washington, and put myself at the head uv the anti-nigger labor movement now bein inogurated there.

PETROLEUM V. NASBY, P. M.
(wich is Postmaster).

12. The Fifteenth Amendment: "A More Enraged Gatherin I Never Saw"

HARP UV ERIN S'LOON, 6TH WARD,
NOO YORK, April 2, 1870.

The proclamation uv the President announcin the ratification uv the Fifteenth Amendment prodoosed a profound sensashen in this Ward.

It wuz told to our people by a reporter uv a daily paper at 11 o'clock this mornin, and it got pretty well around among us by 3 this afternoon, wich wuz tollably rapid, considerin that intelligence in this Ward hez to be conveyed orally. In the afternoon it wuz resolved that a meetin be held in the evenin to consult ez to wat ackshen the Dimocrisy shood take in the matter, wich wuz akkordingly so done. I hed the back room lit up, the barrels moved into a safe place under the strongest kind uv locks, and the bar closed and draped in mournin in token uv the hoomiliashen wich I felt had fallen onto the people in consekence uv this outrage. I hung crape onto the door; I put crape around the portraits uv Jaxon, Chief Justis Chase, Bookannon, and Fernandy Wood, and likewise around the bottles and over the redheaded barrel, wich gave the establishment a highly funereal and mournful look wich wuz entirely satisfactory.

In the evenin the Dimocracy assembled, and a more enraged

gatherin I never saw. They wuzn't jist clear ez to wat the President hed done; indeed the most uv em wuz labrin under the impreshn that the enfranchisement uv the nigger wuz the work uv the Democratic Legislacher at Albany, and ther wuz indicashens uv a determinashen to go thro some of the houses uv the Dimocratic members in this city, but I stopt em by tellin em the strate uv it.

I asoomed the chair, uv course, and hed, in addishen, to do the dooties uv Sekretary, bein the only one then in the meetin who cood write.

Teddy McGinnis remarked that he felt a hoomiliashen wich wuz actooally beyond expreshen. The dirty nagur wuz now his ekal. The only difference between em hed bin removed by this infamus law. Does any one spose that he'd iver consint to vote all day beside niggers? Niver! He called upon the Dimocracy to jine him in a croosade agin em. "Follow me," sed Teddy, "and in Noo Yorrick, at least, we won't be bothered with nagur suffrage, be gorra."

Pat McLaughlin held simlar views. Sooner than vote beside nagurs, he'd relinquish the biznis uv votin altogether, and go to sawin wood. Repeetin is a good enuff biznis, and the small conthract wich he hed, ez a reward thereof, wuz betther, but he coodent stand nagurs, nor woodent. His voice wuz for killin uv em.

The others made similar speeches, when Sandy McGuire offered a resolooshen that the offerin uv a vote by a nagur be considered ez a declarashen uv war agin the Democracy uv Noo York, and that they then be immegitly exterminated. Sandy wuz for no half-way measures. He remembered the glorious Jooly days in 1863, when the Democracy uv Noo York assertid itself. He hed assisted in destroyin the nagur orphan asylum; with this good rite hand he hed beat out the brains uv two nagurs, to say nothin uv the wimin and children wich he didn't consider worth countin. He longed to get at em agin.

The meetin bein all so yoonanimus in their feelin, I wrote the follerin resolooshens:—

"*Resolved,* That the Dimocrisy uv Noo York, considerin and beleevin the nigger to be a beast, a burlesk on hoomanity, and incapable uv dischargin any uv the dooties uv citizenship, do hereby protest agin his bein give the ballot on an ekality with white men.

"*Resolved,* That the Dimocrisy uv Noo York, ruther than

submit to this degredashen, pledges itself to the exterminashen
uv the accussid race."

The resolooshens wuz adoptid without a dissentin voice,
and the enthoosiastic McGuire, brandishin a shillala, rushed out
and attackt a couple uv niggers wich wuz passin, and knockin em
down, stamped onto em vigrously with his boots, exclaimin the
while, "Want to vote, do yez!"

The meetin wuz about to break up, when Tim O'Grady, a
man uv Fernandy Wood's, come rushin in. He hed heard uv the
meetin, and come immejitly to see about it. I told him in a breath
wat hed bin done. "Thunder!" he remarkt to me in a whisper,
"this won't do. Yoo eggrejis old ass, the niggers hev votes, and
will vote now in spite uv us. We must git em, for without em,
with all the rebels disfranchised, wat kin we do in the Southern
States? Call the meetin to order agin."

I didn't like the tone uv his aloosion to me, but I called the
meetin to order onct more.

O'Grady remarked to em that there hed bin a misunderstandin. He felt ashoored that the Dimocrisy uv Noo York, alluz
the friends uv the oppressed and down trodden, wood now gen-
rously extend a helpin hand to our colored brethren jist elevated to full citizenship. The Dimocrisy hed not assisted in their
elevashen, but they had no feelin agin our brethren uv color.
When our colored brethren come to analyze the matter, they
wood love the Dimocrisy the more for not doin uv it. He wood
move the substitooshen uv the follerin resolooshen for the one
wich hed bin unadvisedly passed:—

"*Resolved*, That the Democrisy uv Noo York hail with a
feelin uv pleasure wich we hev no words to express, the elevashen
uv our colored fellow-citizens to full citizenship, and that we
pledge ourselves to pertect em in the enjoyment uv ther newly-
found rites."

The meetin didn't want to pass it. The feelin agin em wuz
too deep sot to be rooted out in a minit, but O'Grady wuz determined. O, wat a minit wuz that! Wuz the niggers to be killed by
us, or wuz they to be taken to our buzzums? Ther fate hung tremblin in the balance. Finally it wuz put to vote, and the niggers
wuz safe. By one majority the resolushen wuz passed.

At that minit a groan wuz heard outside.

"What is that," asked O'Grady.

"Some nagurs I jist now bate!" remarks McGuire.

"Beatin niggers!" sed O'Grady. "Good Lord, bring em in."

And he rushed out and brought in the two unfortunates. They were badly banged up about the face, and breast, and stumick, and legs, but O'Grady wuz ekal to the emergency. He washed their wounds, and revived em with whiskey, and bound up ther sores, and finally sot em on ther feet.

"McGuire!" sed he, when he hed the work finished, "Mc-Guire, embrace em."

McGuire hed his shillala in his hand. Never did I see a man so torn with contendin emoshens. Nateral instinks compelled him to drop that shillala on their heds ez usual, but the politikle considerashens restraned him. Twict under O'Grady's eye he lowered it, until at last he dropt it, and fell sobbin with emoshen onto their buzzums.

I took the crape off the door, bottles, and picters, and immejitly illoominated in honor uv the event, and the next mornin I put up a placard at my door, "No distinkshen at this bar on account uv color. Ekal rites!"

The ward committee is takin prompt and vigerous ackshen to secoor this vote. They hev adoptid the same means they yoose to control ther other vote. They hev already startid ten s'loons, run by colored men, to wich they give all the profits, and are arrangin ten more. There will be a nigger or two put onto the police to-wunst. The force will be increased enuff to make room for these new ones, ez we darsn't discharge any uv the Irish. I'm goin for em also. Those wich I kin git to drink my likker will vote my tikket. It will fetch em sure.

PETROLEUM V. NASBY
(wich wuz Postmaster).

13. Difficulties with the Negro Vote: "I Can't! I Can't! for I'm 'Spectably Connected!"

HARP UV ERIN S'LOON, IN THE SIXTH WARD,
NOO YORK, April 12, 1870.

The Noo York World, in a recent ishoo, remarkt that the Nigger vote must come to us, becoz the Dimocrisy had alluz hed success in managin the ignerant and degradid classes. This determined us to set about sekoorin the vote uv the nigger populashen in our ward immejitly. Father McGrath insisted that it be done to-wunst, becoz the minit they become Dimokrats the

way wuz paved for their comin under the speritooal direckshen
uv the Catholic Church; Timmy McGee insisted that it shood be
done becoz the element, ef opposed to us, mite become dangerous; Timmy O'Ryan, becoz we hed either to incorporate em
into our ranks or kill em, and he didn't beleeve it wood pay to
raise another riot jist now; and I wantid em attached to our
party becoz I wantid em in front uv my bar reglerly.

We decided that the shoorest way to git at em wood be to
git one nigger interestid with us, who wood serve ez a decoy duck
to bring in the others. We wantid a nigger to assoshate with; to
embrace and sich; to show other niggers that we cood and wood
affilyate with em. We hed a terrible time a gittin uv it startid,
however. We got one uv that race in my back room, and
attempted to argoo the questions uv the hour with him, confident in our ability to crush him by facts into submishen to our
doctrines, but the mizable devil pulled out uv his pockit a copy
uv the Constooshn, and askt Teddy the Lifter to read and con-
stroo a sentence therein, which finisht that pertikler effort.
Teddy, and Patsy O'Rourke, and Micky Doolan, who hed him
in hand, startid back at the site uv that book ez tho they hed been
shot. THE CUSS COOD READ, and wat cood any uv em do with sich
a man?

We caught a sick nigger, and hed him in tow three days. We
nussed him, and fed him, and hed in a doctor for him, wich doctor give him medicine and Dimocrisy in ekal doses, all uv wich
he seeminly gulped down with ease. We got him on the skore uv
gratitood, and he went away, promisin that he wood jine us, but
the second day he came back, and laid down on the bar twenty
dollars, with the remark that that sum wood pay for all the cost
and trouble we hed been to on his account.

"What do yoo mean?" sed I, sternly, sweepin the money into
the drawer, however, to make sure uv that.

Bustin into a paroxysm uv teers, he remarkt that ez low and
mean a nigger ez he wuz, he coodent reely jine us. It wuz unfair
in us, he sed, to take advantage uv his illness to put him under
obligashens to us.

"I can't be a Dimokrat," he sobbed, claspin his hands pit-
eously, "I can't, reely. I hev a gray-haired mother livin, and a
younger sister! I can't! I can't! for I'm spectably connected!"

And he rushed out. It wuz forchnit for him that I wuz alone
at that time.

All our efforts to sekoor a Ethiopian to our standard seemed to come to naught, and we wuz just on the confines uv despair, when one mornin Johnny O'Shoughnessy came rushin in, exclaimin, "I've got it—I've got it!"

"Got wat?" I askt.

"The nigger we want. In the Polece Court there's a nigger up for drunkenness, vagrancy, steelin, assault and battery, and some other things, and ez he hezn't a blasted cent, uv course he'll be sent up in short metre. We kin git him shoor, ef we go about it quickly. I got the Judge to hold on a bit till I cood see you."

To-wunst I seed a lite. Rushin frantically down to the courtroom, I gave myself ez bail for his appearance, wich the Judge, who is a politikle friend of mine, acceptid, without question, and seezin the nigger by the coat collar, I hustled him off to my place in triumph. Tim Doolan spoke up.

"Will yoo," sez Tim, "ef we get yoor discharge, promise to alluz vote the Dim—"

"Hold!" sez I quickly, for I wuz afeerd Tim's thoughtless precipitancy mite rooin all. "Hold! He ain't in condishen to hev that question put to him. Wait a minnit. I understand wat's required to make a convert better than yoo do."

And seezin a bottle from behind the bar I put it to his lips. The nigger drank with a eagernis wich gave me hope. Teddy spoke up agin,—

"Will yoo promise to alluz vote—"

"Hold!" sed I. "He hain't enough. Drink!"

And the nigger emptied the bottle.

"Now," sed I, "are yoo willin to promise to alluz vote the Dimocratic tikkit; to labor with your colored brethren to bring em into the fold uv the Dimocrisy, and to do your level best to promote the interests uv the Dimocratic party, now and forever?"

The nigger, by this time crazy drunk (the likker wuz from my own private bottle and unwatered), swore that he would promise all this. "Gib me some mo' dat whiskey," he shrieked.

I gave him another bottle, and in fifteen minits he wuz sleepin the deep sleep wich the tite man only knows.

In about four hours he awoke, and I thought it time to approach him on the main question.

"Ceezer," I remarkt, "you must commence yoor work tonite. We shel git up a meetin uv colored men at this place for the purpose uv organizin a Colored Democratic Club, and you must address em."

"Must I indoose em to jine a Dimocratic Club?" he asked.

"Certinly."

"Did I promise to do it?"

"Certinly," I replied; "and, my buck, yoo'd better keep that promise or I'll hev yoo back in the dock at the Polece Court in a jiffy."

"I'll do it," sed he, with the desperate air uv one who hed determined that life ain't worth livin for, and is prepared for anything. "I'll do it, but I must hev likker enuff to drown my con—wich is to say, give me nerve."

"Certinly," I replied, "all the likker you want, but speek yoo must."

The nite come, and there wuz a decent show uv niggers in the back room. But the speeker! Alas! he wuz too far gone to speek, and I hed to dismiss em.

The next mornin he swore he never wood do it; and to git him to the pint uv consentin I give him more likker, and he got drunk again, and so on it went, all the week. The fix we wuz in wuz suthin like this:—

1. We coodent approach a nigger who hed any standin or inflooense.

2. When we capcherd sich a wun, he woodent hev anything to do with us when he wuz sober; and to hold him, we hed to keep him drunk.

3. When drunk enuff to stay with us, he wuz too drunk to do wat we wantid.

After squandrin on this poor wretch at least a half barrel of ez good likker ez ever soothed my shrinkin sole, I wuz compelled to hev him re-arrested and sent up for a year or two. I coodent stand no sich drain on my finances, nor cood I bear to see so much likker wastid on a nigger.

The cuss took his sentence joyfully. "It's hard," he sed, "but it's better than wat yoo perposed."

This nigger question is the problem uv the age. How it will be solved puzzles me. May Heaven send us wisdom.

PETROLEUM V. NASBY
(wich wuz Postmaster).

IV. "Ef Androo Johnson Wants Me,

He Knows the Terms"

(1866-1868)

NOTE TO THE CHAPTER

Andrew Johnson's enemies always had the last laugh. To be sure, the President's retorts to hecklers also delighted his audiences, but in the next day's paper his words had lost their conviction and become garbled harangue. Steeped in the political practice of back-country Tennessee, Johnson could be relied on, if sufficiently provoked, to snap back, damage his cause and ruin his reputation.

His "bad slip" of March 4, 1865, became grist for the Radical mills. On the day of his inauguration as vice-president, Johnson, weak from illness, had taken whisky to steady himself for the ceremony. The liquor had gone to his head, and his enemies were to recall the scene again and again. Soon the country spoke of the "drunken tailor" from Greenville. Whenever he made an impetuous address, the Radicals accused him of drunkenness; and newspapers repeated the charge. And all the good folk hung their heads in shame over the man in the White House who, in the days of hard drinking, was hardly one of the hard drinkers.

Johnson's impromptu address on Washington's Birthday, 1866, opened the final sequence of disastrous utterances. Goaded by hecklers, his tactless remarks shattered the reserve which his friends had preserved since the assassination of Lincoln. Two men, however, were delighted: Thaddeus Stevens and Petroleum Vesuvius Nasby. The leader of the Radicals in Congress had been waiting for the opportunity to engineer the downfall of Johnson. The President's blunder filled the Lait Paster uv the Church uv the Noo Dispensashun on Confedrit X Roads with hopes of a different nature. After long years, Nasby's coveted political appointment, the postmastership, suddenly seemed to come within reach. But doubts and disappointments continued to plague its attainment when Congress overrode the President's veto of the Civil Rights bill. Even Johnson's first defeat by the Radicals and such setbacks as the election of Republican Joseph Roswell Hawley as Governor of Connecticut were forgotten in August: the Swing 'round the Circle promised to recoup Johnson's faltering fortunes. Having accepted an invitation to the laying of the cornerstone for a Stephen A. Douglas monument at Chicago, the President intended on the trip to appeal to the people in Northern cities for support of his moderate Reconstruction policy.

At the end of August the party got off to a good start. Some had joined the group with Nasby's devotion, among them members of the Cabinet which had endorsed the project enthusiastically. On the trip Postmaster General Alexander W. Randall tended to post office business, mending political fences, but Secretary of the Navy Gideon Welles and Secretary of State William H. Seward were at the President's side. Others, like the country's idols, General Ulysses S. Grant, General George A. Custer and Admiral David G. Farragut, the political strategists took along to assure the party's welcome. However, the heroes frequently stole the show from Johnson. Several ladies, Mrs. Martha Johnson Patterson (the President's daughter and hostess), and Mrs. Welles and Mrs. Farragut also graced the group.

All went well until Niagara Falls, with the exception of the few unpleasantries which Reuben E. Fenton, the Republican Governor of New York, had for the President during his stop in Albany. Then troubles started and never ceased. In Cleveland, Toledo, Ann Arbor, St. Louis, Indianapolis, Steubenville, Pittsburgh and Johnstown, hecklers and tumultuous crowds clamoring for their war heroes got the best of Johnson. He "struck out crazy, but the starch wuz out of him, and he was worsted," Nasby sadly recollected. When Johnson was back at his desk after less than three weeks' absence, he had traveled two thousand miles and delivered eleven major and twenty-two minor speeches. But the President had missed the opportunity to build up another Union party out of loyal Democrats, conservative Republicans and old Whigs, and had supplied his opponents with ammunition for a tirade of abuse and distortion that surpassed anything they had instigated before.

Johnson made their work easy. He relied on a few themes, initially developed at a banquet in New York's Delmonico's, a restaurant Nasby fondly remembered for quite different reasons. The technique had worked well in Tennessee where an old speech was still new to each new audience. In the North, however, once he had delivered an address a couple of times, the extensive news coverage familiarized all potential listeners with its content. Hecklers struck with deadly regularity, safely relying on the audiences' acquaintance with the President's real and alleged blunders. Moses and the Veto, New Orleans and Memphis made up their standard repertoire.

Johnson's ill-starred "Moses" speech of October 24, 1864, dated back to his service as Lincoln's war governor of Tennessee. "You are our Moses," Nashville's Negroes had cheered Johnson at the end of an emotion-charged address when the speaker felt "almost inclined to wish that, as in the days of old, a Moses might arise who should lead them safely to their promised land." Shortly before his Swing, Johnson's veto of the Civil Rights bill, designed to undo the intrusion of the federal government into the sphere of the states, made irreparable the breach between the President and Congress.

The New Orleans riot at the end of July 1866 had deepened impressions the North gained earlier in the spring by a clash at Memphis between Negro soldiers and Irish policemen, and by other sporadic cases of violence upon freedmen. Carefully exaggerated for partisan purposes, the reports strengthened the notion that the Rebels were abusing the Negroes. Lieutenant-Governor Albert Voorhis, Mayor John T. Monroe of New Orleans, and Judge Edmond Abel fought Louisiana Radicals, who were alarmed to see the state government falling into the hands of pardoned Confederate sympathizers. One of the Radical leaders, Dr. A. P. Dostie, a Northern dentist who had settled in New Orleans, was among the casualties of the riots, most of them Negroes.

The President's friends were helpless in the face of the impending disaster enveloping Johnson. Henry Ward Beecher, the New York Congregational minister, reaped much criticism and abuse for his "Cleveland letter" which expressed sympathy with Johnson's policy. Senator James R. Doolittle of Wisconsin and Senator Edgar Cowan of Pennsylvania strengthened the handful of loyal administration Republicans in the Senate. In the House the outstanding Johnson supporter was Henry J. Raymond, founder of the New York *Times*. And there were, of course, such friends as Mrs. Lucy Cobb, who was not unwilling, for a fee, to obtain pardons for former rebels by appealing to Johnson's sympathy.

The Blairs, "a family of some merit, of admirable audacity, and execrable selfishness," Thad Stevens observed, had a habit of trying to seize the White House during every administration. Even "our late sainted President," he sarcastically remarked, "was for a time in the hands of the Blairs," Francis Preston and his sons Montgomery and Francis Preston, Jr. The youngest Blair's loyalty to presidential policies led the Senate to reject his nominations as revenue collector in St. Louis and as minister to Austria. Johnson, who had no interest whatsoever in acquiring Alaska, and went along simply because Seward wanted the territory, might have given more than his "unenthusiastic approval" to the purchase had he only shared Nasby's vision of "Seward's Icebox" as a prospective haven for the crowd of office seekers that constantly harassed him. "This territory kin," the presidential adviser oracled, "be divided up into—say, forty—which, by makin a few more offises for each . . . will be sufficient to give places to all who really have claims upon us and who are pushin us."

Johnson's struggle with the Radicals overshadowed all of his other difficulties. On February 28, 1868, the House impeached him for removing Secretary of War Edwin M. Stanton in defiance of the Tenureof-Office act. With unpolitical tolerance and out of respect for Lincoln's choice, Johnson had continued Stanton in the Cabinet, although he remained mainly as an informer of the Radicals. The flimsiness of the charges betrayed the impeachment as a partisan attack. The Senate sat as the trial court, presided over by Chief Justice Salmon P. Chase. The President himself did not attend. Week after week, the trial dragged through endless days of bitter controversy until May, when Johnson was acquitted by one vote, as Fessenden of Maine, Grimes of Iowa, Trumbull of Illinois and four other Republicans sided with twelve Democrats against the Radicals.

These "recusant Senators" sealed their political fate by their vote. Charles Sumner's label for the heretics suggested the bitter denunciation the seven men were to encounter. None of them ever held elective office again. The wrath of the Radicals fell most heavily on Edmund G. Ross of Kansas, who cast the decisive vote. The roll was called alphabetically, each Senator rising in his seat to answer the Chief Justice. When Ross's turn came, there were fourteen votes for Johnson and four more were certain, bringing the total to one less than the nineteen necessary for acquittal. Everything depended on Ross, who had been under intense pressure to vote for impeachment. When his "Not Guilty" came, Johnson was safe, but Ross realized that "friends, position, fortune, everything that makes life desirable to an ambitious man, were about to be swept away by the breath of my mouth, perhaps forever" and that he was destined "to be a bigger man dead than . . . alive."

Chief Justice Chase's efforts to preserve the semblance of a trial earned him the undying hatred and ridicule of the Radical press. Since Chase had subjected integrity to ambition for years, his enraged friends found it difficult now to separate his opposition to their attempted take-over of the government from his incurable desire for the presidency and his animosity for his political rival, Ben Wade, who as president pro tempore of the Senate would automatically be the new President if Johnson were found guilty. Having fought for the Republican nomination in 1856, 1860 and 1864, Chase made no attempt in 1868 to lead his party, which was irresistibly drawn to Grant. Instead, he allowed himself to become a Democratic hopeful, to the disgust of those who cherished party regularity. Ohio had let Chase down in 1860 and now disappointed him again at the convention in New York, which selected Horatio Seymour by acclamation. Nasby's vision of the presidential race between the Chief Justice and the general never materialized, and Samuel J. Tilden, John Van Buren and other Democrats (instead of Franklin Pierce, Clement L. Vallandigham, John Morrissey and Fernando Wood) demolished Chase's prospects effectively.

1. "I Hev Hopes uv Androo Johnson Myself": Is Johnson Manageable?

CONFEDRIT × ROADS (wich is in the Stait uv Kentucky),
February 29, 1866.

I notice, all over the North, the Democrisy is a firin guns, and marchin after brass bands, and hirin halls for endorsin Androo Johnson. Ez a sentinel on the watch-tower, I protest! In the name uv suffrin Kentucky, uv wich State I am a adopted citizen, I protest! In the name uv common sense and ordnary politikle sagacity, I protest!

Androo Johnson may possibly be on the high road to Dimocrisy but, ez yet, what ashoorence hev we? Am I datin my letters from "Post Orfis, Confedrit × Roads?" Hez there bin, as yit, any well authenticated case uv the removal uv a Ablishnist, and the apintment uv a constooshnel Democrat in his stead? Not that I hev heard of. Per contra, the Ablishnists—them ez wuz appinted by Linkin—are still holdin on, ez calm ez a summer mornin, without any apparent fear uv any change affectin them.

Who pays for the Halls? Who pays the music? Who pays the Powder? Dimocrats who do these scent Post Offises in the distance. Are they like the war hoss in Job's writins, who smelled the battle afar off, and remarked Ha, Ha! to the trumpets? Let me entreat sich that they kin make a better investment uv their means. The cost uv one meetin, put in korn whisky, wood not only solace theirselves, but start half a dozen Ablishnists on the road to Dimocrisy.

Men is deceptive. I hev hopes uv Androo Johnson myself, and principally becoz Vallandigum and Fernandy Wood hev hopes. Them buzzards kin smell carrion a long distance, and they are seldom at fault. In this case, they may be. They base their hopes on Johnson's speech, at Washington, on the 22d. There may be suthin in it; but ain't it possible that the stench wich they took for Dimocrisy, and wich they sposed cum from Johnson, ariz from them ez surrounded him?

"But," sez a Dimocrat, whose nose, from long continued lack of supplies, hez softened down from a generous crimson to a ghastly bloo, and who woodent hev a small post orfis at no price, ef it wuznt offered him, "look at the class he spoke to."

Wat noncence! Androo wuz mad. There wuz a mass uv bile

"Ef Androo Johnson Wants Me . . ."

on his politikle stumick wich must be got rid uv. He had sum nasty things to say, and it wuz a part uv the eternal fitness uv things that he shood hev a nasty audience to say em to.

I don't propose to go orf into spasms over the present situ-ashun. Johnson proposes to continue the Freedmen's Buro, and hezn't no noshen of repealin the test oath, or uv drawin the mili-tary out uv the Dimocratik States. So far as heard from, we uv the South is still in a stait of abject cussitood. Our habis corpuses wich Linkin took away from us hevn't bin returned, and we are obleeged to git along ez best we kin without em. I knocked down a small nigger yisterday, for the purpus uv assertin the sooperi-ority uv the Caucashun race over the Afrikin, and wuz to-wunst hauled up afore a Freedmen's Buro, and fined. Our high-toned and chivalrous members are exclooded from Congris on the frivolus plea that they wuz kernels and briggydeer Ginerals in the Confederit servis; and all these outrages agin Dimocrisy Androo Johnson, by permittin, absolootly approves.

I could probably swaller all these things. I am a Dimokrat uv thirty years standin, and, uv course, hev bin on both sides uv every politikle fence. The seat of my politikle pants is full uv slivers. But, before I take down these things, I WANT TO KNOW WHAT I AM GOING TO GIT FOR IT. Ef Androo Johnson goes back on his party and his pledges, he, uv course, asks us to go back on ourn. In sich transactions, where both par-ties, by bein engaged in it at all, confess themselves ruther a low grade of scoundrels, I think it well enuff to hev the consideration paid down.

Ef Androo Johnson wants me, he knows the terms. I am his to command, for a consideration; ez much so ez is the thousands uv Demokrats who hev bin, for the past week, gittin up demon-strations. But I want suthin to go on. When I hev his permission, under the broad seel uv the Post Orfis Department, to write "P. M." after my illustrious name, I shell be prepared to wade in. I hev bin huntin up several reasons for supportin him. I hev em all ready. I only want this additional one, and then I fling my banner to the breeze. Faith is sed to be the sun of all religious systems. Post Offis is the central figger in all Democratic creeds —the theme uv conversation by day, and the staple uv dreems by night. How long! oh, how long!

Petroleum V. Nasby,
Lait Paster uv the Church uv the Noo Dispensashun.

2. Hope Springs Eternal: "I Think He's Changed His Israelites"

CONFEDRIT × ROADS (wich is in the Stait uv Kentucky),
April 2, 1866

Kin it be? Is it troo, or is it not troo? Is Androo Johnson all my fancy painted him, or is he still a heaven-defying persekooter uv the Democratic Saints? That's wat I and some thousands uv waitin souls wood go suthin handsome to know. I confess I never quite lost faith in Androo. Pro-slavery Democracy sticks to a man ez does the odor uv the gentle skunk to clothes, and it is got rid uv only by the same means, to-wit, buryin the victim thereof.

Androo started out to be a Moses, and he is one; but I think he's changed his Israelites. I onst saw a woman skinnin live eels, and I reproached her, sayin, "Woman, why skinnest thou eels alive? Doth it not pain em?"

"Nary!" retorted she. "I've skinned em this way for going on to twenty years, and they're used to it."

Even so. The negroes hev bin in bondage so long that they're used to it, and Androo feelin a call to continue in the Moses bizniss, hez, I hope, turned his attention to the Dimocrisy. It's us he's a-goin to lead up out uv the Egypt uv wretchedness we've bin in for nearly five years; it's us that's a-goin to quit brick making without straw, and go up into the Canaan wich is runnin with the milk and honey uv public patronage. We shel hev sum fites: there's Amakelitish post masters and Phillistine collectors to displace, but with a second Jaxon at our hed what can we fear?

I feel to-night like a young colt. To me it seems ez though my venerable locks, wich hangs scantily about my temples, hed grown black agin, and that my youth wuz returnin. Ef I hed any notion uv sooicide, that idea is dismist. I'm young agin. Wat hez worked this change? yoo ask. It's the proclamation declarin the war at an end, and withdrawin from the Dimocratic States the odious hirelins uv the tyrant Linkin, and the doin away uv that terrible marshal law. That's wat's done it for me. Now I feel like sayin, with one uv old, "Mine eyes hev seed thy glory; let thy servant depart in peace."

We hev bin dooly subjoogated some time, and a waitin for

this. We wantid it, and longed for it ez the hart does for the water course, and considerably more, onless the hart wuz thirsty in the extreme. For now we are in the Union agin; we are under the shadder uv that glorious old flag wich protects all men ceptin niggers and Ablishnists. The nigger is left to be adjustid by us, who is to be governed by the laws wich control labor and capital. Certainly he is—uv coarse. I saw two uv my neighbors adjustin one last nite. They wuz doin it with a paddle, wich wuz bored full uv holes. He didn't seem to enjoy it ez much ez they did. By that proclamation our states are agin under their own control. Let em go at wunst to work to destroy all the vestiges uv the crooel war through wich they hev past. There ain't no soldiers now to interfere, for the policy uv keepin soldiers in and among free people is abhorrent to freedom and humanity. Go to work at wunst, and build up the broken walls uv your Zion.

We must hev Peace and unanimity; and Peace cannot dwell among us onless there's a oneness uv purpose and sentiment. To prokoor this is yoor fust dooty. If there be among you them ez opposed yoo doorin yoor late struggle for Rites, hist em. Their presence is irritatin, and kin not be tolerated. Ablishnism is as abhorrent now as ever, and the sooner yoo are rid uv it the better. It is safe to assume that every man who opposed the lately deceased Confederacy is a Ablishnist.

The next step, and the most important, is to tear down the nigger school-houses and churches wich hev bin built here and there, and kindly take the nigger by the ear, and lead him back to his old quarters, wich is his normal position. The Yankee school teachers sent here by Freedmen's Aid Soceieties shood properly be hung for spreadin dissatisfaction and spellin books among the niggers, but I wood advise mercy and conciliation. Tar and featherin, with whippins, will perhaps do ez well, and will go to show the world that our justice is tempered with charity; that we kin be generous ez well ez just. Yoor Legislatures shood be instantly called together, and proper laws for the government uv the Freedmen should be passed. Slavery is abolisht, and the people must live up to the requirements of the act in good faith. I protest agin any violation uv good faith, but labor must be done, for the skripter commands it, and our frail nature demands wat can't be got without it. We don't like to do it, but shel skripter be violated? Not at all. The nigger must do it hisself, not ez a slave, for slavery is abolished, but ez a free man. Ethiopian citizens uv Amerikin descent (wich is mulatters), and full-blooded blacks, and all hevin in the veins a taint uv Afrikin blood, must be restrained gently, and for their own good I suggest laws ez follows:—

1. They must never leave the plantation onto wich they are, when this act goes into effect, without a pass from the employer, under penalty uv bein shot.

2. They shel hev the privilege uv suein everybody uv their own color, ef they kin give white bail for costs.

3. They shel hev the full privilege uv bein sued the same ez white folks.

4. They shel be competent ez witnesses in cases in wich they are not interested, but their testimony is to go for nothin ef it is opposed by the testimony uv a white man or another nigger.

5. No nigger shel be allowed to buy or lease real estate outside uv any incorporated city, town, or village.

6. No nigger shel be allowed to buy or lease real estate within any incorporated city, town, or village, except as hereinafter provided for, to wit:—He shel give notice uv his desires by publication for six consecutive weeks in some newspaper uv general circulation in sed village, for wich publication he shel pay invariably in advance. He shel then give bonds, in sich sums ez the mayor shel decide, that neither he, nor any uv his ancestors, or descendants, or relations, will ever become public charges, and will always behave themselves with due humility, the bondsmen to be white men and freeholders. Then the mayor shel cause a election to be proclaimed, and if the free white citizens shel vote "yea" unanimously, he shel be allowed to buy or lease real estate. If there is a dissenting vote, then he shel be put onto the chain gang for six months for his impudence in makin sich a request.

7. Their wages shel be sich ez they and the employers shel mutually agree; but that the negroes may not become luxurious and effeminate, wich two things is vices wich goes to sap the simplicity and strength uv a people, the sum shel never exceed $5 per month, but not less than enuff in all cases to buy him one soot uv clothes per annum, wich the employer shel purchase hisself.

8. The master shel hev the privilege uv addin to this code sich other rules and regulations for their proper government ez may strike him ez being good for em from time to time.

These provisions secure the nigger in all the rites wich kin reasonably be asked for him, just elevated ez he is from slavery, and thrown upon the world, ignorant of the duties of his new position and status. He is simple, and needs the guidin hand uv the stronger race.

My hart is too full to make further suggestions. Organized into a tabloo, with the constitooshun in one hand (wich beloved instrument kivers a great deal uv ground), a star-spangled banner in the other, and a tramplin on a bloo coat wich I stript off uv a returned nigger soldier wich wuz sick, I exultinly exclaim, "The Union ez it is is ez good ez the Union ez it wuz. 'Ror!"

PETROLEUM V. NASBY,
Lait Paster uv the Church uv the Noo Dispensashun.

3. Civil Rights Prevail: "I Am a Kittle Full of Cusses"

CONFEDRIT × ROADS (wich is in the Stait uv Kentucky),
April 9, 1866.

I am a kittle full of cusses.

Under me is a burnin fire uv rage, wich is bein continually fed with the oil uv disappointment.

And I bile over.

The civil rites bill, wich our Moses put his foot onto, we thought wuz dead.

And we fired great guns, and hung out our flags, wich we laid aside in 1860, and made a joyful noise.

For we said, one unto another, Lo! he is a true Moses, inasmuch ez he is a leadin us out uv the wilderness.

The civil rites bill wuz the serpent wat bit us, and he histed it, that we might look and live.

Now let us be joyful!

For the Ethiopian is delivered into our hands, bound hand and foot.

Blessed be Moses!

We will make him grind our corn; but he shel not eat thereof.

Blessed be Moses!

We will make him tread out our wheat; but we will muzzle his mouth.

Blessed be Moses!

He shall pick our cotton; but the hire he receiveth, he shall stick in his eye without injuring the sight thereof.

Blessed be Moses!

He shall toil in the sugar mill; but the sugar shall he not sell.

Blessed be Moses!

His sweat shall nourish our corn; but he shall eat nary ear thereof.

Blessed be Moses!

We will burn his school houses, and destroy his spellin books (for shall the nigger be our superior?), and who shall stay our hand?

The school teachers we will tar and feather, and whar is the bloo-coated hirelins to make us afeerd?

Blessed be Moses!

We looked at the nigger, and said, Ha, ha! the last state uv that chattle is wuss nor the fust; for before, we hed his labor while he wuz strong and healthy, but hed to take care on him when he wuz sick and old; and now we kin git his labor without the care.

Blessed be Moses!

The Ablishnists cast out one devil, and garnished the room; but there wuz seven devils more stronger and hungrier, which rushed in and pre-empted the premises.

Blessed be Moses!

But our song uv joy wuz turned into a wale uv anguish.

Moses sought to hist the serpent, but the serpent histed him.

He's on a pole, and the bitin North wind is a blowin onto him.

He can't get up any higher, because his pole ain't any longer; and he can't get down, because he ain't no place to light onto.

He vetoed the bills, and Congress hez vetoed him; the civil rights bill they passed in a uncivil manner.

Now, bein the nigger hez rights, he is our ekal.

Our ekil is the nigger now, and onless the skool houses is burned, and the spellin books destroyed, he will soon be our superior.

We wuz willin to give him the right uv bein sued; but, alas! he kin sue.

He kin be a witness agin us, and he kin set his face agin ourn.

Our wise men may make laws to keep him in his normal speer, but uv wat avail is they?

We kin buy and sell him no more, neither he nor his children.

The men will cleave unto their wives, and the wives unto their husbands, and our hand is powerlis to separate em.

Their children kin we no more put up at auction, and sell to the highest bidder, we pocketing joyfully the price thereof.

They hev become sassy and impudent, and say, "Go to; are we not men?"

I bade one git off the sidewalk, and he bade me be damned.

I chucked a nearly white one under the chin, and smiled onto her, and she squawked; and her husband, hearing the squawk thereof, came up and bustid my head, even ez a white man wood hev dun.

I chastised wun who gave me lip; and he sood me, a Caucashun, for assault and battery, and got a judgment!

Wale! for Moses put out his hand to save us these indignities, but his hand wuz too weak.

We killed Linkin in vain.

Our Moses is playin Jaxson. He fancieth he resembleth him, becoz his inishals is the same.

He resembleth Jaxon muchly—in that Jaxon hed a policy wich he cood carry out, while our Moses hez a policy wich he can't carry out.

And ez he can't carry out his policy, the people are carryin it out for him.

Wich they do, a holdin it at arm's length, and holdin their noses.

Moses is a cake half baked; he is hot on one side, and cold on tother.

He darsn't let go uv Ablishnism, and is afeerd to come to us.

He hez been takin epsom salts and ipecac; and one is workin up, and the other is workin down.

Where kin we look for comfort?

Do we turn to the people? Connecticut answers, " 'Ror for Hawley!" and Noo Hampshere goes Ablishun.

Do we turn to the courts? Lo! Taney hez gone to his reward —him who aforetime dealt out Dimekratic justice, and who understood the nacher uv the nigger,—and Chase, who is pizen, reigns in his stead.

Raymond is growin weak in the knees, and Doolittle is a broken reed on which to lean.

We are too short at both ends.

Shall we go to Brazil? Lo! there they put niggers in office.

Mexico holds out her hands to us; but, lo! the nigger is considered a man.

We hev no escape from the Ethiopian; he is around us, and about us, and on top uv us.

I see no post orfis in the distance, no hope for the future.

Hed I bin a Ablishinist, so ez to make the thing safe in the next world, I shood be glad to die, and quit this.

For my sole is pregnant with grief; my hart bugs out with woe.

PETROLEUM V. NASBY,
Lait Paster uv the Church uv the Noo Dispensashun.

4. An Appeal to the White House: "Yoo, and Yoo Alone, Kin Remedy This"

CONFEDRIT × ROADS (wich is in the Stait uv Kentucky),
April 26, 1866.

The work uv death is a goin on. The sakred precepts uv the Holy Skripters is bein daily violated by an insane majority, who hev substitooted their own noshens for the safe and pleasant revelashens uv Holy Writ, and the practices of their fathers.

Cood Noah, when he cussed Ham, and declared that he shood be a servant unto his brethren, hev foreseen how his cuss wood hev bin disregarded in these degenerate days, he wood, I boldly assert (and I make the assertion from wat I know uv the character uv that eminent navigator), hev kep sober, and not cust Ham at all. For wat's the use uv sich a cuss ef it's to be removed jist when you want it to stick? Hed it bin taken off afore cotton wuz profitable, and afore the Southern people hed learned to depend onto their labor, it wouldent hev bin so bad, and they cood hev endoored it without murmurin. But, alas! not only is the South in a state of abject cussitood, but the Northern Dimocrasy is likewise.

The case stood thuswise: The South depended on the Nigger; and the Northern politicians, like me, depended on the

South. The nigger wuz the foundashun upon wich the entire structur rested; and now that he's knocked out, it falls.

I wuz in Washington the other day, and wuz a unwillin witnis uv a scene wich filled me with unutterable disgust. The niggers wuz a celebratin suthin connected with their onnatural removal from their normal condishun, and wuz a paradin the streets with bands uv music, and with banners and inscriptions. They hed the impudence to dress up in good clothes,—clothes wich I cood not afford to wear,—and three uv the impudent cusses hed the ashoorance to go so far in their imitation of human beins ez to make speeches; and to my horror, the mass uv em had ben so well trained by somebody that they actily cheered, and ez near ez I cood make out got in the applause at the right place, and all without the assistance uv a indivijual to commence applaudin at the right time, wich we hev generally found nessary at Dimmekratic meetins.

Their inscripshuns wuz insultin. They hed em all spelt rite, and they wuz full uv alloosions to ekal rites, and onqualifyed suffrage, and sich, planely showin that the poor, misguided critters hed no idee that they wuz loaded down with a cuss and that becoz uv that cuss they hed no rites watever.

In Richmond I saw other evidences uv the terrible breakin down uv the barriers wich Noah set up atween the races. I wuz sittin in a hoss car, when a nigger hed the onparalleled asshoorence to enter and set down. I remonstrated with the chattel, who laft in my face.

Thus the old landmarks is bein removed, and thus the foundations uv society is a bein broken up. I saw in Richmond fair wimmin who hed, in olden times, never known wat labor wuz, a washin dishes, and cookin their own vittles; and I saw men, who hed wunst lived luxuriously on the labor uv a hundred niggers, now drivin drays, and sellin dry goods and groceries, and sich, and my soul sunk within me. Wuz the cuss a mistake? Wuz the nigger not the race that wuz cussed? or has he becum so bleached, so lost in the white by amalgamation, that there ain't enough uv the black left in each indivijual for the cuss to hang to?

Andrew Johnson! in your hands rests our cause; on your ackshen depends our weal or woe! Yoo, and yoo alone, kin remedy this. Wat if a corrupt and radikle Congress does override your vetoes, and legislate for these cuss-ridden people? Yoo hev yet a power wich yoo must not hesitate to make em feel. Clear

out the rump Congress; declare our Southern brethren entitled
to their seats, and see that they hev em. The Dimocrisy uv the
North, wich wuz latterly for peece, are now fur war. They will
sustain yoo. Reverse yoor ackshen, and yoo kin attach em to yoo
with hooks uv steel. There ain't no risk in it—nary risk. Turn
the Ablishnists out uv the Post Offices, and replace em with Democrats; let it be understood that yoo hev come back to yoor fust
love, and no longer abide in the tents uv Ablishunism,—and all
will be well. Talk less uv yoor policy, and put more uv it into
acts. Combine Post Offices with Policy, and proclaim that only he
who sustains the latter shel hev the former, and yoo kin depend
on the entire Democrisy North. We are waitin anxiously. From
the South comes up the cry, wich the North reëkkoes.

Will Androo Johnson, wich Ablishnists call Moses, but wich
we, for obvious reasons, style the 2d Jaxson, heed that cry? or
will he persist in clingin to the black idol he embraced four years
ago?

PETROLEUM V. NASBY,
Lait Paster uv the Church uv the Noo Dispensashun.

5. An Arc of the Circle: "Step by Step I Am Climbin to a Proud Eminence"

AT THE BIDDLE HOUSE (wich is in Detroit, Michigan),
September the 4th, 1866.

Step by step I am ascendin the ladder uv fame; step by step
I am climbin to a proud eminence. Three weeks ago I wuz summoned to Washington by that eminently grate and good man,
Androo Johnson, to attend a consultation ez to the proposed
Western tour, wich wuz to be undertaken for the purpose uv
arousin the masses uv the West to a sense uv the danger wich
wuz threatnin uv em in case they persisted in centralizin the
power uv the Government into the hands uv a Congress, instid
uv diffusin it throughout the hands uv one man, wich is Johnson. I got there too late to take part in the first uv the disucssion.
When I arrove they hed everything settled cepting the appintment uv a Chaplain for the excursion. The President insisted
upon my fillin that position, but Seward objected. He wanted
Beecher, but Johnson wuz inflexibly agin him. "I am determined," sez he, "to carry out my policy, but I hev some bowels

left. Beecher hez done enuff already, considerin the pay he got. No, no! he shel be spared this trip; indeed he shel."

"Very good," said Seward; "but at least find some clergyman who endorses us without hevin P. M. to his honored name. It wood look better."

"I know it wood," replied Johnson; "but where kin we find sich a one? I hev swung around the entire circle, and heven't ez yet seen him. Nasby it must be."

There wuz then a lively discussion ez to the propriety, before the procession started, of removin all the Federal offis-holders on the proposed route, and appintin men who bleeved in us (Johnson, Beecher, and Me), that we might be shoor uv a sootable recepshun at each pint at wich we wuz to stop. The Anointed wuz in favor uv it. Sez he, "Them ez won't support my policy shan't eat my bread and butter." Randall and Doolittle chimed in, for it's got to be a part of their religion to assent to whatever the President sez, but I mildly protested. I owe a duty to the party, and I am determined to do it.

"Most High," sez I, "a settin hen wich is lazy makes no fuss; cut its head off, and it flops about, for a while, lively. Lincoln's office-holders are settin hens. They don't like yoo nor yoor policy, but while they are on their nests, they will keep moderitly quiet. Cut off their heads, and they will spurt their blood in your face. Ez to bein enshoord of a reception at each point, you need fear nothing. Calkulatin moderately, there are at least twenty-five or thirty patriots who feel a call for every offis in your disposal. So long, Yoor Highnis, ez them offisis is held just where they kin see em, and they don't know wich is to git em, yoo may depend upon the entire enthoosiasm uv each, individually and collectively. In short, ef there's four offises in a town, and yoo make the appointments, yoo hev sekoored four supporters; till yoo make the appointments yoo hev the hundred who expect to get em."

The President agreed with me that until after the trip the gullotine shood stop.

Secretary Seward sejested that a clean shirt wood improve my personal appearance, and akkordingly a cirkular wuz sent to the clerks in the Departments, assessin em for that purpose. Sich uv em ez refoosed to contribute their quota wuz instantly dismissed for disloyalty.

At last we started, and I must say we wuz got up in a highly conciliatory style. Every wun of the civilians uv the party wore buzzum pins, et settry, wich wuz presented to em by the Southern delegates to the Philadelphia Convention, wich wuz made uv the bones uv Federal soldiers wich hed fallen at various battles. Sum uv em were partiklerly valuable ez anteeks, hevin bin made from the bones uv the fust soldiers who fell at Bull Run.

The Noo York recepshun wuz a gay affair. I never saw His Imperial Highness in better spirits, and he delivered his speech to better advantage than I ever heard him do it before, and I bleeve I've heard it a hundred times. We left Noo York sadly. Even now, ez I write, the remembrance uv that perceshun, the recollection uv that banquet, lingers around me, and the taste uv them wines is still in my mouth. But we hed to go. We hed a mishn to perform, and we put ourselves on a steamboat and started.

ALBANY.—There wuz a immense crowd, but the Czar uv all the Amerikas didn't get orf his speech here. The Governor welcomed him, but he welcomed him ez the Cheef Magistrate uv the nashen, and happened to drop in Lincoln's name. That struck a chill over the party, and the President got out uv it ez soon ez possible. Bein reseeved ez Chief Magistrate, and not ez the great Pacificator, ain't His Eggslency's best holt. It wuz unkind uv Governor Fenton to do it. If he takes the papers, he must know that His Mightiness ain't got but one speech, and he ought to hev made sich a reception ez wood hev enabled him to hev got it off. We shook the dust off uv our feet, and left Albany in disgust.

SKENACTADY.—The people uv this delightful little village wuz awake when the Imperial train arrived. The changes hadn't bin made in the offices here, and consekently there wuz a splendid recepshun. I didn't suppose there wuz so many patriots along the Mohawk. I wuz pinted out by sum one ez the President's private adviser—a sort uv private Secretary uv State; and after the train started, I found jest 211 petitions for the Post Offis in Skenactedy in my side coat pocket, wich the Patriots who hed hurrahed so vociferously hed dexterously deposited there. The incident wuz a movin one. "Thank God!" thought I. "So long ez we hev the post offices to give, we kin alluz hev a party." The Sultan swung around the cirkle wunst here, and leaving the Constooshun in their hands, the train moved off.

UTICA.—The President spoke here with greater warmth, and jerked more originality than I hed before observed. He introdoost here the remark that he didn't come to make a speech; that he wuz goin to shed a tear over the tomb uv Douglas; that, in swingin around the circle, he hed fought traitors on all sides uv it, but that he felt safe. He shood leave the Constooshn in their hands, and ef a martyr wuz wanted, he wuz ready to die with neetness and dispatch.

ROME.—Here we hed a splendid recepshun, and I never heard His Majesty speek more felicitously. He menshuned to the audience that he hed swung around the Southern side uv the cirkle, and wuz now swingin around the Northern side uv it, and that he wuz fightin traitors on all sides. He left the Constitooshun in their hands, and bid em good bye. I received at this pint only 130 petitions for the post office, wich I took ez a bad omen for the comin election.

LOCKPORT.—The President is improvin wonderfully. He rises with the occasion. At this pint he mentioned that he wuz sot on savin the country wich hed honored him. Ez for himself, his ambishn wuz more than satisfied. He hed bin Alderman, Member uv the Legislacher, Congressman, Senator, Military Governor, Vice-President, and President. He hed swung around the entire circle uv offises, and all he wanted now wuz to heal the wounds uv the nashen. He felt safe in leavin the Constooshn in their hands. Ez he swung around the cirkle—

At this pint I interrupted him. I told him that he hed swung around the cirkle wunst in this town, and ez yooseful ez the phrase wuz, it might spile by too much yoose.

At Cleveland we begun to get into hot water. Here is the post to which the devil uv Ablishnism is chained, and his chain is long enough to let him rage over neerly the whole State. I am pained to state that the President wuzn't treated here with the respeck due his station. He commenst deliverin his speech, but wuz made the subjeck uv ribald laffture. Skasely hed he got to the pint uv swingin around the cirkle, when a foul-mouthed nigger-lover yelled "Veto!" and another vociferated "Noo Orleans!" and another remarked "Memphis!" and one after another interruption occurred until His Highness wuz completely turned off the track, and got wild. He forgot his speech, and struck out crazy, but the starch wuz out uv him, and he wuz worsted. Grant, wich we hed taken along to draw the crowds, played dirt on us here, and stepped onto a boat for Detroit, leavin us only Farragut ez a attraction, who tried twice to git away ditto, but wuz timely prevented. The President recovered his ekanimity, and swung around the cirkle wunst, and leavin the Constooshn in their hands, retired.

Professor Nasby (wich is also Postmaster)

At the next pint we wuz astounded at seein but one man at the station. He wuz dressed with a sash over his shoulder, and wuz wavin a flag with wun hand, firin a saloot with a revolver with the other, and playin "Hail to the Chief!" on a mouth organ, all to-wunst.

"Who are you, my gentle friend?" sez I.

"I'm the newly-appinted Postmaster, sir," sez he. "I'm a perceshun a waitin here to do honor to our Cheef Magistrate, all alone, sir. There wuz twenty Johnsonians in this hamlet, sir; but when the commishn came for me, the other nineteen wuz soured, and sed they didn't care a d—n for him nor his policy, sir. Where is the President?"

Androo wuz a goin to swing around the cirkle for this one man, and leave the Constooshn in his hands, but Seward checked him.

At Fremont we hed a handsome recepshun, for the offises hevn't bin changed there, but Toledo didn't do so well. The crowd didn't cheer Androo much, but when Farragut wuz trotted out they gave him a rouser, wich wuz anything but pleasin to the Cheef Magistrate uv this nashen, who bleeves in bein respected.

Finally we reeched Detroit. This bein a Democratic city, the President wuz hisself agin. His speech here wuz wun uv rare merit. He gathered together in one quiver all the sparklin arrows he had used from Washington to this point, and shot em one by one. He swung around the cirkle; he didn't come to make a speech; he hed bin Alderman uv his native town; he mite hev been Dicktater, but woodent; and ended with a poetickal cotashun wich I coodent ketch, but wich, ez near ez I cood understand, wuz,—

> "Kum wun, kum all; this rock shel fly
> From its firm base—in a pig's eye."

Here we repose for the nite. To-morrow we start onward, and shel continue swingin around the cirkle till we reach Chicago.

PETROLEUM V. NASBY, P. M.
(wich is Postmaster),
and likewise Chaplin to the expedishn.

6. *"The Rooshen Purchis": The Real Reason We Bought Alaska*

WASHINGTON, April 14, 1867.

It's done! Seward did it—him and me! The American Eagle hez coz now to screem with redoubled energy. Ef the Nashnel bird wuz a angel, I shood remark to it, "Toon yoor harp anoo;" but it ain't, and therefore sich a rekest wood be ridiculous. This rapsody hez refrence to the Rooshen purchis.

The idea originatid in these massive intelleck. When I wuz here afore, the Blairs, all uv em, wuz a crowdin the sainted Johnson for a mishun. Cowan wantid a mishun, and so did Doolittle; and that day pretty much all uv the delegates to the Cleveland and Philadelphy Convenshens had bin there, wantin some kind uv a place; wat, they wuzn't pertikeler. One gentleman, whose nose (wich trooly blossomed as the lobster) betokened long service in the party, urged that he hed bin a delegate to both Convenshens. "Thank God!" sed Johnson. "Wood that both them Convenshens hed bin made up uv the same men. I wood then hev bin bored for places only half ez much ez I am."

I wuz a helpin him out in my weak way. When the crowd wantin places become too great for human endoorance, I wood say, in a modrit tone, "Let's go out and git suthin;" and to-wunst fully half wood exclaim, "Thank yoo, I don't keer if I do!" It wuz a great relief to Johnson, but wuz pizen on me. With the most uv em, the anguish, anxiety, and solissitood in the gittin uv offises and free drinks wuz about an ekal thing. The offisis they wantid wuz merely the means to that pertikeler end; and so long ez they wuz gittin the latter without the trouble uv the former, they wuz content. A good constooshen and a copper-lined stumick carried me thro this tryin ordeel, until I came across a Boston applicant, who, in consekence uv the perhibitory law, hed bin for some time on short rashens, and wuz keen set. Napoleon hed then met his Wellington, and I succumd. The man's talent wuz wonderful.

Sekretary Seward wuz in trouble about the Blair family. He hed did his level best for em. He hed appinted em to Collekterships and furrin mishuns; but the crooel Senit, wich hed no respeck for us, took delite in fastening uv em onto us by perpetooally rejectin em. Jest after a long siege by Montgomery and the old man, I sejestid the purchis uv the Rooshen Territory, to wich not only they cood be sent, but a thousand uv others wich we hed on our hands; and the Sekretary wuz so pleased at the idea that he wept like a child. He set imejitly about gittin testimonials ez to the valyoo uv the territory, to inflooence the Senit in ratifyin the treaty he was agoin to make. He wrote to a naval officer about it, who answered more promptly than I ever knowd a naval offiser to do, ez follows:—

"It's trooly a splendid country! The trade in the skins uv white bears kin be, if properly developed, made enormous. There is seals there, and walruses so tame that they come up uv their own akkord to be ketched.

"P.S.—In case the purchis shood be made, a naval stashen will be necessary. May I hope that my long services on the Floridy Coast will prove suffishent recommendashen for the command uv the depot? May I?

"I hev the honor to be," &c.

A distinguished Perfessor wrote:—

"The climate is about the style uv that they hev in Washinton. The Gulf Stream sweeps up the coast, causing a decided twist in the isothermal line, wich hez the effeck uv making it ruther sultry than otherwise. Anywheres for six hundred miles back uv the coast strawberries grow in the open air. I recommend strongly the purchis.

"P.S.—In case the purchis is made, a explorin expedishen will be necessary. May I hope that my scientiffik attainments are suffishently well known to yoo to recommend me as a proper person to head the expedishen? May I?

"I hev the honor to be," et settry.

The President wuzn't favorably inclined. He wuz full uv the old fogy idea that it wuz rather chilly there than otherwise. He hedn't faith in the Isothermal Line, and wuz skepticle about the Gulf Stream. It wuz his experience that the further North yoo got the colder it wuz. For instance, he remarkt, that while the people wuz warm toward him in Virginny and Maryland, last fall, they became very cold ez he got North. Wher wuz the Isothermal Line and the Gulf Stream then?

Randall, who will hev his joke, remarkt that the isothermal

line twisted. He notist that the people made it ez hot for em ez he wantid it ez fur North ez Cleveland; to wich Sekretary Welles replied, that it only confirmed him in the opinion that for platin vessels uv war, iron wuz preferable to pine plank any time.

Seward removed the President's objections to-wunst. He read his letters, wich set forth the beauties and advantages uv the country twict over. Here wuz whales, and walrusses, and seals, and white bears, and pine-apples, and wheat, and sea-lions, and fields uv ice the year round, in a climit ez mild and equable ez the meridian uv Washinton. The isothermal line wuz more accommodatin ther than in any other part uv the world. It corkscrewed through the territory so ez to grow fine peaches for exportation to the States, and ice to the Sandwich Islands, side by side. He drawd a picter uv the white bear a rushin over the line, and disportin hisself in fields uv green peas! Imagine, he remarked, the delicacy uv polar bear meat fattened on strawberries; think uv the condishn the sea-lions must be in which leave their watery lairs to feed on turnips wich grow above the 60th parallel; think uv—

"It won't do," sed the President.

"Think uv," retortid the Sekretary, with a quicknis uv intellek remarkable, *"think uv gettin rid uv the Blairs forever!"*

"Will the Ablishn Senit ratify the treaty?" askt Johnson, eagerly.

"I convert with many on the subjick, and they sed ef we cood promise that the Blairs would accept posishens ther, they wood do it cheerfly. For sich a purpose, sed one uv em to me, $7,000,000 is a mere bagatelle."

"I'll do it," sed Johnson. "I agree with the Senators for once. Rather then hev it fail, I'd pay it out uv Mrs. Cobb's share in our jint spekelashens. Freedom from the Blair family! Good Hevings! kin one man be so blest? Is ther sich in store for me? $7,000,000! Pish!"

My opinyun being askt, I give it. Ez hefty ez the vencher is from a commershl stan-pint, in a politikle pint uv view, the advantagis will be still heftier. The Rooshn territory will finally be the chosen home uv the Dimocrisy. Ther is already a populashen there adaptid to us, who kin be manipulated without trouble, and the climit is favorable to a strickly Democratic populashen. The trouble with us here is that the amount uv likker necessary to the manufakter uv a Democrat kills him afore he hez a opportoonity uv votin many times, wich keeps us in a perpetooal minority. Our strength is, for climatic reasons, our weaknis. Far diffrent is it in Roosha. Ther the happy native may drink his quart per day—the bracin atmosphere makin it abslootly nessary for him. Ther is the troo Democratic paradise. How offen hev I sighed for sich a country. Then again, ther are posishens uv profit. The delegates to Congriss will, ef I hev figgered it rightly, draw about $15,000 per session, mileage, wich is $30,000 per year, $60,000 per term. He cood afford to serve without the paltry $5,000, wich wood be cheep legislatin, indeed.

And so it wuz agreed upon, and the treaty wuz made by telegraph at a expense uv $20,000. Before it wuz finely conclooded, some other little incidentals wuz inclooded by the Zar, wich run the price up to $10,200,000, but that wuz nothin for us. Seward went at his work with great energy. The purchis wuz divided up into six territories (for the number uv delegates to our convenshuns wuz large, and they all hed to be provided for), wich wuz named, respectively, Johnson, Seward, Cowan, Doolittle, Randall, and Welles. For the one in the extreme North, the furthest off, Frank Blair wuz appinted Governor; for the next, Montgomery; and the next, the old man, and the other three wuz held in reserve for the pure but unfortunate patriots wich might be hereafter rejected for the Austrian mishun. A list wuz prokoored uv the delegates to our various convenshuns, and them ez hed bin martyred by the Senit; ther names wuz put into a wheel ez at Gift Enterprises, and the Judgeships, Marshalships, Clerkships, et settry, wuz drawd by lot. This ijee waz sejested by Postmaster-General Randall, ez bein the easiest way of doin it. He statid that the appintments from his department hed alluz bin made in this manner, ez it saved time in eggsaminin petitions, cirtifikets uv fitnis, and sich. In this way, about ez near ez I kin estimate, two per cent. uv those claimin posishens at our hands hev bin provided for.

The idea is capable uv unlimited extension. The Administration feelin the releef it hez gin em, are already negotiatin for the British Provinces. This territory kin, by makin uv em a little smaller, be divided up into—say, forty—which, by makin a few more offises for each, and bein libral with explorin expedishuns and sich, will be sufficient to give places to all who really have claims upon us and who are pushin us.

The President breathes easier, and the Secretary is placid ez a Summer mornin. He hez cut the Gordian knot; he hez releeved hisself uv the boa constrickter wich wuz crushin him in its folds. Happiness pervades the White House.

PETROLEUM V. NASBY, P. M.
(wich is Postmaster), and likewise Professor.

7. *Impending Impeachment: "Ef They Do Not, the Ku Klux Will Be on Hand"*

WASHINGTON, May 2, 1868.

The President is uv the opinion that he will be impeeched, wich opinion is shared by his confidenshel friends. Indeed, Randall fell onto his neck when he told him that he hed come to that conclooshun, and remarkt that that wuz the first correct conclooshun he hed come to sence he hed bin President. Ef anything will stop it, it will be the speeches wich are delivered for the prosecooshun. He hez some hope that the people, when they see the avalanche uv words that hez bin piled onto him, will hev their hatred turned into pity, and that pity will in this, ez in other matters, melt into love. But that's a thin reliance, and he knows it, and is, therefore, preparin to leave Washinton. He hez alreddy bid adoo to Mrs. Cobb. They met for the last time this mornin. She wood hev accompanied him to Greenville; but he sed, "Nay. To yoose the words uv another—

'My fate it is too cold for thee, Mrs. Cobb;
 'Twould chill thy deerest joy;
 I'd rather weep to see thee free, Mrs. Cobb,
 Than keep thee to destroy.'

"Here we part. I hev no longer the pardnin power, or disposal uv offices. Ef I shood git to be Mayor uv Greenville, which is in State uv Tennessee, I mite, perchance, give yoo the disposal of the one polece uv that anteek town; but, alars! he cood not afford to pay yoo enuff to keep yoo in garters. No! no! Farewell! I'm scooped. A. Johnson's okkepashun's gone."

Mrs. Cobb wuz led out, bathed in teers. I am informed, however, that she is in comfortable circumstances, havin bin ruther savin doorin that halcyon period uv pardnin rebels. She bled em handsome, and put suthin by for a rainy day. I told the President this, and he wuz visibly releeved. It wuz sejested by a council uv his friends, that he shood return quietly and by the neerest route, to wich he assented. He wood go, he sed, unostentashusly and without display to Greenville, by way uv Baltimore, Philadelphia, Noo York, Noo Haven, (Conn.), Savannah, Mobeel, Noo Orleens, Looisville, and Dubuke, Iowa. "Write to all my friends," sed he, "and beg uv em not to offer me any ovashens, or anythin uv the sort. I desire to glide into history ez a martyr (with a halo round my head), wich bowed meekly and uncomplaininly to the behests uv the d—dest tyranny on the globe. Tell em that the most I desire in the larger cities is processions, with appropriate moosic, banners, and sich, to receeve me at the cars and to escort me to my hotel, and a simple balcony from wich to address my fellow-citizens, that I may set their hearts at rest by asshoorin uv them that I am ez devoted to the constitooshen now ez ever, and to tell em how much I hev suffered in their behalf. I want no wreath, no gaudy chaplets wove for me; no illuminashens, no nothin. I wood merely sejest that at each place the percession be headed by a tomb—a mausoleum—on wheels, drawed by ten black horses, all clothed in mournin, the tomb to bear the inscription, "Impeachment: In this is buried Androo Johnson, and with him the constitooshen, the flag, and the liberties uv his country, wich he wood hev saved." It mite be well to hev another follerin behind it with a wax figger uv Columby bustin the mausoleum, and histin a wax figger uv me out uv it, chuckin the constitooshen at me ez she does it, exclaimin the while, "Rise, second Washington—rise, step-father uv yer country." These little allegories wood inculcate a great moral lesson, and wood inspire the people with awe."

Randall objected. "Wat's the yoose?" he sed. "Ef I am in the car with yoo,—and I spose I shel hev to see this thing out,—the Ablishnists will jeer and flout me, and say, 'Go up, bald head!' The inscripshens they will laff at, and they won't do our people eny good, for not one in ten kin read em."

Welles wuz in favor uv the mausoleum, only he wood hev a slite change. He wood hev Columbia supported by him, ez Neptoon, the God uv the briny deep, puttin a wax sceptre, labelled "Veto," in the hands uv the wax President, with the inscripshen, "With this he wood hev saved the Constitooshn." Randall wuz overpowered, but he did not give up his pint.

"I hev decided on this," sed the President. "I shel not pervent the people from testifyin their devoshen to me, and bearin witness to my many virchoos. I hev already received tenders of percessions ez terrible ez armies with banners. The Blood Tubs uv Baltimore, the Killers uv Philadelfy, and the Ded Rabbits uv Noo York, hev all expressed a desire to do me this honor. In Noo Haven, the Noo Yorkers kin go ther to make the percession, jist ez easy ez they went up ther to vote our ticket in the spring, ez I shel not be in two places the same day. In the South, ef the Confedrits I hev pardoned will all turn out, the percessions will be miles in length, and ef they do not, the Ku Klux will be on hand."

Randall cautioned him not to count double. "Yoo are probably aware," sed he, "that the Ku Klux is made up almost entirely uv the patriots yoo pardoned. But that don't matter; yoo will still be ovatid to yoor heart's desire. I hev correspondence. Here is a letter from a prominent Noo York Dimocrat: 'Hev him come this way. The nigger orfan asylum burnt in 1863 hez bin rebilt, and the boys are achin for a chance to go for it agin. His comin wood stir up our voters to some extent, and help to swell the majority for Seymour.'

"Another one says,—

" 'I hev no objeckshun to yoor funeral percession passin thro Noo Haven. I don't think it wood hurt us. It wood hev the effeck uv gittin up some excitement, wich possibly we cood turn to account in the fall election. But it must be managed nicely.'

"Another remarks:—

" 'He hed better come to Richmond, I think. We cood git up a percession wich wood terrify the niggers and white loyalists, and possibly keep em from ratifyin the Constitooshun. I will make the speech, and will say any good things uv Johnson yoo may sejest, for I am an old man and hev no further hopes for myself, and am consekently reckliss.'

"I hev," said Randall, "others uv similar import from Noo Orleens, Mobeel, Vixburg, and Memphis. The writers all manifest the most ardent devoshen to—"

"I knowd they wood," exclaimed the President. "I yit hev friends."

"—To the candidate uv the Noo York Convenshun, and ez they all appear to think that this percession thro the country wood help em, I am willin. I can stand it. Like my Richmond friend, I hev nothin to hope for."

The tour wuz desided upon, and the President retired comparatively happy. The people must compliment him to his face, and he's a goin out in a sort uv a blaze uv glory any how.

PETROLEUM V. NASBY, P. M.

(wich is Postmaster).

8. *Impeachment Fails: "Our Shepherd Boy Hez Met This Goliath uv Radicalism"*

WASHINGTON, D. C., May 19, 1868.

The happiest hours I hev enjoyed for years past over me last nite. The failyoor to impeech filled me with joy inexpressible.

Thank Hevin! Halleloogy! Ef I wuz David I shood restring my harp, ef I wuz Miriam I shood order a fresh timbrel, ef I wuz Herodias I shood dance afore the King! For we hev pervaled. Our shepherd boy hez met this Goliath uv Radicalism, and with weapons wich he took from his pouch hez conkered him. This rapsody hez reference to impeechment excloosively.

When the vote wuz announced ther wuz the wildest enthoosiasm manifested. The streets wuz immejitly filled with the faithful. Baltimore and the cities further South hed vomitid all over Washinton. Mrs. Cobb, no longer in teers, hed returned, the pardon-brokers, whisky-spekilaters, and those who hed difficulties with courts on account uv irregularities in the currency they manufactured, wuz all here, and joyful. Confedrit Captains, Kernels, and Brigadiers forgot their respective ranks and embraced each other in the public streets; the gray-coats wich hed seen servis at Anteetam and Harper's Ferry made their appearance agin, the drinkin saloons filled up ez ef by magic, in fact, the sceen remindid me very much uv the revival uv the coz on the 22d uv Febrooary, 1866.

At the White House there wuz the most terrific exhilerashun. The President sat smilin serenely, Sekretary Welles (blessins on his frosty pow) wuz ez lively ez the Dunderberg, and Patterson wuz normal. The room wuz crowded with persons to congratoolate the President on his success, and every minit congratulatory despatches wuz bein reseeved, uv wich the follerin is samples:—

CONCORD, N. H., 19th.

The Dimocrisy uv Noo Hampsheer send greetin to Noo Hampsheer's noblest son, Salmon P. Chase. We forgive and welcum him.   F. PEERCE.

NOO ORLEANS, 19th.

The city is ablaze with enthoosiasm. My old poleece is now paradin the streets, a cheerin for Chase. Ez I write they are givin nine cheers and a tiger ez they pass the spot at wich Dostie wuz shot. Judge Abell desires me to add his congratulashuns.

MONROE, EX-MAYOR.

PEORY, ILL., 19th.

The circle wich hez a interest in the handlin uv ardent sperits at this place, congratulates the President on his triumph over his (and our) enemies. Ther confidence in the integrity uv the Senit wuz not misplaced. They consider the money they contributed to bring about this result well spent, and will promptly honor any draft made upon em for means to carry His Eggslency safe thro the remainin ten articles.

By order uv the Circle.

The President promptly answered this telegram, statin that no more money was needed to be yoosed for impeachment purposes, ez the contract with Senators kivered the entire eleven articles.

There were others from Morrissey, Vallandigham, and others, all breethin the same sperit uv thankfulnis for the result, and all acknowledgin indebtednis to the noble Republikins wich hed brot it about. These come from my old Kentucky home:

Halleloojy! I'll hev my niggers agin! Thank Hevin! My son Josier is even now findin out ther whereabouts. The Lord be praised! Hev already subjoogated three uv em. Selah! Bells is ringin and bonfires is blazin.   POGRAM.

The Corners congratulates yoo and the President. I commence work to-morrer on the enlargement uv my distillery, wich wuz suspended when the impeachment onpleasantnis wuz begun. All hale!   McPELTER.

"Why," sed I to Randall, who sat moody and alone, "don't yoo and the President share in the general exileration? He doesn't seem to be the least eggscited."

"Why shood we?" retorted he. "Doth the shepherd go into

spasms over the sheep he hez safe in his fold? The fact is, our eggscitin time wuz several weeks ago, while we wuz a buyin uv em, and arrangin for this. The Black Crook is ruther startlin to the beholder from the front, but to the managers who contracted for the legs at so much a pair, and arranged the tablo it ain't so startlin."

"Thinkst thou the new programme will result ez the President hopes?"

"No; the new party can't succeed, no more than our last vencher did. It ain't made up uv the right material. There's more intelleck than sole in it—more bowels than heart. There's Chase, Fessenden, Trumbull, and Grimes. Chase hez ambition, Grimes hate, and Trumbull and Fessenden dyspepsia, making the engregencies in the new organization half ambition and hate and half dyspepsia. Never trust a man whose stumick is out of order; take no stock in him whose bowels is unsound. Intelleck is nothin, heart is nothin, onless there's a stumick under em on wich to build. Chase hez no conshense, Trumbull and Fessenden no gastric joose. Sich men alluz conspire and alluz fail. Still, I'm glad the thing occurred."

"Ef it amounts to nothin, why glad?"

"Becoz it lets Johnson and me out. When Arnold went back on his countrymen, his countrymen forgot Joodis Iskariot; when Aaron Burr ariz, they to-wunst forgot Arnold; Pierce drove Burr out uv the public mind, Bookanan made em forget Pierce, Johnson made em forget Bookanan, and now Chase will make em forget Johnson and me. That's what I wuz drivin at. Under the storm I shell leeve for my quiet Wisconsin home and live in peece, for beside these latter cusses I shel loom up into comparative respectability. Good nite. All is well."

At a late hour I retired to my virchus couch, and fallin into the deep sleep wich only visits the pillers uv them whose conshences ain't bothered much, uv whom I am wich, ez my conshence sheds convickshen uv wrath to come ez a duck does spring rain, I dreemed a most curis dreem.

Methawt the Presidenshel course wuz reely and trooly a race course, and the candidates hed to run that course, the winner uv the race to be glorified. At one end uv the track wuz a weighin stand and at the other the winner's post, which wuz the White House. The runners wuz to carry the candidates for Vice President, and sich other weights ez their backers shood put onto em.

The Republicans hed Grant on the ground, promptly and ready for the race. He come up splendid. He wuzn't so mighty immense, but he wuz clean-limbed, decently develop all over, and showed first-rate in the back and loins. Colfax vaulted onto his shoulders, and he wuz ready.

Our people hed some difficulty in selectin a man to run agin him. Finally Chase wuz selected to run, and he wuz brot to the weighin stand. To the naked eye he wuz a splendid specimen, and he come up to the stand so galliant, that notwithstandin he carried in his hand a silver pitcher wich the niggers uv Cincinnati give him for defendin a fugitive from Kentucky, our people cheered him vociferous. Tall, strong, and muscular-lookin, in good flesh, deep-chested, broad-shouldered, strong-backt, he wuz ez perfect a specimen ez I ever beheld, and all felt confident that he wood hev no trouble in beatin his opponent out uv site.

At this pint Vallandygum, Peerse, Vorhees, Morrissey, and Wood, who hed charge uv our arrangements, took him in hand.

"We must prepare our man," sed they.

"Take orf this Ablishn coat," sed Voorhees.

"And this imparshel suffrage vest," sed Morrissey; "the nigger hezn't the moral qualificashens for the ballot."

"And this free soil shirt," sed Wood.

"And that anti-fugitive slave law wig," sed Voorhees.

"And them ekal justice shoulder-braces," sed Peerse.

"And them humanitarian pants," shreeked Wood.

"We can't abide none uv these things," yelled the crowd. "Peel! All uv these yoo got from the Ablishnists, free-soilers, and Republicans. We'll none uv em."

The silver pitcher he carried in his hand they trampled into the mud, and one by one the obnoxious garments wuz pulled off from him. Heavens! wat a change! Ez they wuz removed he shrunk. When the coat wuz taken off he wuzn't so broad and massive; when the vest wuz gone he wuz positively flat-chested; when the shoulder-braces wuz removed he became hump-backed; and when the pants wuz snaked off he stood afore us the merest skeleton I ever beheld—a weak, shaky, wheezin skeleton. Our folks looked disappointed, but it wuz too late to change. A loose two-sided wrapper wuz thrown over him, Gov. English climbed onto his shoulders, Vallandygum jumped into one pocket and Fernandy Wood into the other, the brass band tooted, the crowd yelled, he made one convulsiv start, but in vain. The stiffnin wuz all out uv him. His poor, weak knees gave way, his back doubled up, and he came to the ground, every bone in him rattlin ez he fell, while Grant made the race serenely.

"My God," sed Morrissey, lookin at the poor wreck, "what he got from the Ablishnists wuz all ther wuz uv him, after all!"

At this pint I awoke, and wuz saddened. There's where our trouble lies. We hev to strip these fellows, when they come to us, uv all that gives em any strength. Chase, without his Ablishnism, can't get a Ablishen vote, and the Democracy will vote for their own men in preference. Names ain't worth a d—n any more, and men without principles ain't uv the slightest account. And that's what's the matter with Democracy.

PETROLEUM V. NASBY, P. M.
(wich is Postmaster).

V. Professor Nasby

(1862-1867)

NOTE TO THE CHAPTER

Necessity, Petroleum Vesuvius Nasby knew, was the mother of invention. The military collapse of the political bulwark of inequality among men required the construction of new defenses. His own futile struggle against the teachings of abolitionism had also convinced him that the influence of learning in the country was proportional to its distribution. Unable to block the spread of knowledge any longer, Nasby set out at least to control its content. As a remedy for the evil times on which the South had fallen, he invented "The Southern Classikle, Theologikle, and Military Institoot uv Confedrit × Roads" to protect the youth "uv a Northern or levelin tendency" and to prepare the "stoodents for comin out strong on the holinis uv Slavery." Needless to say, the educator was also eager to settle an old score and to check once and for all the influence of Oberlin, the "figgerative . . . fountainhead . . . for the entire Ablishen party."

Anti-slavery evangelists transformed Oberlin College in Ohio into a hotbead of Abolitionism right under Nasby's eyes. In 1835 the trustees had agreed that the anti-slavery faculty should have full control and resolved that "the education of people of color . . . should be encouraged & sustained." Few of the nine thousand students who matriculated before the Civil War escaped complete conversion to the cause. Oberlin was always ready to aid Negroes who escaped from slavery. Fugitives were constantly passing through on the Underground Railroad to Canada. The most aggressive students crossed the border into the Southern states and enticed and guided slaves to freedom. One of them claimed to have liberated forty-seven slaves in the few years of his life which he spent outside of Southern prisons. On another line of their attack against the peculiar institution, Oberlinites formed an emigrant aid society and encouraged Free Soil settlers to move to Kansas to save the territory from slavery by their votes and moral influence. Some of them were actively involved in the fight over "Bleeding Kansas."

After the passage of the Fugitive Slave act in 1850, Oberlin was in a practical state of rebellion against the national government. The law directed Federal officials to return fugitives to the South, required

Northern men to aid in their recapture, and prescribed penalties for those who interfered with the act's execution. The rescue of John Price from the custody of a Federal officer agitated the country in 1859. The liberators, citizens of Oberlin and professors and students of the college, were indicted and jailed in Cleveland. Before the charges were dismissed they had printed a newspaper, received in their cells the correspondents of Eastern journals and deputations of churches and philanthropic societies, and addressed mass meetings of sympathizers through the barred windows. No wonder that Nasby saw Oberlin at the core of all the troubles besieging the country.

Nasby's "Institoot" was artfully designed to keep its students on the right path. The "young men confided to our care," the "Professor uv Biblikle Politicks" emphasized, "will receive not only a solid collegiate educashen, ez it is understood at the North, but careful attention will be paid to the accomplishments so necessary to the troo Southern gentlemen." A selected faculty and purged textbooks guaranteed success. General Nathan B. Forrest, a Confederate cavalry commander whose military instinct bordered on genius and whose spelling and language gave rise to the tradition that he was illiterate, taught moral philosophy. He himself had grossly ignored the subject during the war by sharing responsibility for the slaughter of Negro soldiers which followed his capture of Fort Pillow in April 1864.

Southern chivalry was represented by General John B. Magruder, whose entertainments were the envy of fashionable society at Newport before the war, and whose courtly bearing had earned him the title "Prince John." As one of the best trained of the Virginia officers, he lectured on the classics. Colonel John S. Mosby, a taciturn daredevil who had harassed the North with his rangers' raids, covered rhetorics and belles-lettres. The important field of biblical studies was entrusted to worthy Copperheads. Henry Clay Dean, an erratic Iowa Democrat, had mixed politics and preaching with considerable success during the war. His advocacy of peace and his criticism of the Lincoln administration had cost him his license as a Methodist minister. Charles Chauncey Burr, a Northern apostle of states' rights, had publications on the Constitution and Lola Montez to his credit.

The faculty of the Institoot relied for inspiration on the disjointed utterances of unreconstructed rebels against Negroes and Abolitionists. The ignorance and bias of other Southern men were not less useful. In 1861, Thomas E. Bramlette of Kentucky had made a determined stand for the preservation of the Union, had served in the Federal army, and as United States district attorney had enforced Kentucky's wartime laws against Confederates and Southern sympathizers. His two terms as governor turned him into a bitter opponent of Washington. When Lincoln ordered the enlistment of Negro troops in 1864, he threatened to turn his state against the Federal government. He continuously quarreled with the Union army in Kentucky, welcomed back the returning Confederate soldiers and recommended the repeal of all laws against them. Together with other Southerners, he favored the Thirteenth Amendment, but he objected sharply, with "words uv wisdom" it seemed to Nasby, to any attempts to abolish the Negro's enforced inferiority since he was convinced that colored men lacked the power to rise to the white man's level.

The growing concern of all politicians for the vote of the newly enfranchised Negroes jeopardized the ingenious attempts of "Drecktors and Faculty" of the Institoot to make the leopard spots, the signs of inherent inferiority, stick on the freedmen. "The nigger vote," Postmaster General Alexander Randall's fictitious instructions demanded, "must be capcherd," and it did not take Wade Hampton, who in his native state of South Carolina began cultivating the art of persuading Negroes to vote the Democratic ticket, to remind Nasby that in politics victories were won by votes cast. Nasby's resolution quickly turned the Institoot into "The Ham and Japhet Free Academy for the Development uv the Intelleck uv all Races, irrespective uv Color." Among the new members added to the faculty was Beverley Nash, a colored porter who became one of the most prominent figures of the South Carolina Constitutional Convention in 1868. "Times changes, and men change jist ez fast ez times," the Professor meditated, and "I shood like to see the times wich kin change faster than I kin."

1. Early Concern for Higher Education: "Oberlin! Wher Ablishnism Runs Rampant!"

COLUMBUS, O., June the 21st, 1862.

I wuz onto my way to Columbus to attend the annooal gatherin uv the faithful at that city, a dooty I hev religusly performd for over 30 yeres. Ther wuz but wun seat vakent in the car, and onto that I sot down. Presently a gentleman carryin uv a carpitbag sot down beside me, and we to-wunst commenst conversashen. After discussin the crops, the weather, et settry, I askt wher he resided.

"In Oberlin," sez he.

"Oberlin!" shreekt I. "Oberlin! wher Ablishnism runs rampant—wher a nigger is 100 per cent. better nor a white man— wher a mulatto is a objik uv pity on account uv hevin white blood! Oberlin! that stonest the Dimekratik prophets, and woodent be gathered under Vallandygum's wings as a hen-hawk gathereth chickens, at no price! Oberlin, that gives all the profits uv her college to the support uv the underground railroad—"

"But—" sez he.

"Oberlin," continyood I, "that reskoos niggers, and sets at defiance the benificent laws for takin on em back to their kind and hevenly-minded masters! Oberlin!—"

"My jentle frend," sez he, "Oberlin don't do nuthin uv the kind. Yoo've bin misinformd. Oberlin respex the laws, and hez now a body uv her gallant sons in the feeld a fightin to maintane the Constooshn."

"A fightin to maintane the Constooshn," retortid I. "My frend" (and I spoke impressivly), "no Oberlin man is a doin any sich thing. Oberlin commenst this war. Oberlin wuz the prime cause uv all the trubble. What wuz the beginnin uv it? Our Suthrin brethrin wantid the territories—Oberlin objectid. They wantid Kansas for ther blessid instooshn—Oberlin agin objecks. They sent colonies with muskits and sich, to hold the territory—Oberlin sent two thousand armed with Bibles and Sharp's rifles—two instooshns Dimokrasy cood never stand afore—and druv em out. They wantid Breckinridge fer President. Oberlin refused, and elektid Linkin. Then they seceded; and why is it that they still hold out?"

He made no anser.

"Becoz," continyood I, transfixin him with my penetratin gaze, "Oberlin won't submit. We might to-day hev peese ef Oberlin wood say to Linkin, 'Resine!' and to Geff Davis, 'Come up higher!' When I say Oberlin, understand it ez figgerative for the entire Ablishn party, wich Oberlin is the fountinhead. There's wher the trouble is. Our Suthern brethren wuz reasonable. So long as the Dimokrasy controlled things, and they got all they wanted, they wuz peeceable. Oberlin ariz—the Dimokrasy wuz beet down, and they riz up agin it."

Jest exsactly eighty-six yeres ago, akordin to Jayneses Almanac, a work wich I perooz annually with grate delite, the Amerykin eagle (whose portrate any wun who possessis a 5-cent peece kin behold) wuz born, the Goddis uv Liberty bein its mother, the Spirit uv Freedom its sire, Thomas Jefferson actin ez physician on the occasion. The proud bird growd ez tho it slept on guano—its left wing dipt into the Pacific, its rite into the Atlantic, its beek thretened Kanady, while his majestik tale cast a shadder ore the Gulf. Sich wuz the eagle up to March, '61. What is his condishn now? His hed hangs, his tale droops, ther's no strength in his talons. What's the trouble? Oberlin. He hed been fed on nigger for yeres, and hed thrived on the diet. Oberlin got

the keepin uv him—she withholds his nateral food; and onless
Oberlin is whaled this fall, down goes the eagle.

PETROLEUM V. NASBY.

2. A Postwar College: "That the Southern Yooth May Be Properly Trained"

CONFEDRIT × ROADS (wich is in the Stait uv Kentucky),
December 9, 1866.

Square Gavitt, Deekin Pogram, Captain McPelter, and myself wuz in the Post Offis last nite, wich, next to Bascom's, hez got
to be the cheef resort uv the leading intellex uv the Corners,
a talkin over matters and things, when the Deekin happened to
menshun that next week his second son, Elijer, who hez intelleck
into him, was a goin to start for Michigan to enter a college.

"Wat!" sed I, "do yoo perpose to send that noble yooth,
Elijer Pogram, to a Ablishn State, to enter a Ablishn college, to
suck his knollege from a Ablishn mother? Good Heavens! Frailty,
thy name is woman."

[I hedn't any ijee that this last remark wuz appropos, but it
sounds well, and I hev notist that it don't make much difference
wat the cotashun is, so ez yoo end a remark with a cotashun.]

The Deekin remarked that it wuz painful; but the fact wuz,
Elijer must hev a ejucashen. He didn't bleeve in ejucashen, generally speekin. The common people wuz better off without it, ez
ejucashen hed a tendency to unsettle their minds. He hed seen
the evil effex uv it in niggers and poor whites. So soon ez a nigger
masters the spellin book and gits into noosepapers, he becomes
dissatisfied with his condishn, and hankers after a better cabin
and more wages. He to-wunst begins to insist onto ownin land
hisself, and givin his children ejucashen, and, ez a nigger, for our
purposes, ain't worth a soo markee. Jes so with the poor whites.
He knowd one meloncolly instance. A poor cuss up toards Gar-
rittstown, named Ramsey, learnt to read afore the war, and then
commenst deterioratin. For two years he refoozed to vote the
Dimocratic ticket, then he blossomed out into a Ablishnist, and
tried to make the others uv his class discontented by tellin uv em
that Slavery wuz wat kept them down, and finally, after pashense
ceased to be a virchoo, and we tarred and fethered him one nite
for a incendiary, he went to Injiany. That cuss cum back here,

doorin the late onpleasantniss, kernel of a regiment, wich he campt on my farm and subsisted em off it. Sum ejucashen is, how ever, nessary. I design Elijer for Congris, and he must hev it. He's a true Pogram, and nothin will strike in wich kin hurt him.

"Why not," sez I, "that the Southern yooth may be properly trained, start a College uv our own? Why, Deekin, run risks uv hevin the minds uv our young men tainted with heresy?"

The entire company wuz struck with the idea, and it wuz earnestly canvassed, and finally decided upon; and I wuz deppy-tized to start it, wich I immejityly did. The name by wich the new college is to be known is "The Southern Classikle, Theologikle, and Military Institoot uv Confedrit × Roads (wich is in the Stait uv Kentucky)."

The college grounds is to comprise one hundred akers taken from corners uv the farms uv Deekin Pogram, Elder Slathers, and Capt. McPelter, wich ground they sell the college, seein it's for that purpose, for $300 per aker.

The faculty will be, ef we kin sekoor em, composed uv these trooly great minds:—

Genril Forrest, late C. S. A., Professor uv Moral Philosophy.

Kernell Mosby, late C. S.A., Professor uv Rhetoric and Belles Lettres.

Capt. McGee, late C. S. A., Professor uv Natural Sciences.

Genril Magruder, late C. S. A., Professor uv watever is understood by them ez is posted in college matters ez Classics, wich I shel look up ez soon ez I have time.

This is a killin two birds with one stun. We not only pervide ejucashen, wich is safe for our young men, but we pervide com-fortable places for the heroes uv the late onpleasantniss.

In addition to these, Deekin Pogram, Square Gavitt, and my-self, each pledged ourselves to endow a Professorship in the Theologikle Department, to be known by our names, and we to hev the appintin uv the Professors.

The Pogram Chair uv Biblikle Theology will be offered to Rev. Henry Clay Dean, uv Iowa, provided he will stipulate to wash his feet wunst per quarter, and change his shirt at least twice per annum.

The Gavitt Chair uv Biblikle Literatoor will be offered to Rev. C. Chauncy Burr, uv Noo York.

The Nasby Chair uv Biblikle Politicks will be filled by Rev. Petroleum Vesoovius Nasby, whose eminent fitness for the place is undispooted.

In the Scientific and Classikle Departments the text-books will be keerfully revised, and everything uv a Northern or levelin tendency will be scroopulously expergated. In the Theologikle Department speshl attenshun will be given to the highly nessary work uv preparin the stoodents for comin out strong on the holinis uv Slavery, and to this end the three years' course will be devotid thus:—

1st year—To the cuss uv Noer.
2d year—To provin that the Afrikin nigger wuz reely the descendants uv Ham.
3d year—Considerin the various texts wich go to show that Afrikin slavery is not only permitted by the skripters, but especially enjoined.

I shell myself lectur, from time to time, on Ham, Hager, and Onesimus, that the bearins uv these individooals upon our system may be fully understood, and also on sich subjects ez the inflooense uv stimulatin flooids upon the human system, the cat-o'-nine-tails ez a evangelizer, and sich other topics ez may from time to time sejest themselves.

The young men confided to our care will receive not only a solid collegiate educashun, ez it is understood at the North, but careful attention will be paid to the accomplishments so nessary to the troo Southern gentleman. They will be taught draw poker, pitchin dollars (real Spanish dollars will be provided for the purpose), spittin at a mark, revolver and bowie knife practice, tournament ridin at rings (real injy rubber rings will be provided—this'll be extra), and cat-o'-nine-tails. The morals uv the stoodents will be scroopulously looked after. No card-playin will be allowed afore servis on Sunday, and none whatever with the servants. They will be taught to respeck themselves.

Uv course, there will hev to be a large outlay uv money, wich it stands to reason can't be outlayed till it's inlayed. We, therefore, formed an Executive Committee, whose dooty it wuz made to solissit funds for this purpose, and to inaugerate a series uv Gift Enterprises, and sich, wich is ez follows:—

Deekin Pogram, President. Elder Slathers, Vice-President. Capt. McPelter, Corresponding Secretary. Myself, Financial Secretary and Treasurer.

The high standin uv the Board, particklerly the Treasurer, wich hez the handlin uv the funds, is a suffishent guarantee that all money subscribed will be faithfully applied. It wuz resolved, in order that the Board may present that respectable appearance wich their posishen demands, that the first funds reseeved should be applied to the purchis uv each uv em a new soot uv clothes, a step, I am confident, the friends uv southern educashen will approve uv and heartily endorse.

I hev hopes in the course uv a week to report progress. Every subscriber uv $2.50 and upwards, will hev a Honorary Professorship named after him, or will be made a Honorary Member uv the Board uv Directors, ez he chooses. We hev high hopes uv a libral support from the Dimocrisy North. They cannot but realize the dangers uv sendin their sons to sich institooshens uv learnin North ez must turn em out Ablishnists, or chill, at least, the ardor uv their Dimocrisy.

It is to be hoped that contributions for the buildin uv the institooshen and its proper endowment will be commenst immejitly, ez there is a morgage on Deekin Pogram's farm, and I am in pressin need uv a substanshel soot uv winter clothes.

PETROLEUM V. NASBY, P. M.
(wich is Postmaster).

3. Lecture-Sermon: "Kin the Leopard Change His Spots, or the Ethiopian His Skin?"

POST OFFIS, CONFEDRIT X ROADS
(wich is in the Stait uv Kentucky),
Janooary 10, 1867.

I wuz rekested a week ago to preech a discourse from the text wich the noble and high-minded Guvner Bramlette used with sich crushin force in his last annual message, to wit: "Kin the Leopard change his spots, or the Ethiopian his skin?" and alluz feelin anxious to do wat I kin for the cause, I did it last nite, or rather essayed to do it.

And here let me remark, that there ain't a more devoted people in Kentucky than them lambs ez compose my flock. It wuz a tetchin site, and one wich filled my sole with joy, to see em pour out uv the groceries at the first tootin uv the horn, and to see Pennebacker, wich owns the Distillery, stoppin work to come; but the most cheerin and encouragin sign to me wuz to see Deekin Pogram, who wuz playin seven-up for the drinks with Elder

Slathers, at Bascom's, lay down his hand when he hed high low and jack in it, and hed only three to go. "Elder," sed he, his voice tremblin at the sacrifice he wuz a makin, and a tear steelin down his cheek, "Elder, them's the horn. Let us to our dooties. 'Ligion must take the front seat uv temp'ral matters," and, sighin ez he cast a partin glance at his hand, he strode out resolootly to the sanktooary.

I opened by readin the follerin from Guvner Bramlette's message:—

" 'The nigger is the inferior uv the white—he lacks the power to rise. Ontil the Leopard kin change his spots, or the Ethiopian his skin, all efforts to repeal or nullify God's laws will be unavailin."

"My bretherin, these words is words uv wisdom, and fur em let us be thankful. The skin uv the Ethiopian wuz inflicted onto him for the express purpose uv distingishin him from his bretherin, whose servants he wuz condemned to be, for all time, ez a punishment for the sin uv Cain or the improodence uv Ham, wich, Democratic divines heven't settled on. With the black skin he wuz given all the other marks uv inferiority. He wuz cust with long arms, immense hands, flat nose, and bowed legs, and that ther mite be no mistake in the matter, he wuz given wool instead uv hair. Halleloogy! Wat a blessid thing for us is this Ethiopian! Wat a consolation it must be to yoo all to know that ther is a race below yoo, and how blessid the refleckshun that they can't change ther skin, and by that means git above yoo! That's the comfort we draw from the skripters. Wat a horror it wood be for Deekin Pogram, snorin so peacefly, ef when the Soopreme Court decides the Ablishn amendment unconstooshnl, and he gits his niggers back agin; ef ther shood be a new dispensashun, and niggers shood be permitted to change ther skins! Wat sekoority wood we hev for our property? Some mornin he'd wake up and find em all white persons, wich it wood be unconstooshnel to wollop.

"My brethern, ther has bin many efforts to change the skin uv the Ethiopian, or rather ther hez bin many who wanted to. The Boston Ablishnists hev tried it, but wat hez bin the result? Ain't they niggers yit, and ain't they still the degraded wretches they alluz wuz? I paws for a reply."

I made this latter remark becoz it sounded well, not that I hed any idee that anybody wood reply. Imagine my surprise at seein a gray-headed nigger, wich hed bin, doorin and after the fratrisidle struggle, employed in the Freedman's Burow, rise, and

remark that he hed a word to say onto that pint. There wuz a
storm uv indignashun, and the impudent nigger, who wuz so
sassy ez to presoom to speak in a white meetin, wood hev bin
sacrificed on the spot, hed not Joe Bigler, who wuz half drunk,
drawd a ugly-lookin navy revolver, and remarkin that he knowd
that nigger, that he hed more sense than the hull bilin uv us, and
he shood hev his say.

"Ef," sed this recklis Joe, "ef he beats yoo, Perfesser, trooth
is trooth; let's hev it. Ef he don't, why, it's all the better for yoo.
Ef yoor Websterian intelleck kivers the ground, all rite; ef his
ponderous intellek gets the best on't, jist ez rite. 'Out uv the
mouths uv babes and sucklins.' Elder, I go my bottom dollar on
this sucklin. Speak up, venerable: there won't none uv em tech
yoo;" and he cockt his revolver.

"Beggin pardon," sed the nigger, "I agree with yoo, Perfesser, that the Ethiopian can't change his skin hisself, but does
the Scripter say that it can't be changed for him?"

"Anser the venrable babe," sed Joe Bigler, pintin his revolver at me.

"I can't say that it does," sez I.

"Very good," retorted the nigger, "hezn't there a change bin
a goin on in Kaintuck from the beginnin? My mother wuz ez
black ez a crow—I'm considble lighter—my wife's a half lighter
than I am—my gal's children is a half lighter than their mother,
and I want to know wat Guvner Bramlette's got to say to that.
The white man ain't got no cuss onto him, hez he?"

"Speek up, Perfesser—the sucklin wants yoo to be prompt,"
sed Joe Bigler.

I answered that "he hed not—that it wuz piled onto Ham
or Cain and ther desendants, and nobody else."

"Very well, then," sed the nigger, "ez I am only half Ham
or Cain, then uv course there's only half a cuss onto me, only a
quarter onto my wife, only an eighth onto my daughters, only a
sixteenth onto my daughters' children, and there's lots uv niggers
in this yer visinity wat hezn't got the thirty-second or the sixty-
fourth part uv it hangin to em. Guvner Bramlette also sed suthin
bout niggers bein degraded coz twuz their nacher, didn't he,
and that edducashen woodent do for em?"

"Perfesser," sed the tormentin Bigler, wich hed just whisky
enuff into him to be ugly, "I must remind you that the partikeler
babe and sucklin, out uv whose mouth yoor bein immensely condemned, expex prompt ansers."

I ansered that sich wuz the tenor uv the Guvner's remarks.

"Ef that's troo, why don't the mulattoes come up faster? Ef it's the nateral stoopidity uv the nigger, the white man ain't affected by it, and the mulatto only half. I am 'quainted with the heft uv the people afore me, and I'll bet my last year's wages, wich Deekin Pogram ain't paid yit, that half uv em can't read any mor'n I kin. 'Pears to me I'd like to hev Guvner Bramlette take the load off us for a year or two and see whether we'd rise or not. We moutn't and then agin we mout. But I ruther think its a leetle too much to put a millstone on top uv a man and then kick him for not gettin up."

"Bully!" sed Joe Bigler. "Go on! go on!"

"It ain't square playin to make laws agin our risin, to flog us for hevin spellin-books, to make it a penitentiary offence to learn to read, and to burn our skool-houses, and then because we ain't just ready to enter college, to insist on't that we are naterally incapable. And above all, ain't it presoomin a little to charge it onto the Lord? Ain't yoo mistakin yoor own work for hizzen? 'Praps ef Guvner Bramlette's father hed bin flogg'd for wantin to learn to read, and Guvner Bramlette's mother hed bin brought up ez a feeld hand, and the same strategy hed bin practised on Guvner Bramlette's grandfather, and great grandfather, and great, great grandfather, and great, great, great grandfather, and his great—"

"Hold on, venerable," sed Joe Bilger, "don't enumerate. Jest say his ancestors, back to the identicle time they wuz slaves to them Normans, wich held his projenitors jist ez closely ez yoo've bin held, and it'll be suffishent."

"I plead guilty to the big hands, flat nose, and bowd legs. Possibly the first nigger hed em—possibly not. Ef Guvner Bramlette's ancestors hed bin kept at the hoe, his hands wood hev bin ez big ez mine; ef they'd borne burdens forever his legs wood be bowed, and ef ther noses hed bin perpetooally smasht hizzen wood be flatter than it is."

"Hev yoo eny more questions to put to the Perfesser?" sed Joseph.

"No," replied the Ethiopian, "I hev sed my say."

"Then," sed this Bigler, "I dismiss this congregashun, with this remark, that that nigger is under my protectin care, and ef a single lock uv his wool is disturbed, I shel feel it a sollum but painful dooty devolvin upon me, to put a ball into the carcass uv each uv the offishls uv this Church, commencin with the Paster, and continuin all the way down to the scribe. Git!"

And pell-mell the congregashen piled out—one over another.

It will be necessary to dispose of Joe Bigler somehow. He lost wat property he hed in the war, and is becoming exceedingly loose in his talk. He can't be tolerated long.

PETROLEUM V. NASBY, P. M.
(wich is Postmaster), and likewise Professor.

4. "Adaptid Especially to the Southern Intelleck": How to Choose Textbooks

POST OFFIS, CONFEDRIT × ROADS
(wich is in the Stait uv Kentucky),
Febrooary 20, 1867.

The Institoot is a success. Contribushens flow in slowly but shoorly,—fast enuff indeed to give each uv the Board a noo soot uv close; and we, espeshelly, who hev the fust handlin uv that money, sevral other comforts. But that corner-stun troubles us. Sum hundreds uv people saw that a bottle uv likker and a greenback wuz deposited under it, and regerly every nite it's bin overturned by persons in serch uv them relics. At great expense we built onto it a section uv wall; but makin no account uv our expenditoor, they overturned it. We then histed a sign-board bearing this legend: "The whisky is gone, and the greenback also," signed by the Board; but one half uv the citizens uv that lokality don't read, and tother didn't hev the nessary confidence in the truthfulness uv the Board to prevent em from goin for the artikles, tho the very knowlege uv us wich brot about this state uv disbelief, shood, wun wood suppose, hev taught em that the greenback and likker coodent possibly be there after so long a period hed ensood. So, ez a last resort, we stuck two posts in the ground and drawd an iron chain over it. That got em. Force is about the only thing uv any account in this country.

The Board met last nite at the Post Office, wich, ontil we git the Institoot built, will be the headquarters uv the Trustees, to consider the propriety uv publishin a series uv skool books, adaptid especially to the Southern intelleck, and calculated to

keep alive in the minds uv the buddin yooths uv the late Confederacy, wich is unfortunately deceest, a lively opinion uv themselves and a corresponding hatred uv Noo England and the
North generally. We hev hed serious doubts whether proper ideas
cood be instilled into a youth from a book written by a Boston
man, and printed in Cincinnati.

I submitted to the Board a example for a noo Arithmetic,
to wit:—

"A Yankee sent a substitoot into the Federal army at a cost
uv $1000, passing off onto him two counterfeit ten dollar notes.
To make up the expenditoor, he to-wunst swindles a innocent
Kentuckian out uv $100 in a patent rite, a Alabamian out uv $200
in a Western land trade, and the balance he makes up by sellin
wooden nutmegs, wich he turns out uv basswood at a profit uv
4 cents per one. The grate moral question is, how many nutmegs
must this ingenius but unprincipled cuss manufaktur, and how
long does it take him, with the improoved machinery they hev, to
do it?

"The Southern soljers, at the battle uv the first Bull Run,
captured 18 Federals, one uv whom hed upon his person $12 in
greenbax, and tothers $8 each. How many uv Johnson's Post-
masters cood be bought with the proceeds uv the capcher?"

Deekin Pogram approved uv these examples; but he kept
insistin that there wuzn't enuff in em to fire the Southern heart.
The Southern heart wuz a perpetooal funeral pile wich needid
continyooal firin. Onless fired it wuz a gloomy mass uv very on-
sightly black cinders. He proposed that the forthcoming book
shood be coal oil on the slumberin embers uv the yoothful Southern heart. He hed a example:—

"The battle uv Chickamauga wuz fought a certain number
uv miles from Chattanooga. One regiment uv Confedrit soljers
druv a division uv Fedral mercenaries into the town. Allowin
that each Fedral, ez well ez Confedrit, hed two legs, how many
more steps did the Fedrals take to get em into Chattanooga,
where they wuz comparatively safe from Confedrit rage and
valor, and sich, than it did the Confedrits to drive em thar?"

Bascom remarkt that he hed one wich he felt it his dooty to
propose:—

"A strickly conscienshus grocery keeper starts in biznis worth
four hundred dollars in clean cash. He pays for his whiskey two
dollars per gallon in Looisville, and hez for a reglar customer a
Postmaster, wich drinks forty or sixty times per day, and alluz

tells him to 'jist chalk it down.' Required the length uv time nessary to bust him under them afflictin circumstances?"

Bascom remarkt that long before the book appears in print, he wood be able to furnish the anser to that little problem. Considerin the example a dig direct at me, I wuz uv a noshen to retort; but ther wuz sich a look uv injerd innosense onto Bascom's countenance that reely I coodent. Suthin must be done for Bascom,—I hev lived onto him too long. The next contribushen I reseeve from frends North shel be devoted to liquidating, in part, the debt I owe him. I cood bust him, by not givin him at least cost for his likker; but wat follows? There's the rub. Wood he who come after give me credit? Better bear the ills we hev than fly to them to wich we hevn't bin interdoost.

Joe Bigler, the drunken Confedrit soljer, happened in, and heard the last two examples, and remarkt that he cood furnish any number uv examples at site. We never stop Joseph in anything he perposes to do, for he hez a habit uv carryin a navy revolver slung to him. Joseph wuz permitted to perceed.

"Ef a Southern man pants for his rites, and fites four years for em, gittin licked like the devil, how long after is it advisable for him to continyoo to pant, pervidid he didn't know at the beginnin wat his rites wuz?

"Ef a Southern soljer kin whip five Northern soljers, why in bloody thunder, they hevin hed a suffishency uv opportoonities uv doin it, didn't the South gain her independence?

"Ef fitin four years, and loosin every doggoned cent's worth uv property a man hed wuz profitable biznis, how many struggles for independence wood a man uv modrit means be justified in goin thro with?

"Ef two gallons and a half uv Kentucky whisky kin be got from a bushel uv corn, how many Democratic voters, takin young men ez they run, kin be manufaktured from the produck uv an aker uv good land in a modrit year for corn?

"A high-toned shivelrous Virginian, twenty years ago, hed a female slave wich wuz ez black ez a crow, and worth only $800. Her progeny wuz only half ez black ez a crow, and her female grandchildren wuz suffishently bleached to sell in Noo Orleans for $2500 per female offspring. Required, 1st. The length uv time nessary to pay off the Nashnel debt by this means. 2d. The number uv years nessary to bleach the cuss of color out uv the niggers uv the United States.

"A. Johnson hed the idea uv carryin a certin number uv

deestricks, by speekin in em with Seward, all uv wich gave increased majorities agin him. Required the number uv miles uv travel, and the number uv repetitions uv the speech, to enable him to carry out his policy?

"Ef two nips at Washington wuz suffishent to perdoose the speech at the inaugerashen on the 4th uv March, 1865, how many must have bin slung into A. J. to perdoose the 22d uv Febrooary effort, and how many must he hev taken between Washinton and St. Louis?"

"These examples," sed Joseph, "I consider nessary for this book; and ef it is published without em I shel take it ez a personal affront, for which I shel hold the Board personelly responsible. The Southern yooth must be properly instructed—my orphans must hev proper notions instilled into em, and these examples is nessary to that end. Let this Board remember that, when this book is publisht, ef these examples is not in them, they hev me to settle with."

And Joseph departed. We are in a quandary. We dare not publish the book without his examples, for he alluz keeps his word, and is a ugly cuss to deal with; and uv course puttin em in coodent be thought uv. We finally decided that Joseph must be got out uv the way ez soon ez possible, and therefore votid that Bascom give him unlimited credit at his bar for a week, chargin the same upon the account uv the Institoot. I know that a free run at his barrels would finish me or any one uv the Board in that time. Happy Bigler! He hez at least one satisfactry week afore him,—I cood almost wish the Board wood try it on me. It wood be a short but glorious career.

Petroleum V. Nasby, P. M.
(wich is Postmaster), and likewise Professor.

5. Push-Button Integration: "I Shood Like to See the Times Wich Kin Change Faster than I Kin"

Post Offis, Confedrit X Roads
(wich is in the Stait uv Kentucky),
April 22, 1867.

Times changes, and men change jist ez fast ez times. I shood like to see the times wich kin change faster than I kin; but this last shift I hev bin forced to make, ruther took my breth. It wuz sudden. The Connecticut eleckshun didn't do us much good after all. We felt well over it for perhaps a day; but ez we begun to git other indicashens from the North, we didn't jist see how that little spirt wuz agoin to help us. Cincinnati went Ablishin stronger than ever. Chicago ditto; and most everywhere the Dimocratic rooster wuz flattened. The cabinet, when they heerd uv Deekin Pogram's assault upon a nigger, on the receet uv the intelligence uv the election news, notified me officially that a repetishen uv sich loonacy wood be equivalent to a reseet uv my resignation, even tho the post offis shood be discontinyood. *"The nigger vote must be capcherd. It's essenshel. Wade Hampton sez so,"* wrote Randall to me, and I reprimanded the Deekin for his recklessniss, and borrowed four dollars uv Bascom, who is the only man in the vicinity who hez any ready money, to make it all rite with him.

We held a meetin uv the Drecktors and Faculty uv the Southern Military and Classicle Institoot last evening, to decide wat course that instooshn wuz to take in the grate work uv surroundin the Ethiopian. In sich a time ez this, ez I menshened to Captain McPelter, it won't do for our institooshuns uv learning to stand back. These great levers, the molders uv public opinion, must be ez progressive ez the progressiveist, and must change like other things to meet the requirements uv the times. We hev commenst our march into Africa, and thus far hev we gone into the bowels uv the land without impediment, to speak uv—let us persevere. Let us capcher the Ethiopian, stink and all.

The meetin wuz held in the back room uv Bascom's, owin to the fact that it wuz rainin, and the roof uv the Post Offis leaks. I hed an appropriashen some time since from the Department for repairs; but bein in doubt whether it wuz intended for repairs on the Post Offis or the Postmaster, I gave the prizner the benefit uv the doubt, and got a new pair uv boots. I cood better endoor the slite inconvenience uv occasional rain than to go barefoot.

I made a statement uv the case, and sejested a radical change in the Institoot. Captain McPelter agreed with me. He felt that ther hedn't bin that complete, hearty recognition uv our Afrikin brethren as there ought to be. He hed on several occasions allowed his nateral vivacity to git the better of his proodence, and hed waded into em alarmin. The old ijee of Ham and Hagar and Onesimus hed bin so drilled into him in his yooth, that he hed to wrestle with it to keep it in control, and in spite uv himself it often got the better uv him. He sejested that the name uv the Institoot be changed from "The Southern Military and Classikle Institoot," to "The Ham and Japheth Free Academy for the Development uv the Intellek uv all Races, irrespective uv Color." That he thought would anser the required end. The colored men who choose to avail theirselves of the priviliges afforded by this institooshn, when it is finished, kin find in this no cause uv complaint. They are recognized. They are given the precedence. They stand first in the matter and foremost. Wat more kin they ask?

Bascom hed a series uv resolooshuns wich he desired to present. He sed it mite be looked upon ez strange that he shood favor the concentrashun uv free niggers at the Corners, but he hed good and suffishent reasons. First, he hed faith that constant contact with the Board wood bring em to the pint uv patronizin his bar; but ef it didn't, he knowd perfectly well that the Board and Fakulty wood manage to git all they hed, for board and tooition, wich he wuz perfectly certin he'd git in the end. Wat he wanted wuz people here; to yoose an illustration borrered from his biznis, the offishels uv this Institoot wuz the tunnel through wich the wealth uv all uv em wood be conducted to his coffers. I fell onto his neck in rapcher, and then vowed that I wuz willin to die for his good—that I cared not how much uv other people's money run through me to him ef 'twas thus dilooted. The resolooshens presented read ez follows:—

"*Resolved,* That the name uv the Southern Military and Classikle Institoot be changed to 'The Ham and Japheth Free Academy for the Development uv the Intelleck uv all Races, irrespective uv Color.'

"*Resolved,* That in makin this change, we, the Board uv Directors, do so, assertin,

"1. That in this emergency we are justified in doubtin whether Noer got tite at all, the statement in the Skripters to that effect bein ondoubtedly an error uv the translators.

"2. That ef he did git tite, he didn't cuss Ham at all.

"3. That ef he did cuss Ham, the cuss wuzn't intended to extend beyond Canaan at the furthest, and hence his descendants go scot free.

"4. That ef the cuss wuz really and trooly intended to attach to all uv Ham's descendants, irrespective uv color, to the end uv time, it ain't uv no effeck in Kentucky, ez that State hez allus run irrespective uv any code, 'ceptin sich ez hez bin adopted by her Legislacher.

"5. That the theory that the nigger, irrespective uv color, is a beast, is a deloosion, a snare, which we hev alluz practically held, no matter what we may, for effect, hev sed, ez the number uv mulattoes, to say nothin uv them still farther bleached in Kentucky, abundantly proves.

"6. That the Ethiopian, irrespective uv color, is trooly a man and a brother; and the female Ethiopian, also irrespective uv color, trooly a woman and a sister.

"*Resolved,* That this Institoot, whose name is now so happily changed, shel be conducted upon the principles uv strict ekality, irrespective uv color.

"*Resolved,* That when we reflect that the bloated aristocracy uv England interdoost, and the early settlers uv Massachoosets sankshund, slavery on this continent, forcin it really onto us, we bile with indignashun towards em, and kin hardly restrane ourselves.

"*Resolved,* That at the tables, in the choice uv rooms, and in all matters where there is a choice, the African man and brother, irrespective uv color, shel heve the precedence.

"*Resolved,* That Oberlin College, by not givin the sons uv Ham, irrespective uv color, the precedence, shows clearly that it is actooated by narrer-minded prejudice, wich deserves the reprobashen uv every lover uv his kind.

"*Resolved,* That the Ethiopian, irrespective uv color, kin change his skin, and that his oder, ef he hez any, is rather pleasant than otherwise.

"*Resolved,* That we look with loathing upon the States North, wich, alluz professin friendship for the noble black man uv the cotton fields, refoose to take him to their buzzums, irrespective uv color.

"*Resolved,* That ef Massachoosits and Vermont, and Northern Illinois, and the Western Reserve in Ohio, are honest in their professions uv love for the negro, they will come down with donashuns to assist in the completion uv the Academy."

Deekin Pogram didn't know about all this. He hed bin edikated in Ham and Hager, and wuz a bleever in Onesimus. He doubted. Sposen after all this concesion the nigger shood play off onto us? Sposen he shoodent vote with us after all, but cling to his Northern friends? Or spose he shood vote with us, and we

shood, thro his vote, git control, wat then? How cood we redoose
em to their normal condition agin after all this palavrin?

Bascom replied that he wuz surprised at the Deekin's
obtoosnis. First, ef they did vote with the Ablishnists, we wuz no
worse off, ez that wuz wat they proposed to do any how. Ef, on
the other hand, they didn't, what then? The trouble with em
now is, they know too much. "Let em," sed Bascom, warmin up,
"let em associate with us a year, let em vote with us, et cettry,
and in twelve months they're precisely fitted agin to be servance
unto their brethren. Look," sed he, "at the Northern Dimocrasy,
and see to what we may hope to bring these men in time."

But little more bizness wuz transacted. Beverly Nash, of
South Caroliny, wuz unanimously called to a professorship; and
a young gentleman uv color, who, from his strong resemblance
to Elder Gavitt, ought to hev biznis capacity, wuz unanimously
elected a member of the Board. The yoonyun is perfect. Ham
and Japheth hev shaken hands, and are embracin each other.

May prosperity attend the nupchels, and may the isshoo be
fortunate. I hev got over the disgust attendant upon the fust
chill, and am consekently feelin well.

PETROLEUM V. NASBY, P. M.
(wich is Postmaster), and Professor in the
Ham and Japheth Free Academy for
the Development uv the Intelleck uv
all Races, irrespective uv Color.

6. Nasby Regulates a Country School: "A Minglin with Our Daughters ez a Ekal"

POST OFFIS, CONFEDRIT X ROADS
(wich is in the Stait uv Kentucky),
November 25, 1867.

When the Almighty made niggers, he ought to have made
em so that mixin with the sooperior race would have been an
impossibility. I rite these lines, propped up in bed at my boardin
house, my face beaten to a jelly, and pefeckly kivered with stickin
plaster; my nose, alluz the beauty and glory uv my face, is en-
larged to twict its fair proporshens; my few remainin teeth hev
bin knockt down my throat, my lips resemble sausages, my left
ear is forever no more, and wat little hair wuz a hangin about my

venerable temples is gone, my head is ez bald as a billyard ball, and twict its normal size. It come about thus:—

There was trouble in one of the Southern counties uv Ohio. In a reliably Democratic township in that county is a settlement uv niggers, who, in the old time, ran away from Kentucky, and settled there where they could hev wat they earned, wich was jest so much swindled out uv Kentucky. Uv course comin from Kentucky, these niggers are, many uv em, ez near white ez they can be. One uv em who carried with him the name uv his master, and, ez he says, father, LETT, is ez near a white man ez may be, and ez he married a wench who wuz a shade whiter than he, their children are jist a touch whiter then both uv em. Uv these he hed three daughters, rangin from sixteen to twenty.

Now this LETT is a disturber. He hed a farm uv perhaps 200 akers, and wuz taxed heavy for skool purposes, but his children wuzn't uv course allowed to attend the skool. None uv the nigger children were. But LETT got the ijee into his hed that there wuzn't no propriety in his payin taxes without enjoyin the benefits arizin from em, and aided and abetted by other niggers, who were wicked enough to complain uv payin taxes to the support uv white skools, he sent his daughters to the skool, directin them to present theirselves boldly, take their seats quietly, and study perseverinly. They did so, the skoolmarm, who wuz a young huzzy, with black eyes and nateral curls, from Noo Hampsheer, where they persekoot the saints, not only assented to recevin em, but gave em seats and put em into classes—think uv that— with white children.

There wuz trouble in that township. I wuz sent for to-wunst, and gladly I come. I wuz never so gratified in my life. Had smallpox broken out in that skool, there woodent hev bin half the eggs-citement in the township. It wuz the subjick uv yooniversal talk everywhere, and the Democrisy wuz a bilin like a pot. I met the trustees uv the township, and demanded ef they intended tamely to submit to this outrage? I askt em whether they intended to hev their children set side by side with the decendants uv Ham, who wuz condemned to a posishen uv inferiority forever? Kin you, I asked, so degrade yourselves, and so blast the self-respeck uv yoor children?

And bilin up with indignashen, they answered "never!" and yoonanimously requested me to accompany em to the skoolhouse, that they mite peremptory expel these disgustin beins who hed obtrooded themselves among those uv a sooperior race.

On the way to the skoolhouse, wich wuz perhaps a mile distant, I askt the Board ef they knowed those girls by site. No, they replied, they hed never seed em. "I hev bin told," sed I, "that they are nearly white."

"They are," sed one uv em, "quite white." "It matters not," sed I, feelin that there wuz a good opportoonity for improvin the occashen, "it matters not. There is suthin in the nigger at wich the instink uv the white man absolootly rebels, and from wich it instinktively recoils. So much experience hev I had with em, that put me in a dark room with one uv em, no matter how little nigger there is in em, and that unerrin instink wood betray em to me, wich, by the way, goes to prove that the dislike we hev to em is not the result uv prejudis, but is a part uv our very nacher, and one uv its highest and holiest attriboots."

Thus communin, we entered the skoolhouse. The skoolmarm wuz there, ez brite and ez crisp ez a Janooary mornin; the skolers wuz ranged on the seets a studyin ez rapidly ez possible.

"Miss," sed I, "we are informed that three nigger wenches, daughters of one LETT, a nigger, is in this skool, a minglin with our daughters ez a ekal. Is it so?"

"The Misses LETT are in this skool," sed she, ruther mischeeviously, "and I am happy to state that they are among my best pupils."

"Miss," sed I sternly, "pint em out to us!"

"Wherefore?" sed she.

"That we may bundle em out!" sed I.

"Bless me!" sed she, "I reely coodent do that. Why expel em?"

"Becoz," sed I, "no nigger shel contaminate the white children uv this deestrick. No sech disgrace shel be put on to em."

"Well," sed this aggravatin skoolmarm, wich wuz from Noo Hamshire, "yoo put em out."

"But show me wich they are."

"Can't yoo detect em, sir? Don't their color betray em? Ef they are so neer white that you can't select em at a glance, it strikes me that it can't hurt very much to let em stay."

I wuz sorely puzzled. There wuzn't a girl in the room who looked at all niggery. But my reputashun wuz at stake. Noticin three girls settin together who wuz somewat dark complectid, and whose black hair waved, I went for em and shoved em out, the cussid skoolmarm almost bustin with lafter.

Here the tragedy okkerred. At the door I met a man who

rode four miles in his zeal to assist us. He hed alluz hed an itchin to pitch into a nigger, and ez he cood do it now safely he proposed not to lose the chance. I wuz a puttin on em out, and hed jist dragged em to the door, when I met him enterin it.

"Wat is this?" sed he, with a surprised look.

"We're puttin out these cussed wenches, who is contaminatin yoor children and mine," sed I. "Ketch hold uv that pekoolyerly disgustin one yonder," sed I.

"Wenches! You d—d skoundrel, them girls are my girls!"

And without waitin for an explanashen, the infooriated monster sailed into me, the skoolmarm layin over on one uv the benches explodin in peels uv lafter. The three girls, indignant at bein mistook for nigger wenches, assisted their parent, and between em, in about four minutes I wuz insensible. One uv the trustees, pityin my woes, took me to the neerest railroad stashen, and somehow, how I know not, I got home, where I am at present recooperatin.

I hev only to say that when I go on sich a trip again, I shel require as condishen precedent that the Afrikins to be put out shel hev enuff Afrikin into em to prevent sich mistakes. But, good Lord, wat hevent I suffered in this cause?

Petroleum V. Nasby, P. M.

(wich is Postmaster).

VI. "Paster uv Sed Church, in Charge"
(1863-1866)

NOTE TO THE CHAPTER

Nasby's interest in the Scriptures originated in the politics of the day and not in the realm of religion. The Bible provided him and other Americans with a defense of slavery. Alternative arguments seemed less satisfactory. Southerners discerned an assault upon orthodox Christianity in the scientific doctrine of multiple origins and found socio-economic arguments in favor of the peculiar institution unconvincing in a world that knew poor whites. While Abolitionists increasingly attacked the Bible, many Southerners read assiduously of Noah's curse on Ham in the ninth chapter of Genesis or pointed to Paul's request for the return of Onesimus as a clear sanction of the Negro's perpetually low position and an obvious foreshadowing of the fugitive slave laws.

"Eternal viggilence is the price uv liberty," the pastor exhorted. Nasby urged his flock to labor ceaselessly to realize the political implications of his interpretation of the Scriptures. The deeds of his "Dimekratik trinity" pointed the way. Clement L. Vallandigham, who denounced the war bitterly and advocated peace by conciliation, attained the heaven of Democratic martyrs. Fernando Wood, the New York politician, joined him in 1863 by organizing the Peace Democrats. In 1862 the Senate expelled Jesse Bright of Indiana after the arrest of the bearer of a letter of introduction which he had addressed "To His Excellency Jefferson Davis, President of the Confederation of States."

Nasby's own political demands followed closely the footsteps of these patron saints of his Church. His stand against the Morrill Tariff of February 20, 1861, parroted the objections of nearly every Democrat, while Eastern protectionists demanded an even higher tariff wall. An amendment and the tariff act of July 14, 1862, reduced the free list and increased the rates of items on the protected list. Nasby wanted to abolish the Republican measure but insisted on retaining the tariff on sugar to protect Louisiana against imports from the West Indies. He felt that Horace Greeley's *Tribune*, which supported the Free Soil Movement, Abolitionism and the Republican Party, should be suppressed, no doubt to eliminate the paper's influence on the rural North.

Another step was to hang such leading Abolitionists and Radical Republicans as Thaddeus Stevens, Charles Sumner, Benjamin F. Wade, Joshua R. Giddings and Owen Lovejoy, whose brother Elijah Parish had been shot by a mob at Alton, Illinois, on November 7, 1847, when he tried to protect the press on which he had printed his anti-slavery paper. To this list of his arch enemies Nasby added Benjamin F. Butler, who reaped abuse and ridicule for his controversial administration of New Orleans after his troops had entered it on May 1, 1862.

Indefatigably, Nasby battled "Methodist, Presbyterian, Lutheran and other hetrodox Churches" which insisted that "the nigger is human, and that he hez a sole to saiv and fit it for the skies." As head of the "Church uv the Noo Dispensashun" he diligently devoted "its entire intellek to constrooin the Skripters in accordance with the Dimekratic ijee." The authority of Sir William Blackstone, the most famous of English jurists, was enlisted to supply a modicum of legality for his dictum that the Negro was a beast and belonged to whoever tamed him. For the propagation of the faith he advocated sending missionaries to Northern Illinois, to the Western Reserve in Ohio, and to Massachusetts and other strongholds of Abolitionism.

Step by step the Civil War shattered Nasby's dreams. The smashing defeat in 1864 of the Democratic Presidential candidate, General George B. McClellan, in Nasby's eyes seemed comparable only to the Russian annihilation of Thaddeus Kosciusko's army in 1794 at the battle of Maciejowice, which ended Polish independence. However, even in the darkest hours of democracy, Nasby never uttered his "Finis Poloniae." He endured the two-year imprisonment of Jefferson Davis at Fortress Monroe and the hanging of Mrs. Mary E. Surratt, who was executed with three others for their complicity in John Wilkes Booth's plot against Lincoln. The eagerness with which people bought the treasury bonds of a Republican government, popularly called Seven-thirties from their rate of interest, only further inspired Nasby to fathom the promises of the ninth chapter of Genesis.

His unwavering faith found its reward. All over the country, signs indicated the re-emergence of Nasby's democracy. In the Memphis riots of May 1866, whites hunted down Negroes. In August, a convention in Philadelphia attempted to build up a Union party out of loyal Democrats, conservative Republicans and Old Whigs to support Johnson. A fellow Kentuckian furnished another bright moment. Lovell H. Rousseau, who had served as general in the Union army, entered Congress after the war, where his opposition to Radical Reconstruction and his irritation over the vindictive speeches of congressmen who had fought the war only with their tongues led him to cane the Abolitionist Congressman Josiah B. Grinnell of Iowa in the corridors of the Capitol.

The moral lessons of these signs were clear to Nasby and all his faithful. "You kin find in the Skripter suthin applicable to every occasion," he assured his friends, but it was curious "what different sermons kin be preached from the same text."

1. The Church's One Foundation: "This Work Is Wat My Hart Delites In"

Nuthin hez dun so much agin the Dimokrasy ez churches, skool-houses, Sundy skools, preachers, and sich. Here, our people hev awoken to the dangerous tendencies uv sich instooshns, and hev set about viggerously to suppress em. Ez this work is wat my hart delites in, I organized the pious portion uv the Dimokrasy, that we mite do our work well and thorough. When my gigantic intellek hez a chance, the work is shoor to be well done, and I hev the satisfaction uv announcin the complete destruction uv two churches, the drivin off uv five preachers, and the frightnin uv many wimin.

But my mission is not alone to tear down—I bild up. The ijee segestid itself to my fertile mind, that a strikly Dimekratik church and Sunday skool wood not only help the cause, but afford me an easy livin.

It wuz dun, and I am reglarly installed ez the pastor uv the First Dimekratik Church uv Ohio.

The follerin is the order uv exercises:—

1. People assemble at the second tootin uv the horn.

2. Readin uv one uv the follerin passages uv Skripter: 9th chapter uv Gennysis, wich relates the cussin uv Canaan, provin that niggers is skriptoorally slaves; and the chapters about Hayger and Onesimus, wich proves the Fugitive-slave Law to be skriptooral. (The rest uv the Bible we consider figgerative, and pay no attenshun to it watever.)

3. Singin—"O, we'll hang Abe Linkin on a sour apple-tree," or some other improvin ode, hevin a good moral.

4. Readin extrax from the Noo York Argus.

5. Singin—"O, John Brown's body hangs a danglin in the air."

6. Lecture on watever phase uv the nigger question may seem appropriate.

We heve also organized a Sundy skool on a pure basis. I spent much time in gettin up a katekizm, uv wich the follerin is a sample:—

Q. Wat is the cheef end uv man?

A. To whale niggers and vote the Dimekratik tickit forever.

Q. Wat do the Skripters teach?

A. That a angel sent Hayger back to her mistress; that Paul sent Onesimus back; and "Servance, obey yoor masters."

Q. Who wuz Onesimus and Hayger?

A. Onesimus wuz a mulatter, and Hayger a octoroon.

Q. Wat is sin?

A. Skratchin a ticket.

Q. Who compose the Dimekratik trinity?

A. Vallandigum, Brite, and Fernandywood.

Q. Wat is the first duty uv man?

A. To beware uv Ablishn lies; to rally to the poles; to vote early; and to bring in the agid, the infirm, and the ideotik.

To stimoolate the infant mind, I heve institootid a sytem uv rewards, ez follows:

For commitin two verses uv Vallandigum's address, one check for beer, good at the Corners; five verses, two checks; twelve verses, four checks; and to the child hevin the most verses, a copper-mounted butternut pin.

We hed a festival yesterday. The tables wuz bounteously spred with bolony, liver-worst, and crackers, wile a barl uv native whisky furnisht the flooids nessary. It wuz a tetchin site to see the mothers, with maternal solissitood, a mixin nacher's great restorer with water and sorgum surup, to adapt it to the infantile stumick. For my part, I alluz take mine strait.

I bleeve good will be accomplisht. Last week, in makin a pastoral visit, jest about noon, to the house uv wun uv my flock, who hez fine poultry, I wuz amoosed at heerin a meer infant, only three years uv old, swinging his little hat, and cry, "Hooraw for Jeff Davis." It wuz tetchin. Pattin the little patriot on the head, I instantly borrowed five cents uv his father to present to him.

Petroleum V. Nasby.

2. Missionary Journey: "The Apossel Biznis I Like"

October the 6th 1863.

The sole uv Nasby's foot knows no rest. Eternal viggilence is the price uv liberty, and a old Dimekrat who hez never skratched a tikkit, and who never spiles his likker by dilooshn,

kin work in these perilus times. I am engaged in organizin societies on the basis uv the Union ez it wuz, the Constitution ez
it is, and the nigger wher he ought to be. This employment soots
me. The apossel biznis I like. Brot into continool contack with
the best uv Dimekrats, I hev the run uv a thowsand jugs—pay
regler and libral—facilities for borrerin unekalled—I am kon-
tent. I send a few extrax from my journal.

MUNDY, 2d.—Kum into Whartensberg afoot. Wuz reseevd
with enthooziasm, invited to drink twenty times in ez menny
minits, wich invitashens I acceptid, solely for the good uv the
coz. Hevin cast-iron bowils, I survived the trial. Hed a meetin,
and adminsterd the oaths to resist drafts and shelterin deserters;
and after exhortin uv them to stand by Dimokrasy, borrered
thirty dolers and a clean shirt, and departid. [Poskrip.—The
clean shirt I borrered frum a line about 9 P.M.]

TOOSDY, 3d.—Houktown wuz the next pint. Dimokrasy all
rite to opperate on. Never wuz in a place in wich nigger wuz so
hated and feerd. They hev a holesum prejoodis agin every thing
black. Wun old patriark shot all his black sheep, paintid a black
hoss red, and his dawter, a gushin maiden uv thirty-too askt the
objik uv her affeckshins too dy his raven locks white. A rumor
that a provo mashel wuz in the visinity did the job for him in a
single nite. Found em well organizd. Addrest em at length,
showin conclusively that hed Linkin resined in favor uv the
great Davis, we shood never hed this war; that sich a compermise,
and the follerin concessions, wood hev averted blud-shed, to-
wit:—

The rite uv suffrage to be held only by slave-owners, and
sich ez they may designate. The repele uv awl tariffs ceptin the
wun on sugar. The fillin up uv Boston harber. The suppreshun
uv the Triboon. The hangin uv Giddins, Wade, Stevens, Sumner,
and Oin Luvgoy.

I dwelt at length on the horrors uv amalgamashen, and
closed with an elokent appele to stand by Vallandigum and pure
Dimokrasy. Borrered three dolers on a prommis to remit, wich
I shell do sum time after next Presidenshel eleckshin. I made the
wictim eazy by givin him my note. When men can be made comfortable by simply a note, I alluz do it, if they furnish paper.
Benevolens is a prominent trate in my karicter.

WENSDY, 4th.—Van Buren wuz my next pint. The Dimokrasy here hav their lamps trimd and burnin. They indoost more

soljers to desert than any township in the county, ceptin Amandy and Union. I organized a branch society to wunst. A blessid feelin pervades here. They jest more than hate niggers, and mor'n twenty babies hev bin named Vallandigum within six months. One enthoosiastic old butternut named a femail infant Vallandighamia, and another named his boy Vallandigum Woods Bright. The boy hez a strong constitooshn, and may live. Things is workin in Allen. I borrered only eight dollers uv the fatheful, wich I shel pay wen one of my rich uncles pegs out.

PETROLEUM V. NASBY,
Paster uv sed Church, in charge.

3. "I Proved That Slavery Was Scriptooral": Orthodoxy and Heresy

CHURCH UV THE SLAWTERD INNOCENTS
(Lait St. Vallandigum), January the 16th, 1864.

Trouble are comin upon me thicker and faster. "Men change, but principles, never," hez bin a motto uv mine for years, and bleevin in the grate principle of the strong owning the weak—or, in other words, slavery—I shel never cease my efforts to make it universal. Ther bein a onreasonable prejudice in the minds uv the weak uv my congregashen aginst bein the perpetooal servance uv them as nacher hez made to rool, I called a special meetin of my flock, to consider the matter. I interdoost it thus:—

By Hager, I proved that slavery was scriptooral.

By "cussid be Kanan," et settry, I shode concloosively that the nigger wuz the identikle indivijjle who wuz to be the sed slave aforesed.

Then it wuz put to vote, and it wuz unanimusly resolvd, that Afriken slavery be interdoost amongst us. I notist, with pleasure, that the poorer the indivijjle, the more anxshus he seemed to own a nigger.

Opinions were then interchanged. Absolum Kitt, who is a carpenter, and who never saved a dollar, hevin alluz hed a sick wife and a large family of children, sed he felt that a grate work hed bin dun that nite. The prowd Anglo-Saxun, whom nacher intended to rool, hed bin that nite elevatid to his normal speer.

"Paster uv Sed Church, In Charge"

Hentzforth ther wuz no more labor for him. He hed a contrak to bild a house for brother Podhammer, and he hed no doubt that the brethrin who wuz blest with means, wood make up a puss, and enable him to buy a nigger carpenter to do his work.

Brother Podhammer aroze. He, uv coarse, wood be glad to assist brother Kitt, but dooty to his own family required a diffrent line uv action. His idee wuz to purchis a nigger carpenter hisself, and—

"WHAT!" exclaimed Kitt.

Brother Podhammer resoomd. He intended to buy a nigger carpenter hisself, and bild his house. The cheef beauty uv the grate system, and the wun that makes it altogether luvly, is, that yoo kin BUY yoor labor.

"But," sed Kitt, "what kin I do if yoo work nigger carpenters?"

"Trooly," sez Podhammer, "I know not. A carpenter kin be purchist for $1000, the interest uv wich is $60, and his keepin, say $100 more, per annum. Now, ef Brother Kitt will cum to them wages, and be modritly umble, I mite, for his sake, forego the exquisit pleasure uv hevin a nigger to flog, and still employ him."

"But," sez Kitt, turnin pale, "my family wood starve on them wages. Why, I mite ez well be a nigger myself."

At this pint I lifted up my voice. I exorted Brother Kitt to patience. The grate Dimekratik idee, that capital shood own labor, must be establisht. It may bare hard upon indivijjles, but wat then? John Rogers went camly to the stake for principle. Ef Brother Kitt doth not like to accept his normal condishen towunst, he kin go to sum less favored country, wher the grate instooshon is not establisht.

Brother Podger, a blacksmith, sed he supposed the rich uns wood buy a nigger blacksmith, and let him emigrate. Brother Snipes, a plasterer, made a similar observashen. Brother Punt, a bricklayer, remarkt likewise.

Whereupon they all, in chorus, similarly exclaimed they'd see us d—d fust, and then they woodent.

Whereupon they reconsidered the resolushen establishin slavery.

Kitt and his herritix wuz not at church last Sundy, and the postmaster told me that they hed sent off a club for the Anti-Slavery Standard.

Trooly, a reformer's Jordan is a hard road to travel I be-leeve.

PETROLEUM V. NASBY,
Paster uv sed Church, in charge.

4. An Ordination: "A Youth uv Much Promise"

CHURCH UV THE NOO DISPENSASHUN,
March the 17th, 1864.

Last Sunday we hed an improvin season. Robert Tooms Punt, who hez bin a studyin for the ministry with me for the past four weeks, wuz licenst and ordained. He is a youth uv much promise. He votid twict for Bookannon, and only 18 yeres old, swarin his votes in with a coolnis and ease that eggscitid the admirashen uv the patriarks at the biznis. I kin safely say that he hez whaled more Ablishnists, bustid more Methodist Brethrin, and other hetrodox Churches, than any Dimekrat uv his age in the Stait. He hez a brilliant future.

After the usual questions wuz put to him, and satisfactorily answered, the congregashen wuz dismist, and, in the presence uv the elders and deacons alone, I delivered the follerin charge.

BROTHER: Hevin bin reglerly ordained, it only remains for me to give yoo a word uv council. Yoo are a goin into the apossel biznis at a rather unfavorable time. Man, wich is born uv woman, hez trouble for his inheritance. I've hed so much uv it that, ef I hed it to do over agin, I woodent be born at all.

The politikle heavins is orecast with portenshus clouds. The litenin uv wrath is leapin frum wun to another, whilst the thunder, wich wuz wunst at a distance, now roars angrily in our ears. The ole ship Dimokrasy is tossin madly onto the wild waves, with nary a sale set, her seams open, the water (a furrin element to her insides) a rushin in. The stiddiest part uv her crew hev seezed the boats and abandoned her, and the rest uv em are a fitin for the helm.

In the mean time the old ship is dashin past the haven uv Success, and is headin strate for the rocks uv Destrucshen. To yoo is intrusted a part uv the work uv savin her. Let me entreat yoo—

1. Avoid the soljers. With them yoo hev nothin in common. They will despitefully use yoo. Wunst a party uv em made me drink a pint uv water and take the oath uv allegianse, wich out-

rages wuz follered by conjestion uv the bowils and inflamashen uv the brain.

2. Alluz preech agin the nigger. It's soothin to a ginooine, constooshnel, suthern-rites Dimekrat to be constantly told that ther is a race uv men meaner than he is. Besides, it's safe—the nigger hez no vote. Ef he hed, we might vary.

3. Alluz hev a marter. The stait-rites Dimokrasy alluz sympathize with a man that's in basteels for sympathisin with the South, for nun uv em know how soon their turn may come.

4. Preech agin amalgamashen at leest four Sundays per month. A man uv straw that yoo set up yerself is the easiest knockt down, pertikelerly if yoo set him up with a view uv knockin uv him down.

5. Alluz diloot yoor whisky for new converts. It takes much to convert a Ablishnist, and ef yoo use the pure artikle, it wood kill a ordnary constooshn afore he'd hev time to vote, wich wood be aggervatin.

6. Sarch the skripters faithfully for sich passages ez "Cussid be Kanan," "Servance, obey yoor masters," and sich.

7. Learn to read, or at least git the shape uv the letters so fixt in yoor mind that when yoo quote from a book or noosepaper, you will hold it rite side up. Eddicashen hez bin a grate help to me.

8. Learn to spell and pronounce Missenegenegenashun. It's a good word.

The great leadin ijees uv our sect, wich it is yoor dooty to inculcate, is these: The nigger's a ape, Linkin a goriller, Jeff Davis a chrischen gentleman, the rebellion a struggle for rites, the soljer a bluddy tool, Benbutler a beast, et settry. Yoo are never to bleeve in Fedral victorys, but must alluz credit Confedrit successes. I woodent advise yoo to let yoor faith in the Confedrisy go so fur as to take their skrip on yer salary, neither wood I burn greenbax. I hev dun. Go, my brother. Let yer polar star be Dimokrasy, yer rallyin cry, "The Yoonyun ez it wuz—the Constooshn ez it is," wich is latitoodinus; fite the good fite, and the day will cum wen yoo kin lay orf yer armor, and with "P. M." after yoor name, enjoy the repose that alluz follows well-directid and viggerus effort.

Brother Punt startid to-day for Suthern Illinoy, wher he hez a congregashen.

PETROLEUM V. NASBY,
Paster uv sed Church, in charge.

5. Slavery and Religion: "Ther Is Grate Gain in Sich Godlinis"

CHURCH UV THE NOO DISPENSASHUN,
July the 3d, 1864.

The Methodist, Presbyterian, Lutheran, and other hetrodox Churches, are, to-day, the most hefty obstacles in the path uv the Dimokrasy; and, to successfully opose em, I institootid the Church uv the Noo Dispensashun, uv wich I am paster uv sed Church, in charge. Wat the Dimokrasy now want is Church extension: hence this appeal.

Dimokrasy is built upon the one ijee that the nigger is a babboon. That's our corner-stun—knock it out, and the entire fabric tumbles.

The hetrodox Churches insist that the nigger is human, and that he hez a sole to saiv and fit it for the skies. This doctrin, ef it pervales, knocks Dimokrasy higher than a kite. For why? Bekause: ef the nigger's human, and not a beast, wher's slavery? Ekko answers, No where. Because: the commandment sez, "Thou shalt not steal," et settry. Ef the nigger's a man, we steal wen we take his labor. Ef he's a beast, wy, then, we hev dominion over him, and may use him ez we do the pashent ox. The pint is plane.

The Church uv the Noo Dispensashun, uv wich I am paster uv sed Church, in charge, devotes its entire intellek to constrooin the Skripters in accordence with the Dimekratik ijee.

Sum uv our brethren, who still hev Methodist and Presbyterin sooperstishuns into em, appologize for their support uv the grate instooshn, by insistin that they bring the Afrikin over to this country for the purpose uv chrischenizin uv him. Away with sich nonsence! I'll none uv it. Is it chrischenlike to ceeze a man in his native land and bring him to a furrin shore agin his will? Agin: Ef that's evangelikle, is it proper to maik the forsibly evangelizd heathen work for his board and wun soot uv cheap close, per annum, continooally bein perswadid to renood effort by the cat-o'-nine tales? Ther is grate gain in sich godlinis—at least 500 per cent. Most anybody will go into the mishnary biznis on them terms. I, week ez I am, kin bare sich a cross. Besides, wen yoo've got a cargo convertid, why don't yoo send em back? Dost thou desire to convert their children? O, mizable subterfuge! Ef the parience wuz convertid, woodent the children be? Ef that's yer ijee, what do ye sell em for? Hev yoo took a morgage onto em for expenses incurd in bringin uv em here, and hev yoo the power uv foreclosin?

Bosh! Ef they're human, they hev a warranty deed for their bodies and soles, the same ez we hev. Hence, ez slavery is nessary to the Dimekratik party, we must defend it on solid ground.

Therefore my Church, uv wich I am sed paster, in charge, strikes out boldly, and teaches that a nigger is a BABBOON —a beast. Wen wild, he's anybody's property that capchers and tames him; after wich, him and his young is abslootly his, to do with as seemeth good in his site. (Blackstun.)

Troo, amalgamashen, wich alluz appears to be practist wher the instooshn exists, is agin us, for wen a slave hez a man for a father, he's only half babboon. But I never seed any Dimekratic principle that hedn't a week pint in it.

We want money to establish our Church. We must send mishnaries to Northrin Illinoy, to the Western Reserve, and to Massachoositts. It takes money for our preachers to live now, for whisky is 10 cents per drink, even in the most obskoor doggerys. Men and brethrin, kum to our aid.

We hev no lack uv labrers in this grate vinyard. Evry yere the other Churches expel more or less uv their preachers, for irregularitis in swappin hosses, and for extreme conviviality and sich, who are willin to be reseevd into our buzm. They are ready; all we want is means to set em aflote.

Remittencies uv 10 cents and upwards thankfly reseeved. I'm President, Secretary, Treasurer, and Board uv Trustees uv the Associashen. Remit librally and to-wunst. The high character uv the offishary is suffishent garantee that the money will be properly applied.

PETROLEUM V. NASBY,
Paster uv sed Church, in charge.

6. Nasby Unfrocked: "They Bleeved Wat I Told Em"

ONTO THE WING,
November the 18th, 1864.

The die is cast! All is ore! Ef Freedom shreekt when Kossikusco fell, she must hev squawkt last Toosdy nite ez she beheld

the innanimate corpse uv the Dimekratik party, which fell, crush-
ing Little Mack, and the hopes uv sum hundreds uv thousans uv
good Dimekrats, who spectid to be persuadid by ther frends into
acceptin the various offisis under the guverment.

I am a lost and rooined man. My people are uv the troo
Dimekratik stripe. They hed faith in me. They bleeved wat I
told em. I told em Micklellan wuz certain uv the elecshun, and
that I hed ded-wood on the disposal uv the offisis in that seck-
shun. It immejitly become a easy matter to borrer money. It wuz
deliteful—wood, O wood that it cood hev bin perpetooal!
Brother Savage lent me $50, with a request that I wood speak
a good word for him for a furrin mishn. I assoomed a virchus
look, and replied that I never sold my inflooence, but that I alluz had a admirashen for his massive intellek and many virchoos.
Brother Guttle lent me money, wantin this, and Brother Sludge
wantin that; in breef, evry individooal uv em who hed a forhead
a inch high, spectid suthin.

The returns cum in. Ohio—Linkin! "Good! 'Rah!" shouts
I, with great presence uv mind.

"Why good?" anxshusly asks the expectants.

"Becoz, to carry Ohio, the Ablishnists must hev brot votes
from Noo York, wich will give us that state, shoor."

Noo York—Linkin!

"Good Lord!" answers I, promptly; "the Noo York Ablishnists must hev voted in Ohio, and hev got home in time to vote
agin. But wait for Pennsilvany."

Pennsilvany—Linkin!

"My frends, ther wuz fraud—Massachoosits soljers, at least
40,000, must hev voted there. Indiana will do it, however."

Indiana—Linkin!

"Not less than 40,000 Massachoosits soljers hev voted there.
Illinois is safe, though."

Illinois—Linkin.

"40,000 Massachoo—"

"Give me my money!" roard Savage, and the same remark,
with variashens, wuz made by Guttle, Sludge, and the rest uv
em.

"Gently, my frends," sed I, backin out uv the door. "We hev
bin defeated but the great principle that a white man is better
than a nigger, for wich we hev so long fought, still lives. Let us
sink all minor considrashens, and—"

The minor considerashens I referred to wuz, however, up-permost in their minds, for they all went for me, yellin like Cuscororious Injins, "Give me my money!" whereupon I re-treated to the meetin-house, lockin myself in. They surrounded it, swearin they'd starve me out.

When a innocent boy, I read a harrowin tale uv a Rooshn mother, who wuz persood by frantic wolves, and who saved her own life by droppin her children to em, wun by wun. My privit barrel uv whisky wuz in my study—I wuz saved! I histid it out uv a winder, and calmly awaited results. They flockt around it—they took turns at the bung-hole. In wun short hour they wuz stretched helpless on the plain, dead drunk. Then and there I resined my charge, and borrerin sich money and watches ez the ungrateful wretches hed about em, to make up arrears uv salary and sich, bid adoo to em forever. I shel go to Noo Jersy.

PETROLEUM V. NASBY,
Lait Paster uv the Church uv the Noo Dispensashun.

7. Searching Scripture: "Last Nite a Lite Bust onto Me"

SAINT'S REST (wich is in the Stait uv Noo Jersey),
August the 11th, 1865.

The contemplashen uv the nigger, hez, in time past, given me a great deal uv trouble. Nigger hez to me bin a incubus—a nitemare. I never cood see why the species wuz created; never cood I understand why they wuz put onto the face uv the earth, any more than toads or other disgustin objects. But last nite a lite bust onto me—I seed it all!

I wuz low-sperited and deprest. Jeff Davis a pinin in a loathsum dungeon—the English capitalists a mournin for their cotton-bonds, and refusin to be comforted because the Confed-racy is not—Mrs. Surratt a danglin in the air—military courts plenty and habis corpusis scarce—the loosenis with wich people put ther munny into 7-30's—the soljers returnin and goin for constooshnel Dimekrats, and the ginral demoralization uv Dim-okrasy, all conspired to give me the horrors, and to add to my distress my jug wuz out! To avoid madness, I took up the Bible (I board with a justice uv the peace, who hez to keep one to swear witnesses on), and happened to open at the 9th chapter uv Gennesis. Yoo know all about the blessid chapter.

Noah, after the water went down, come down from Aryrat, went into farmin, and planted grapes extensive. One day he took a drink too much, and laid down with insuffishent clothin onto him. His second son, Ham, saw him in that fix, and when Noah awoke, while his hair wuz still pullin, he cust him and his posterity, and sed they shood be servants forever.

Ham (wich in the original Hebrew signifies the hind-quarter uv a hog), wuz the father uv the Afrikins, and they hev bin slaves ever sence.

I seed a lite to-wunst—I realized the importance uv the nigger. He is the connectin link in the chain uv circumstances wich led to the formashen uv the Dimekratic party. He hez kept the blessid old macheen a runnin to this day. Observe:

Whisky (or wine, wich is the same thing) made Noah tight.

Ham saw Noah inebriated.

Noah cust Ham, wich turned him into a nigger and a servant.

That the Skripters mite be fulfilled, the childern uv Ham wuz brot to America, to be servants here.

Wickid men set themselves agin the Skripters, and tried to make men uv the niggers.

The Dimekratik party ariz for the purpus uv keepin the nigger down, and that deliteful biznis hez given them employment for more than 30 years.

Ez I shet the book I cood not help remarkin, in the words uv the sammist,—

> "Good Lord, upon what slender threads
> Hang everlastin things!"

Sposin Noah, instid uv plantin grapes, hed gone to practisin law, or into the grocery biznis, or buyin prodoose on commishn, or puttin up patent medicines—he woodent hev got inebriated; he woodent hev cust Ham; Ham woodent hev turned black; there woodent hev bin no niggers, no Ablishnists, and, consequently, no Dimekrats.

Or, sposn all uv Ham's childern hed taken diptheria, and died; the same results wood hev follered.

Whisky made nigger—nigger made Dimokrasy. Take away whisky and nigger, and Dimokrasy woodent be uv no more akkount than a one-armed man at a raisin.

Whisky! Nigger! Dimokrasy! O, savory trinity!
We don't none uv us read the Skripters enuff.

PETROLEUM V. NASBY
Lait Paster uv the Church uv the Noo Dispensashun.

8. *A Heresy Trial: "Wich Bid Fair to Result in a Rendin uv the Walls of Our Zion"*

CONFEDRIT × ROADS (wich is in the Stait uv Kentucky),
June 9, 1866.

They hed a ruction in the church at the Corners yisterday, wich bid fair to result in a rendin uv the walls of our Zion, and the tearin down uv the temple we hev reared with so much care and hev guarded with so much solissitood. When I say "we," I mean the members thereof, ez the church wuz reorganized sence the war by returned Confedrit soldiers and sich Dimekrats ez remained at home nootrel; but inasmuch ez I am the only reglerly ordained Dimokratic paster in these parts I ginerly conduct the services, and hentz hev insensibly fell into a habit uv speakin uv the church ez "my" church, and I feel all the solissitood for its spiritooal and temporal welfare that I cood ef I wuz reglerly ordained ez its pastor, wich I expect to be ef I fail in gettin that post offis at the Corners, wich is now held by a Ablishnist uv the darkest dye, wich President Johnson, with a stubbornness I can't account for, persistently refooses to remove.

The case wuz suthin like this:—

Deekin Pogram wuz charged by Elder Slather with hevin, in broad daylite, with no attempt at concealment, drank with a nigger, and a free nigger at that, in Bascom's grocery, and to prove the charge Deekin Slather called Deekin Pennibacker.

The Deekin wuz put onto the stand, and testified ez follows:—

"Wuz in Bascom's grocery a playin seven up for the drinks with Deekin Slather. Hed jist beet the Deekin one game and hed four on the second, and held high, low, and jack, and wuz modritly certin uv goin out, partiklerly ez the Deekin didn't beg. Wus hevin a little discussion with him—the Deekin insistin that it wuz the best three in five, instead uv the best two in three, jest as though a man cood afford to play five games between drinks! The ijee is preposterous and unheard of, and ther ain't no precedent for any sich course. We wuz settlin the dispoot in regler orthodox style—he hed his fingers twisted in my neck handkercher, and I hed a stick uv stove wood suspended over his head. While in this position we wuz transfixed with horror at seein Deekin Pogram enter, arm-in-arm with a nigger, and,—

The Court.—Arm-in-arm, did you say, Brother Pennibacker?

Witness.—Certainly.

The Court.—The scribe will make a minnit uv this. Go on.

Witness.—They cum in together, ez I sed, arm-in-arm walked up to the bar, and drank together.

By the Court.—Did they drink together?

Witness.—They ondeniable did.

By myself.—The Court desires to know what partikeler flooid they absorbed.

Witness.—Can't say—spose 'twas Bascom's new whiskey—that's all he's got, ez the Court very well knows.

By myself.—The Sexton will go at once to Bascom's and procoor the identicle bottle from which this wretched man, who stands charged with thus lowerin hisself, drunk, and bring it hither. The Court desires to know for herself whether it was really whisky. The pint is an important one for the Court to know.

A wicked boy remarked that the pint wood be better onderstood by the Court if it wuz a quart. The bottle wuz, however, brought, and the Court, wich is me, wuz satisfied that it wuz really and trooly whisky. Ez the refreshin flooid irrigated my parched throat, I wished the trials based upon that bottle cood be perpetooal.

I considered the case proved, and asked Brother Pogram what palliation he hed to offer. I set before him the enormity uv the crime, and showed him that he was by this course sappin the very foundashun uv the Church and the Democratic party. Wat's the use, I askt, uv my preachin agin nigger equality, so long ez my Deekins practis it? I told him that Ham wuz cust by Noah, and wuz condemned to be a servant unto his brethren—that he wuz an inferior race, that the Dimocrisy wuz built upon that idea, and that associatin with him in any shape that indicated equality, wuz either puttin them up to our standard or lowerin ourselves to theirn; in either case the result wuz fatal. I implored Brother Pogram to make a clean breast uv it, confess his sin, and humbly receive sich punishment ez shood be awarded him, and go and sin no more. "Speak up, Brother Pogram," sez I, paternally, and yet severely.

Brother Pogram, to my unspeakable relief, for he is the wealthiest member of the congregashun, and one we darsn't expel, replied,—

"That he DID drink with the nigger, and wat wuz more, he wuz justified in doin it, for THE NIGGER PAID FOR THE WHISKY!!"

"But, shoorly," I remarked, "it wasn't nessary to yoor purpose to come in with the nigger arm-in-arm,—a attitood wich implies familiarity, ef not affeckshun."

The Prisoner.—The nigger and I hed bin pitchin coppers for drinks, and I, possessin more akootnis, hed won. I took the nigger by the arm, fearing that ef I let go uv him he'd dodge without payin. They are slippery.

Overjoyed, I clasped him around the neck, and to-wunst dismist the charge as unfounded and frivolous.

"My brethren," sez I, "the action uv Brother Pogram is not only justifiable, but is commendable, and worthy of imitashun. Ham wuz cust by Noah, and condemned by him to serve his brethren. The nigger is the descendant of Ham, and we are the descendants uv the brethren, and ef Noah hed a clear rite to cuss one of his sons, and sell him out to the balance uv the boys for all time, we hev ded wood on the nigger, for it is clear that he wuz made to labor for us and minister to our wants. So it wuz, my brethren, until an Ape, who hed power, interfered and delivered him out of our hand. Wat shel we do? Wat we cannot do by force we must do by financeerin. We can't any longer *compel* the nigger to furnish us the means, and therefore in order to fulfil the skripter, we are justified in accomplishing by our sooperior skill wat we used to do with whips and dorgs. The spectacle uv Brother Pogram's marchin into Bascom's with that nigger wuz a sublime spectacle, and one well calculated to cheer the heart uv the troo Dimekrat. He hed vanquished him in an encounter where skill wuz required, thus demonstratin the sooperiority uv the Anglo-Saxon mind—he led him a captive, and made uv him a spoil. Wood, O wood that we all hed a nigger to play with for drinks! The case is dismissed, the costs to be paid by the complainant!"

The walls uv our Zion is stronger than ever. This trial, ez it resulted, is a new and strong abutment—a tall and strong tower.

PETROLEUM V. NASBY,
Lait Paster uv the Church uv the Noo Dispensashun.

9. "You Kin Find in the Skripter Suthin Applicable to Every Occasion": The Prodigal Son, Southern Style

CONFEDRIT × ROADS (wich is in the Stait uv Kentucky),
July 6, 1866.

I preached last Sabbath, or rather, tried to, from the parable of the Prodigal Son. We hed a splendid congregashun. I notice a revival of the work in this part uv the Dimocratic vineyard wich reely cheers me. The demonstrashun our friends made in Memphis, the canin uv Grinnel by Rosso, and the call for an Johnson Convenshun in Philadelphia, all, all hev conspired to comfort the souls uv the Dimocrisy, and encourage em to renewed effort. It is bringing forth fruit. Only last week five northern men were sent whirlin out of this section. They dusted in the night to escape hangin, leavin their goods as a prey for the righteous. Six niggers hev been killed and one Burow officer shot. Trooly there is everything to encourage us.

The house wuz full. The weather wuz hot, and the pleasant incense uv mingled whiskey, tobacco, and snuff wich ariz wuz grateful to me. The sun shone in on Deekin Pogram's face ez he gently slept, and when the sun hits him square I kin alluz tell wher he sets, even ef it is dark. He drinks apple-jack instead of corn whiskey, and chaws fine-cut tobacker instead uv plug, and consekently when in the pulpit I kin distinguish the pecooliar aroma uv his breath from those around him.

"My brethren," sed I, "sich uv yoo ez hev Bibles in yoor houses, kin get somebody to read yoo the parable to wich I shel call yoor attention. A man, wunst upon a time, hed sons, ez many men hev since, and wun uv em wuz a tough one, who hed a taste for that pertikeler branch uv agriculture known ez sowin wild oats. He left his home and went into far countries, makin the old man shel out his share uv the estate, and he lived high, jist, my brethren, ez yoor boys do, or rather, did, when they went to Noo Orleans, in the days when yoo hed a nigger or two wich yoo cood sell to supply em with money. He played draw poker and faro; he drank fancy drinks, and boarded at big hotels; and he follered after strange women, which'll bust a man quicker nor any one small sin the devil hez yet invented, ez yoor pastor kin testify. Uv course, his pile give out, and he got down, my friends, did this ingenuous yooth, to rags and wretchedness, and ended in being an overseer uv swine. What did he do? He ariz and went to his father, and the old man saw him afar off, and went out to meet him, and fell onto his neck, and give him a order for a suit of clothes and a pair uv boots, and put a ring onto his finger, and made a feast, killin for the purpose the fatted calf wich he hed saved for another occasion.

"My friends, you kin find in the Skripter suthin applicable to every occasion, and this parable fits the present time like a ready-made coat. The South is the Prodigal Son. We went out from our father's house on a expedition wich hezn't proved altogether a success. We spent our share uv the estate, and a little more. We run through with our means, and hev cum down to rags, and dirt, and filth, and hunger. We are, and hev bin some time, a chawin husks. We run out after them twin harlots, Slavery and State Rights, and they've cleaned us out. Our pockets are empty. No more doth the pleasant half-dollar jingle in sweet unison agin its fellows. Our wallets is barren uv postal currency, and the grocery-keepers mourn, and refuse to be comforted, becoz we are not. We hev got to the husk stage uv our woe, and wood be tendin hogs, ef the armies, wich past through these countries, hed left us any. We hev come back. In rags and dirt we hev wended our way to Washington, and ask to be taken back. Now, why don't our father, the Government, fulfil the Skripter? Why don't it see us afar off, and run out to meet us? Why don't it put onto us a purple robe? Where's the ring for our finger, and the shoes for our feet? and where's the fatted calf he ought to kill? My brethren, them Ablishnists is worse than infiddles—while they preach the gospel they won't practise it. For my part, I—"

At this point a sargent, belongin to that infernal Burow, who wuz in the audience, with enough uv soldiers to make opposin uv him unpleasant, sed he hed bin a sort uv an exhorter in his day, and desired to say a word in explanation uv that parable, ez applicable to the present time; and, sez he, "ef I am interrupted, remember I b'long to the church military, wich is, just now, the church triumphant." And cockin his musket he proceeded, very much uninterrupted.

"The prodigal son," sez he, "wuz received by the old man with considerable doins, but, my worthy friends, he went out decently. He didn't, ez soon ez he withdrawed from the house, turn around and make war onto the old gentleman—he didn't burn his house and barns, tear up his garden, burn his fences, and knock down the balance uv his children. Not any. He went away peaceably, a *misguided* good-for-nothin, but yet a *peaceable* good-for-nothin. Secondly, he come back uv his own akkord. The old man didn't go after him, and fight for four years, at a cost uv half his substance, to subdue him and bring him back, but when he hed run through his pile, and squandered his share uv the estate, and got hungry, he came back like a whipped dog.

"My friends, let me draw a parallel between these cases.

"The Prodigal Son went out,—so did the South,—thus farly the cases is alike.

"The Prodigal didn't steal nothin. The Confederacy took everything it cood lay its hands on.

"The Prodigal spent only what wuz his to spend. The Confederacy spent not only all it stole, but all it cood borrer, when it knowed its promises to pay wuzent worth the mizable paper they wuz printed onto.

"The Prodigal, when he did come, come ez penitent ez the consciousness that he hed made a fool uv hisself cood make him. The Confederacy wuz whipped back, but it still swears hefty oaths that it wuz right all the time.

"The Prodigal didn't *demand* veal pot-pies, and purple robes, and sich, but begged to be a servant unto the more sensible brethren wich stayed. The South comes back *demandin* office, uv wich the fatted calf, and rings, and purple robes is typical, and considerably more share in the government than it had before it kicked over the traces, and went out.

"Spozn the Bible prodigal hed stopped his parient, and remarked to him thus: 'I am willin to come back, on conditions. Yoo must pay my debts—yoo must give me an ekal share uv the farm with the other boys—yoo must treat me in all respecks just ez ef I hadn't gone out, and—this is essential—yoo must take with me all the sharpers who ruined me, all the gamblers and thieves with whom I fell in while I wuz away, and make them head men on the place; and above all, I hev with me the two harlots wich wuz the prime cause of my ruin, and they must hev eleven of the best rooms in the house, and must be treated ez your daughters. To avoid displeasin the others, I'll dress em in different clothes, but here they must stay. Otherwise, I'll go out agin.'

"Probably the old gentleman wood hev become indignant, and would hev remarked to him to go, and never let him see his audacious face agin, or rather, he would hev strangled the harlots, scattered the blacklegs, and choked the young sprout into submission. Them's me. I am anxious to kill that fatted calf, and am also anxious to put on yoo robes and shoes. But, alas! the calf suffered from want uv attention so long doorin the late misunderstandins that he's too poor—the robes wuz all cut up into bloo kotes for the soljers we sent out to fetch yoo in— the shoes they wore out, and the rings—Jeff'son Davis wears the only style we hev. When you come back in good shape, yool find us ready to meet yoo; but till then, chaw husks!"

Lookin around, this armed tyrant remarked that there would be no more preaching that day, and sadly the congregation dispersed.

I am heart sick. At every turn I make that Burow stares me in the face, and counteracts my best endeavors. It's curious, though, what different sermons kin be preached from the same text, and it's also curious how quiet our folks listen to a Ablish-nist who hez muskets to back him.

PETROLEUM V. NASBY,
Lait Paster uv the Church uv the Noo Dispensashun.

VII. "Ameriky for White Men!"

(1862-1867)

NOTE TO THE CHAPTER

The collapse of the Confederacy, the emancipation of slaves, and the progress of Reconstruction left Nasby undaunted. Facing his entire set of lost causes squarely, he diligently and ingeniously remedied the situation. "I'm a anti-slavery man from this time out," he resolutely resolved. "My conshence," he hastened to explain, 'won't allow me to support it no longer, and, besides, it don't pay." The entry of William T. Sherman's artillery into Savannah in December 1864, represented the most effective "car uv emansipashen" and accelerated Nasby's change of mind. He immediately challenged the policies of his idols, James Buchanan and Jefferson Davis, who "took hold uv the Dimekratic kite, tore off its time-honored tale, Ekal Rites, and substitooted Slavery," but praised the "anshent Dimokrasy" of Andrew Jackson, Silas Wright and Thomas H. Benton.

Nasby's faith that "ther will alluz be a Dimokrasy as long as ther's a nigger" remained intact throughout the dark days when Jefferson Davis was held at Fort Monroe for two years and other leading Confederates were excluded from political life or found safety in Mexico, Canada and Europe. His manipulation of the freedmen's political role guaranteed "that the dangers uv negro ekality mite still be kept afore the Amerikin people." The scheme's vital importance impressed him deeply after contemplating "The Last Man," the measured utterances of humanity's lone survivor by the Scottish poet Thomas Campbell.

The drastic actions of leading Democratic politicians, among them Clement L. Vallandigham of Ohio, Fernando Wood and Horatio Seymour of New York, Franklin Pierce of New Hampshire, Jesse Bright of Indiana, William A. Richardson of Illinois and Thomas B. Florence of Pennsylvania, whose suicides plagued Nasby in a nightmare, suggested the dimensions of the disaster facing democracy if the Negro ceased to be a tool for political exploitation. The catastrophe was abetted by the maneuvers of Henry W. Slocum, who had commanded the left wing of Sherman's army on the March to the Sea and after the war joined the Democratic party, and by Horace Greeley's condemnation of the politicos. It drove Nasby to imitate Edwin Forrest's rendition of Othello's suicide, which had captured the imagination of the actor's admirers.

184

Nasby energetically pursued his goal to preserve America for the white man and keep the Negro in perpetual submission. He artfully cultivated fear of Negro equality in men and women of the South and North. Updating his Bible lessons with stories of the mulatto origin of Hannibal Hamlin of Maine, based on the swarthy complexion of Lincoln's first vice-president, he recited his fantastic account of Charles Sumner's life. These tall tales turned Lucretia Mott, the advocate of women's rights and anti-slavery thought, into the Senator's sister, made Anna Dickinson, the lecturer for women's suffrage and reform, his daughter, and selected the runaway slave and Abolitionist lecturer Frederick Douglass as his half brother. His audiences' deep-seated aversion to reformers, suffragettes and Abolitionists guaranteed the impact of his teachings.

After the Radical Republicans took "nigger suffrage into their embrace," Nasby felt finally assured that the Democratic party would become the rallying ground for all enraged white Americans. "Wen yoo desire a Dimekrat to froth at the mouth," the political strategist knew, "yoo will find a black face will answer the purpose." He now confidently dropped the studied sympathy for freedmen as potential voters which he had cultivated since the passage of the Military Bill in March 1867. That Radical Reconstruction measure directed Federal military commanders in the South to supervise the registration of voters and the elections. "Ef the Dimocrasy must hev a race to look down on," he had oracled at that time, "let them turn their attenshun to the Chinese or the Injuns, but . . . the nigger is sacred." Now he again employed his trusted biblical images of Negro inferiority and went out of his way to buttress them with Louis Agassiz's views of the diverse origin of races. Unperturbed, Nasby embraced the scientific hypothesis of a multiple creation and discarded orthodox Christianity. After all, "uv what comparison is religion to a Dimekratic triumph?"

1. Emigration in the Border States: "I Am Bekomin Alarmed"

WINGERT'S CORNERS, OHIO, April the 2d, 1862.

There is now fifteen niggers, men, wimin, and childern, or ruther, mail, femail, and yung, in Wingert's Corners, and yisterday another arrove. I am bekomin alarmed, for, ef they inkreese at this rate, in suthin over sixty years they'll hev a majority in the town, and may, ef they git mean enuff, tyrannize over us, even ez we air tyrannizin over them. The danger is imminent! Alreddy our poor white inhabitants is out uv employment to make room for that nigger; even now our shops and factories is full uv that nigger, to the great detriment uv a white inhabitant who hez a family to support, and our poorhouse and jail is full uv him.

I implore the peeple to wake up. Let us hold a mass meetin to take this subgik into considerashen, and, that biznis may be expeditid, I perpose the adopshen uv a series uv preamble and resolooshens, suthin like the follerin, to-wit:

WAREAS, We vew with alarm the ackshun uv the President uv the U. S., in recommendin the immejit emansipashun uv the slaves uv our misgidid Suthern brethrin, and his evident intenshun uv kolonizin on em in the North, and the heft on em in Wingert's Corners; and

WAREAS, In the event uv this imigrashun, our fellow-townsman, Abslum Kitt, and others, whose families depend upon their labor for support, wood be throde out of employment; and

WAREAS, When yoo giv a man a hoss, yoo air obleeged to also make him a present uv a silver-platid harnis and a $650 buggy, so ef we let the nigger live here, we are in dooty bound to marry him off-hand; and

WAREAS, When this stait uv affares arrives our kentry will be no fit place for men uv educashen and refinement; and

WAREAS, Any man hevin the intellek uv a brass-mounted jackass kin easily see that the two races want never intendid to live together; and

WAREAS, Bein in the magority, we kin do as we please, and ez the nigger aint no vote he kant help hisself; therefore be it

Resolved, That the crude, undeodorizd Afrikin is a disgustin obgik.

Resolved, That this Convenshun, when it hez its feet washed, smells sweeter than the Afrikin in his normal condishun, and is therefore his sooperior.

Resolved, That the niggers be druv out uv Wingert's Corners, and that sich property ez they may hev accumulatid be confiscatid, and the proceeds applide to the follerin purposes, to wit:

Payment uv the bills of the last Dimekratik Centrel Committee; payment uv the disintrestid patriots ez got up this meetin; the balance to remane in my hands.

Resolved, That the Ablishnists who oppose these resolushens all want to marry a nigger.

Resolved, That Dr. Petts, in rentin a part uv his bildin to niggers, hez struck a blow at the very foundashens uv sosiety.

Fellow-whites, arouse! The enemy is onto us! Our harths is in danger! When we hev a nigger for judge—niggers for teachers —niggers in pulpits—when niggers rool and controle society, then will yoo remember this warnin!

Arouse to wunst! Rally agin Conway! Rally agin Sweet! Rally agin Hegler! Rally agin Hegler's family! Rally agin the porter at the Reed House! Rally agin the cook at the Crook House! Rally agin the nigger widder in Vance's Addishun! Rally agin Missis Umstid! Rally agin Missis Umstid's childern by her first husband! Rally agin Missis Umstid's childern by her sekkund husband! Rally agin all the rest uv Missis Umstid's childern! Rally agin the nigger that cum yisterday! Rally agin the saddle-culurd girl that yoost to be hear! Ameriky for white men!

PETROLEUM V. NASBY.

2. Slavery Renounced: "Besides, It Don't Pay"

SAINT'S REST (wich is in the Stait uv Noo Jersey),
January the 15th, 1865.

"The wages uv sin is death." Sich is the substance uv a passage uv Skripter, wich, sence my exile to this lonely shore, hez bin my solace. How troo the remark! How fearfully hez it bin realized!

The anshent Dimokrasy owned this guverment, and mite hev hed it to day. But then they wuz a richus set. They wuzn't dissipatid. They didn't run after harlots. Jaxon, and Benton, and Silas Write, and sich men, who wuz men, kept us strate. But wen they went to their respective rewards, another class uv men occupied us. Jim Bookannon and Jeff Davis took hold uv the Dimekratic kite, tore off its time-honored tale, Ekal Rites, and substitootid Slavery. The result is before the world. Dimokrasy is in the mud, and the Ablishnists hev the post-orfises. Alass!

In the olden time we used to hear this song:—

"Ho! the car uv emansipashen
Is rollin grandly thro the nashen."

I've seen the car. It's on two wheels, and carries balls from 6 to 500 pounds in wate. Sherman rode it into Savanner tother day.

The harder the work yoo do for the devil, the more death yoo git for wages. We labored faithfully in the service uv slavery. We dismist our conshenses, went back on our record, swore black wuz white, and vicy versy, even goin so fur ez to go into two wars to perpetuate it. What is the result?

Linkin hez abolisht it by proclamation. His blood-coated hirelins hev abolisht it, niggers and all, wherever they hev gone, and they hev made sum rather extensive toors. And, finally, the Confederasy, wich wuz institooted to preserve it, is purposin to throw it overboard ez the price uv recognishen, and this they do without stoppin to enquire wat is to bekum uv us Northern Dimekrats, who hev tied ourselves to it.

So reckless sailors fling overboard a priceless cargo, to save a worthless hulk. So Jonah wuz histed into the bilin waves, to save a set uv mariners who wuz not prophets. Wood, O wood that I, like him, cood be gobbled by some friendly whale, who wood, in doo time, vomit me out on dry land.

Slavery wuz a huge Juggernaut. Jest so long ez we Northern Dimekrats lade flat in the mud afore its wheels, we wuz not injured, but merely shoved further into the mire, puttin us, however, in the eggsact posishun to ketch the ile that dript frum the axels. But it finally mashed us.

Ez for me, I am done. I'm a anti-slavery man from this time out. My conshence won't allow me to support it no longer, and, besides, it don't pay. Ez the sole survivin leader uv the Dimokrasy, I shel immejitly ishoo a circular, instructin uv em to make this change uv front.

PETROLEUM V. NASBY,

Lait Paster uv the Church uv the Noo Dispensashun.

3. Democracy's Platform: "But We Hev Wun Resource for a Ishoo"

SAINT'S REST (wich is in the Stait uv Noo Jersey),
June the 23d, 1865.

These is the dark days uv the Dimokrasy. The misforchoons that befell our armies in front uv Richmond, the fall uv our capital, follered by the surrender uv our armies to Grant and Sherman, hez hurt us. Our leaders are either pinin in loathsome dunguns, incarseratid by the hevin-defyin, man-destroyin, tyrannical edix uv our late lamented President, or are baskin in the free air uv Italy and Canady. We hev no way uv keepin our voters together. Opposin the war won't do no good, for before the next elecshun the heft uv our voters will hev diskiverd that the war is over. The fear uv drafts may do suthin in some parts uv Pennsylvany and Suthern Illinoy, for sum time yit, but that can't be depended on.

But we hev wun resource for a ishoo—ther will alluz be a Dimokrasy so long as ther's a nigger.

Ther is a uncompromisin dislike to the nigger in the mind uv a ginooine Dimekrat. The Spanish bull-fighter, when he wants to inflame the bull to extra cavortin, waves a red flag afore him. Wen yoo desire a Dimekrat to froth at the mouth, yoo will find a black face will anser the purpose. Therefore, the nigger is, to-day, our best and only holt. Let us use him.

For the guidance uv the faithful, I shel lay down a few plain rools to be observed, in order to make the most uv the capital we hev:—

1. Alluz assert that the nigger will never be able to take care uv hisself, but will alluz be a public burden. He may, possibly, give us the lie by goin to work. In sich a emergency, the dooty uv every Dimekrat is plane. He must not be allowed to work. Associashens must be organized, pledged to neither give him employment, to work with him, to work for any one who will give him work, or patronize any wun who duz. (I wood sejest that sich uv us ez hev bin forchoonit enuff to git credit, pay a trifle on account, so ez to make our patronage worth suthin.) This course, rigidly and persistently follerd, will drive the best uv em to stealin, and the balance to the poor-houses, provin wat we hev alluz claimed, that they are a idle and vishus race. Think, my brethren, wat a inspirin effeck our poor-houses and jails full uv niggers wood hev on the people! My sole expands ez I contemplate the deliteful vision.

2. Likewise assert that the nigger will come North, and take all the good places, throwin all our skilled mechanics out uv work by underbiddin uv em. This mite be open to two objecshuns, to-wit: It crosses slitely rool the 1, and white men mite say, ef there's jist enuff labor for wat's here, why not perhibit furriners frum comin? I anser: It's the biznis uv the voter to reconsile the contradicshun—he may beleeve either or both. Ez to the second objeckshun, wher is the Dimekrat who coodent be underbid, and stand it even to starvashen, ef the underbiddin wuz dun by a man uv the proud Caukashen race? and wher is the Dimekrat so lost to manhood ez not to drink blood, ef the same

underbiddin is dun by a nigger? The starvin for work ain't the question—it's the color uv the cause uv the starvashen that makes the difference.

Nigger equality may be worked agin to advantage. All men, without distincshun uv sex, are fond uv flatrin theirselves that somebody's lower down in the scale uv humanity than they is. Ef 'twan't for niggers, what wood the Dimokrasy do for sumbody to look down upon? It's also shoor to enlist wun style uv wimmen on our side. In times gone by, I've notist gushin virgins uv forty-five, full sixteen hands high and tough ez wire, holdin aloft banners onto wich wuz inscribd—"Save us frum Nigger Equality." Yoo see it soothed em to hev a chanse uv advertisin, 1st, That they wuz frail, helplis critters; and, 2d, That, anshent and tough ez they wuz, some wun wuz still goin for em.

Ef ther ain't no niggers, central commities must furnish em. A half dozen will do for a ordinary county, ef they're hustled along with energy. Ef they won't steal, the central commities must do it theirselves. Show yer niggers in a township in the mornin, an the same nite rob the clothes-lines and hen-roosts. Ever willin to sacrifice myself for the cause, I volunteer to do this latter dooty in six populous counties.

These ijees, ef follered, will, no doubt, keep us together until our enemies split, when we will reap the reward uv our constancy and fidelity. May the Lord hasten the day.

PETROLEUM V. NASBY,
Lait Paster uv the Church uv the Noo Dispensashun.

4. The Last Negro: "Thou Wust Our Corner-Stun"

SAINT'S REST (wich is in the Stait uv Noo Jersey),
September the 20th, 1865.

Last nite, for amusement, I picked up a volume uv poems, ritten by wun Campbell, and happened to read a piece called "The Last Man." It's a rather heavy piece uv writin. His descriptive powers are rather better than mine, tho, perhaps, ef my too partial friends ain't too partial, he is a long way behind me in the matter uv pathetics, and in them fine touches wich show the man uv sole and sensibility.

Be that ez it may, the poem made an impression on me (wich is proof that there is suthin in it), and it wuz onto my mind ez I retired to my virchus couch.

Scarcely hed I sunk into slumber, when my viggorous intellek, wich even the bonds uv slumber can't chain, wandered away into the misty realms uv speckulashen. I hed the most horrible vision that ever afflicted a sleepin man, wich the bare recollecshun uv causes a involuntary shudder to thrill my susceptible frame.

Methawt a epidemic startid in Africa, and come by reglar steps through Europe, and finally reached Noo York. For a time it raged alike among all classes uv people, and among all colors and complexions. The proud and hawty Caucassian, the bold and patriotic Celt, the noble red man uv the forest (wich is pizen), all, all wuz swept away by the relentless pestilence.

Finally, it abated. The white man and the red man begun to escape the fangs uv death; but among the niggers it raged wuss than ever. Thro the South it swept like a tornado, sparin the whites, but cuttin down every nigger in its path. Ther wuz weepin and wailin. The hawty planter saw in his nigger-quarters the brite octoroon, for whom he hed paid $2500, and who hed solaced his hours uv relaxashen with her charms—who hed bore him girls almost perfectly white, wich, on account uv hevin his blood in their vanes, he hed bin able to sell for $3000 and $4000 to other planters, whose tastes run in that direckshun—he saw her, the objeck uv his affeckshun, and a part uv his estate, lyin a inanimate corpse, not worth a cent for any purpose.

Likewise he saw his robust field-hands, each wun with sinews and muscles uv iron—the males hearty and sound, without blemish; the females capable uv raisin a picanniny wich wuz worth $200 ez soon ez weaned, wunst a year, and by a little extra whippin do a year's work in the field every 12 months, stretched cold corpses in the field, the cotton unpicked, and his last year's gamblin debts unpaid. Thus wuz disease outragin all the finer feelins uv humanity, and destroyin relentlessly all that made life pleasant and lovely.

Finally, nigger after nigger fell, until but two remained in the United States. They wuz a male and female, uv sich perfectly healthy systems, that it seemed impossible for disease to tetch them.

When the epidemic wuz known to hev settled down to niggers alone, the Dimokrasy held a consultation, and fearin the race wood becum extinct, hed selected these, hed carefully secloodid em from the world, and hed employed twenty-four uv the most eminent medical men uv the world to be with em constantly—each stayin an hour—that, in case they showed any symptoms, the proper remedies mite be to-wunst applied, afore the disease got a hold. From these two, ef the rest wuz destroyed, it wuz hoped a new stock cood be raised, that the dangers uv negro equality mite still be kept afore the Amerikin people.

But all to no purpose. The unsparin pestilence smoted em, and, notwithstandin the efforts made by the eminent physicians, notwithstandin the prayers and groans uv the Dimokrasy—they died!

Methawt the heavens wuz hung in black, and ominus litenins shot athwart the skies. In the distance, low, mutrin thunders wuz heard, and the beasts uv the forests run affrighted from their coverts. Dray hosses dropt dead in the streets; dorgs run wildly, with their tongues a hangin out, and the white foam droppin from their distendid jaws. Ever and anon pale, sickly gleams uv lite flashed across the dark, leaden-colored clouds, givin nacher the appeerence uv labrin under a severe attack uv yaller janders.

THE LAST NIGGER WUZ DEAD!

Presently the leaders uv the Dimokrasy began to assemble. Fernandywood cum.

"Alass!" sez he, sobbin ez tho his hart wood break, and kissin the cold corpse—"Farewell, my hopes—a long and last farewell! Thou wust our corner-stun; on thee we built. Thou wust our capital, our cheefest trust. We used yoo—we abused yoo—and in abusin yoo found our profit. Yoo wuz ordained to be the cuss uv Ameriky—we wuz ordained to be alluz fearful uv yoor bein our sooperior—to us wuz entrusted the delightful task uv keepin yoo down, and us over yoo. Our task is ended with thee. Kin we any more rally our people to the poles, by yawpin the dangers uv nigger equality, when ther ain't no nigger? This, now, is a white man's guverment—we hev nothin left to contend for, and thus I foller thee."

And Fernandy, who hed found a jackknife in the nigger's vest pocket, run it into his bowels, and fell a dead corpse across his body.

Franklin Peerse approached and wailed thus:—

"And art thou gone, last uv the Afrikins? Cood not the avengin ministers uv death hev taken sum other race? Cood not the noble Injin bin taken, and thou spared to Dimokrasy? No white man feared his supremacy. Cood not the Chinese hev bin sacrificed in thy stead? The people hed no prejoodis agin his color. Thou wust all that made me uv yoose, and ez thou art gone, so I go also."

And takin the jackknife out uv Fernandy's hand, he stabbed hisself with it, and fell dead atop uv Fernandy.

Vallandigum approached, weepin violently.

"Opposin thy elevation," sed he, addressin the dead nigger, "wunst made a martyr uv me, which martyrdom netted me $30,000 in ten-cent pieces, wich I immejitly invested in 7-30 bonds issued by a tyranikle and onconstooshnal guverment. By carryin a portrait uv thee, and exibitin it at my meetins in the rooral deestrisks, I hev made my constituencies bile with rage, at the ijee uv sich ez thou bein elevatid to their speer. Like Othello, 'my occupashun's gone.' Farewell, pollitics—thou wast my pollitics. Farewell, Congris!—uv wat yoose is a Dimekrat in Congris with no nigger to blat about? Farewell, life!—for wat is life with no nigger to persekoot?"

And takin the jackknife from Peerse's hand, he recklessly plunged it into his bowels, and fell across Peerse.

Brite, uv Injeany; Richardson, uv Illinoy; Seymour, uv Noo York; Florence, uv Pennsilvany, and all the leeders uv the party uv the North, without exception, cum up, and, makin similar orashuns, used the jackknife in like style—fallin across each other ez four-foot wood is corded.

Gineral Slocum, uv Noo York, hed a good mind to do the same thing; but he conclooded he cood turn a somerset out uv the party ez easy ez he somersetted into it, and he didn't.

Filled with anguish uv the heaviest descripshun, and fully appreciatin the feelins uv the noble men who woodent survive their party, I caught the jackknife, and, throwin myself into a attitood—sich ez I hev seen Forist come, when, in Othello, he stabs hisself—I wuz on the pint uv makin it acquaintid with my intestines, when I happened to observe a quart-bottle stickin out uv the nigger's coat pocket. Droppin the knife, I seezed it, and in two gulps swallered the contents. The room spun round and round, and, eggsaustid, I fell senseless across the dead sooicides. Jest then Horis Greely entered the room. Holdin up both hands, he exclaimed,—

"Ez it wuz in the beginnin, so it is in the endin. Behold Dimokrasy!—nigger at the bottom, whisky at the top, and a stink in the middle. We're rid uv two great cusses to-wunst!"

And, instid uv punchin his stumick with the knife, he shuffled out uv the room, holdin his nose.

I awoke, in a feverish sweat, shreekin wildly. So vivid wuz the scene I hed dreamed, that I found it impossible to sleep, and all that long nite I walked the floor in agony.

Wuz the dream prophetik? Is there any danger uv the nigger becomin extinct by disease? I know amalgamashun is whitenin him in the Southern States, but up North, where Dimokrasy is skarse, we kin preserve them in all their original blackness. Hevin grant that this friteful vision wuz simply the result uv a disordered stumick, and not a warnin uv wrath to cum!

PETROLEUM V. NASBY,
Lait Paster uv the Church uv the Noo Dispensashun.

5. *The Diversity of Races: "This Doctrine Kivers the Whole Ground"*

SAINT'S REST (wich is in the Stait uv Noo Jersey),
September the 24th, 1865.

Whenever yoo ask the people to adopt any given line uv ackshen, yoo hev got to give em a tollable good reason therefor. Troo, this never hez bin so necessary in the Dimekratik party, whose members hez alluz follered their leaders, without askin the why or wherefor, with a fidelity beautiful to behold. But people, ginerally, are inquisitive, and wun reason why we hev never succeeded with the slavery question, is becoz we never hev yet given a good reason why the nigger shood be held in slavery.

Wunst it wuz sought to be defended on the ground that the nigger wuz inferior to the white man, but it woodent do. Why? Becoz the full-blown Dimekrat thot to hisself to-wunst, "Ef the stronger shel own the weaker—ef the intellectooally sooperior shel hold in slavery the intellectooally inferior, LORD HELP ME! Why, I might ez well go into a Ablishn township and select my master to-wunst."

The same argument won't do ez to nigger equality. Why shood we say that the nigger shan't vote, on the score uv his not bein fitted by educashen or intelligence, when the fust and chiefest qualificashen uv a strate Dimekrat is his not knowin how to read? Why, to-day, in my county, ef a Dimekrat kin rite his name without runnin his tongue out, we alluz refuse to elect him a delegate in the county convenshun. It exposes him to the suspishun uv knowin too much.

I hev quit all these shaller dodges, long ago. We must hev the nigger, for jest at this time there ain't no other capital for us to run on; but he must be put on maintainable ground. I put my foot on him, on the ground uv the DIVERSITY UV THE RACES! He is not wun uv us. He is not a descendant uv Adam. Goddlemity probably made him, ez he did the ox, and the ass, and the dorg, and the babboon, but not at the same time, nor for the same purposes. He is not, in any sence uv the word, a MAN! His color is different, the size uv his head is different, his foot is longer, and his hand is bigger. He wuz created a beast, and the fiat uv the Almity give us dominion over him, the same ez over other beasts.

Does the theologian say that this doctrine undermines the Christian religion? I to-wunst reply, that that don't matter to us. Dimokrasy and religion shook hands and bid each other a affecshunate farewell, years ago. Uv what comparison is religion to a Dimekratik triumph?

Doth the ethnologist say that the difference atween the Caucassian and Afrikin is no greater than atween the Caucassian and Mongolian? I anser to-wunst that he is rite—that the Mongolian is likewise a beast; becoz, don't yoo see, there ain't no Mongolians in this secshun uv country to disprove it.

Doth the Ablishnist pint to a nigger who kin read and rite, and figure through to division, and in sich other partikulers show hisself sooperior to the majority uv Dimekrats? I alluz draw myself up to my full hite, assoom a virchusly indignant look, and exclaim, "He's nuthin but a d——d nigger, anyhow!" wich is the only effective argument we hev hed for ten years.

Doth the besotted nigger-lover pint to the mulatto, and say, "What will yoo do with him, who is half beast and half man, who hez half a sole that is to be saved—for one half uv whom Christ died?" I anser at wunst, that I don't deal in abstracshuns, and git out ez soon ez possible, for there is a weak pint there, that I hevent ez yit bin able to git over.

This wun weak pint is no argument agin my theory, for happy is the Dimekrat who kin propound a theory that hezent a score, instid uv wun, weak places in it.

This doctrine kivers the whole ground. Ef the nigger is a beast, Dimekrats hev a good excuse for not givin to mishnary societies, for uv what use is it to undertake to Christianize beasts, who hev no soles to save and fit em for the skies? It gives us a perfect rite to re-establish slavery, for doth not Blackstun, who wuz supposed to know ez much law ez a Noo Jersey justis uv the peace, say that we hev a rite to ketch and tame the wild beast, and bend him to our uses? Also, he can't vote; for wood the lowest white man consent to vote alongside uv a beast, even ef he did walk on two legs? Not any.

Let this doctrine be vigorusly preachd, and I hev no doubt suthin will result from it.

PETROLEUM V. NASBY,
Lait Paster uv the Church uv the Noo Dispensashun.

6. *Still Longing for the Old Plantation:* "*A Shadder Hez Fallen*"

CONFEDRIT × ROADS (wich is in the Stait uv Kentucky),
March 19, 1866.

Yesterday I happened to pick up a copy uv a friteful depraved Ablishin paper, and my horror-stricken eyes wuz glued to the follerin passage, which I read:—

"I am happy to state to you that our free negroes are doing finely. We have no trouble with them. They have all gone to work manfully. They give an impetus to trade that we never before had. I have sold John Guttle's negroes, this year and last, more goods than I ever sold Guttle, and he owned two hundred and fifty slaves. So you see the free negro system is working well with us."

Ez I peroozed them lines, tears started involuntarily from my beamin eyes, and coursed in torrents down my venerable cheeks. I know John Guttle well, I may say intimately. He wuz a dear friend,—one uv the few wich I call friend in the most comprehensive sense uv the word. He holds my note for eighteen dollars and 63 cents; and I hev sumwhere among my papers, wich I have always carefully preserved for reference, a memorandum uv his address, that I might be shoor not to forget to send it to him. I give him the note becoz he furnished the paper, and it made him easy in his mind—I put down the memorandum becoz it looked business-like. Benevolence is a prominent trait in my character. When givin my note for borrered money will do a man good, I never begrudge the trouble uv writin it.

But wat I wuz a goin to say wuz, that the feendishnis uv that item passes belief. The writer puts it in print to show that the Ablishn uv slavery benefitted sumbody. I grant him that the merchant, who undoubtedly wuz born in Massachoosetts, wuz benefitted by the change; so are the greasy mechanics who are now pollutin the soil uv Alabama; and so, probably, are the 250 niggers; but, in the name uv Liberty, in the name uv Justice, in the name uv the Constitooshun uv the United States, and the flag uv our Common Country, I ask, How about John Guttle?

John Guttle is robbed. John Guttle is deprived uv his property. The bread is taken from John Guttle's mouth; his staff is broken; his dependence is gone; he is bereft.

Never shall I forget John Guttle or his hospitable mansion, ez I knowed it in the happy years afore the crooel war. He wuz a gentleman uv the old school—one uv the few left us in these degenerate days. His home wuz wun uv unalloyed happiness. Situated just back uv Mobeel, he had the finest plantashun in that section, and hed on it 250 niggers. All shades wuz represented. There wuz the coal-black Cuffee, whose feechers denoted the pure Afrikin, and whose awkward manners showed that he wuz not long from Afrika. There wuz the civilized mulatto, in whose veins the Guttle blood showed; the quadroon, in whom the good old Guttle blood predominated; and the octoroon, which wuz mostly Guttle. The Guttleses wuz eminently a Christian generation. They wuz devoutly pious; and there never wuz one uv the name who cood not repeat, without the book, all uv the texts bearin on slavery. The passages in which Onesimus and Hager figger wuz favorites with em; but on "cussid be Canaan" they wuz strong. For generations they had mourned over the hard fate uv the sons uv Ham, doomed to perpetual bondage becoz uv the sin uv their father; and with a missionary spirit ekaled by few and excelled by none, they did their part towards redoosin that cuss, by makin ez many of em ez possible half-brothers to the more favored race uv Japhet, and thus bringing uv em out uv the cuss; and they hed mellered the color uv their charges down from the hideous black to a bright yeller. Under the old patriarkle system, time passed off smoothly and pleasantly with the Guttle family. Them 250 niggers wuz obliged, uv course, to work, and their labor wuz money. John bought each uv the male sons uv Ham two soots uv clothes per annum, and each uv the female sons uv Ham one soot. It wuz considered healthy for the young ones to go naked, which they wuz religiously allowed to do, ez none uv the Guttles uv that family wood do any thing agin nater or her laws. The girls hed pianos, and wuz educated at the

North; the boys wuz celebrated for horse racing and their skill at losin money at faro. They wuz hospitable and generous to a fault. Their house wuz open house, and their beverages wuz alluz the best. Money wuz no objick to them; for when they had a severe attack of poker, or faro, or hoss racin, they hed plenty uv octoroons and quadroons, with the real Guttle nose, wich brand wuz well known in Noo Orleans, and wood alluz command the highest possible figger that wuz paid in that market; or, ef they had no more than they wanted at home uv that style, why, a few field hands wood be sold, and the remainin ones wood be persuaded by the overseer to do the work uv the whole. John Guttle's sons wuz all in the Confederit army. His daughters, willin to sacrifice every thing fur the cause, heroically pledged theirselves to whip the niggers theirselves doorin their absence.

Now all is changed! A shadder hez fallen across that peaceful home. The nigger quarters is there, but the niggers is not. The broad plantashun is divided up into small farms, and half uv it is owned by Ablishnists from the North, who work theirselves, and who hev a meetin house on one corner uv it, and the niggers a school house on the tother. The race track is plowed up and in cotton; the whippin-post and the stocks is taken down and burned; all, all the evidences uv civilizashun hez faded afore the ruthless hand uv the invader. John Guttle—that generous old man—subsists by the labor uv his own hands. One uv his sons ekes out a miserable existence running a dray in Mobeel; another, who is gifted with no ordinary intelleck, earns a respectable living playing seven-up, in a small way, with his former niggers; and the two girls is runnin a sewing masheen.

Talk not to me uv benefits. What is a dozen tradesmen and two hundred and fifty niggers to the glorious old Dimocratic John Guttle? What is the interest uv a dozen or so uv Noo England mechanics, and the niggers aforesaid, when compared to that glorious aristocracy which can never exist beside em? Kin I go and borrer eighteen dollars and sixty-three cents uv one uv them? No. Becoz, working for their paltry livins, they place a higher value on money, and will not spread it around ez profoosely ez the noble race which preceded em.

Another great wrong is done in this settin free uv John Guttle's niggers. John Guttle hez, uv course, no further interest in the Dimocratic party. Slavery wuz the umbillikle cord which united the Southern slaveholder and the Northern Dimocrat;

and, that cord cut, why hez John Guttle any more interest in Dimocracy? We stood ez a Chinese wall between them and the rushin flood uv Ablishn fanaticism; and we made the wall biznis pay. They furnished money, and we did the work; and, there bein but few uv us, the orfisis wuz easily divided. Alas! our occupashin's gone. The South is forever lost to us; for she hez no dirty work for us to do.

I appeal to the United States uv America. In behalf uv John Guttle, I say, give him back his niggers. In behalf uv the Dimocrisy North, who are out uv employment, give him back his niggers. In behalf uv his son who is runnin a dray, give him back his niggers. In behalf uv his daughters runnin a sewin machine, give him back his niggers. Make things Normal agin. Like John the Baptist, the Guvernment shall hear the voice uv one howlin in the wilderness until all these is done.

PETROLEUM V. NASBY,
Lait Paster uv the Church uv the Noo Dispensashun.

7. Tea-Party Talk: "See Onesimus, Hagar, and Ham"

CONFEDRIT × ROADS (wich is in the Stait uv Kentucky),
April 1, 1866.

Charles Sumner is not a very popular man in this section uv Kentucky; on the contrary, quite reverse. He is known here ez an Ablishnist; ez one who is a chief supporter uv that hidjus sin—the infidelity, I may say, for a man may ez well deny the whole Bible ez to cast discredit upon Onesimus, Hagar, and Ham, onto wich the whole system uv Afrikin slavery rests—the originator, therefore, uv the infidle beleef that Slavery is not uv divine origin, wich, judgin from the experience uv the last five years, appears to be gainin ground in the North. He is not, therefore, popular in this region.

Yisterday I attendid a tea party at Deekin Pogram's, to wich the elite uv the Corners wuz present, incloodin an Illinoy store-keeper uv the name uv Pollock, wich hed bin invited because the Deekin hed, some three months ago, bought a bill uv goods uv him on ninety days' time, and wantid an extension. While at the table enjoyin the

"Cup wich cheers, but don't intoxicate very much,"

ez Dryden hez it (tho I bleeve, to keep off chills, in this country, they mix three and a half parts uv whiskey to one uv tea),
the name uv Sumner wuz mentioned.

Mrs. Pogram to-wunst remarked that she didn't want the
name uv that ojus creecher spoken at her table.

"Why?" sed I, gratified at the ebulition.

"I hate him!" sed she, spitefully.

"So do I," replied I; "but what hev yoo agin him, aside from
his obnoxious political opinions?"

"Didn't he marry a nigger?" sed Mrs. P., triumphantly.
"Didn't he marry a nigger—a full-blooded nigger? and hezn't
he hed nineteen yaller children, every one uv wich he compelled,
agin their will, to marry full-blooded niggers? Didn't he—?"

"Mrs. P.," sed this Illinoy store-keeper, wich his name it
wuz Pollock, "do yoo object to miscegenation?"

"Missee—what?" replied she, struck all uv a heap at the
word.

"Miscegenation—amalgamation—marryin whites with niggers."

"Do I?" retorted she; "ketch a son uv mine marrying a nigger! They are another race; they'r beasts; and who'd marry em
but jist sich men ez Sumner and them other Ablishnists?"

"Then permit me to ask," sed this Pollock, wich wuz bound
to kick up a muss, "ef ther's any race uv pure blood in this section uv Kentucky wich is yaller?"

"No! uv course not," sed Mrs. P.; "them yaller people is mulatters—half nigger, half white."

"And them ez is quite white—not quite, but nearly so—
about the color uv a new saddle, like Jane, there," sed he,
pintin to a octoroon girl uv 18 wich used to belong to the Deekin
afore the isshooin uv the infernal proclamashen, "like Jane,
there, wich is waitin on the Deekin, and—but, good Lord!" sed
he, startin up like a tragedian.

"Wat!" shouted the company, all startin up.

"Nothin," sed he: "only, now that Jane's face is in range
with the Deekin's, wat a wonderful resemblance! She hez the
Pogram nose and ginral outline uv face; not Mrs. P.'s angularity,
but the Deekin all over. My deer sir," sed he, addressin the Deekin, "ef she wuzn't a quadroon, I shood say she looks enough like
yoo to be yoor daughter, by a first wife, I shood say, for she hez
not, ez I remarked, Mrs. P.'s angularity and gineral bonenis; but

uv course, she bein a part nigger, the resemblance may be sot down ez-a-very-remarkable-coincidence!"

The Deekin turned ez white ez a sheet, and Mrs. Pogram turned ez red ez a biled lobster, from wich I inferred that there wuz trooth in a rumor I had heard about the Deekin and his wife hevin a misunderstandin about a nigger woman and her baby, about 18 years ago, wich resulted in his bein made bald-headed in less than a minute, and the baby's mother being sold South. The Illinoy store-keeper, uv the name uv Pollock, re-soomed:—

"I wuz about askin wat them niggers is, ez is nearly white?"

"Why, they'r octoroons, or seven-eights white," sed Mrs. Pogram.

"And no Kentuckian ever marries a nigger?" inquired the store-keeper, who I saw wuz pursooin his investigations alto-gether too far.

"Never!" sed Mrs. Pogram; "we leave that to Ablishnists."

"Well, then," sed this Pollock, who, I spect, wun't half so innsent ez he let on, "I see that yoo hev no objection to mixin with the nigger, providin yoo don't do it legally; that amalga-mashen don't hurt nothin, pervidin yoo temper it with adultery. Is that the idee, Mrs. Pogram?"

Mrs. P. wuz mad, and made no reply, and Pollock persood the subjick.

"Jane there, is, I take it, about one eighth nigger. She got her white blood from whites, uv course; and ez there coodent be no marryin in the biznis, there is proof positive in her face that the 8th commandment hez bin violated about four times somewhere in this vicinity, or wherever her maternal ancestors, on her mother's side, may hev resided. What do yoo think about it, Deekin? Ez a Christian, woodent it be better to marry em than to add a violation uv the commandment to the sin uv amal-gamashen? It wood redoose yoor load jest a half."

The Deekin wuz too indignant to reply, and ez it involved a pint altogether too hefty for his limited intelleck, I took it up.

"My dear sir," I remarked, "yoo don't make the proper dis-tinction, or, rather, yoo don't appreciate the subjick at all. The nigger here sustains only one character with us,—that uv a infe-rior bein, the slave uv the hawty Caucashen, uv whom we are the noblest specimens; that is, the Deekin is, he bein a South-erner. I unfortunately wuz born in the North, and am a hawty

Caucashen only by adoption. To marry a nigger wood be to destroy our idea uv sooperiority, for we marry only our ekals. The intercourse with em, the results uv wich yoo see indications, bein outside uv the pale uv matrimony, is not, ez yoo wood suppose, the result uv unbridled licentiousnis, but is merely the assertion uv our superiority. When the lordly Caucashen (uv whom the Deekin is wich) bids a daughter uv Ham (wich, in the original Hebrew, signifies the hindquarter uv a hog) come to him, and she doth it not, he breaks her head, wich inculcates obedience. One is only a slave indeed when he surrenders all his individual rites. The female slave cannot be considered ez entirely subdooed until she hez yielded to her owner everything. To marry em wood be to elevate em; the intercourse common among us is not a sin, it bein merely the assertion uv that superiority wich we claim is founded on the Holy Scripter. See Onesimus, Hagar, and Ham."

"Yes," sed the Deekin, who wuz now on the right track; "it's a assertion uv our sooperiority; it's a dooty every white man owes to his class, and I, for one, will alluz—"

"Let me ketch yoo at it, Gabe Pogram," shouted Mrs. P., "and I'll give yoo sich a cat-haulin ez yoo never—drat yoor sooperiority, and yoor Ham, and yoor Caucashen. Niggers is niggers, and—"

Noticin that Mrs. Pogram hedn't quite arrived at the proper pitch uv self-sacrifice, I turned the discussion onto Sumner agin, ez a subjick upon wich they cood all agree.

I learned that his father wuz a Dutch grocery-keeper, and his mother an Irish washer-woman; that he run away from home at the tender age uv eight, after murderin, in cold blood, his grandparents, one uv wich wuz a Algerine and tother a Chinese; that he wuz apprenticed to the shoemakin biznis, and hed cut the throat uv his boss and his wife, and immersed the younger children into a biler uv scaldin water, where they were found mostly dead seven hours afterward; that he acquired wealth a sellin lottry tickets and brass clocks, et settry. His servants wuz redoost Southern gentlemen wich he hed swindled into his debt, and wich, under the laws uv Massachoosits, coodent git away, and that his intimate friends and associates wuz niggers, with wich he sot long at the festive board, and drunk champane; that Lucresha Mott wuz his sister, Ann Dickinson his daughter, Fred Douglas his half brother, and that he kissed, habitually, every nigger child he met, and frowned so severely onto white children ez to throw em into spasms, and other items uv information uv wich, livin in the North, I wuz ignorant. Ez I remarked, he isn't popular down here, and cood hardly be elected to Congris from this Deestrick. The tea party broke up shortly after, Pollock winkin at me villainously ez he left the house, feelin good to think how he hed opened a old sore. That Pollock needs watchin.

PETROLEUM V. NASBY,
Lait Paster uv the Church uv the Noo Dispensashun.

8. Problems in Personnel Management: "They Ain't Half ez Stoopid ez They Look"

POST OFFIS, CONFEDRIT X ROADS
(wich is in the Stait uv Kentucky),
April 25, 1867.

We are in trouble down here with these cussid niggers. They are harder to manage than pigs. Pigs don't express ther pecoolyarities. Mules come nearer. Ther is sich a method in their obstinacy—sich a wilful cussidnis, that I reely hev made up my mind that I don't understand em at all. They cuddle up to us ez kind ez a bloomin maiden does to her first adored, and they fling us just ez natral ez that same guileless maiden does when number two heaves in site. They behave well for a season, aperrently for no other purpose than to enjoy our discomfiture when they finally throw us. I hev bin a gittin a suspishen thro me that they ain't half ez stoopid ez they look; and that, after all, we are not fur from the trooth when we say, in our resolooshens, that they are the ekals uv the whites. Why shoodn't they be? Why shoodent the nigger boy, wich is now crossin the street, wich hez Deekin Pogram's feechers ez like ez a photograff, hev ez much sense ez the Deekin? I hev egsamined into the pedigree uv that nigger, and I find that his mother hed the hawtiest blood uv Virginny coursin toomulchusly thro her veins—and that stock the Pogram mix coodent materially depreciate in one generashen.

I hed the niggers uv the X Roads handsomely in tow up to yisterday. I hed em attendin services last Sunday at the meetinhouse, and by private arrangement hed em seated miscellaneously among the awjence. Dekin Pogram hed a wench, wich weighed at least 250 pounds averdupoise, atween him and his wife, while four other niggers ornamentid his pew. Bascom, with alacrity, consented to three; and Elder Gavitt provided seats for four. It wuz a pleasant site! White and black wuz alternatid like the spots on a checker-board—niggers and whites wuz spread out together like the fat and lean in pork; and ez I seed it I cood hardly restrane my emoshens. There before me wuz the regenerashun uv the Democratic party—there wuz wat wuz to bring us out uv the valley and shadder uv death into wich we hed fallen, up on the high ground uv offishel life. I preached that day from two texts, to wit: "Uv one blood did he make all the nashens uv the earth," and "All ye are brethren." I demonstrated with great fervor the loonacy uv the idea that the Almighty wood take the trouble to create two or more races when one wood do ez well —wich idea is alluz well receeved in this region. All men form their idea uv the Deity from themselves; and I never knowd a Confedrit Cross Roader to make two things when one wood anser. I refuted the theory, that there wuz more than one head to the race, by quotin the texts wich treated uv the creashen uv Adam and Eve, and demolished the Ham doctrine at site. "Ef," sed I, "Noer did cuss Ham, and condemn Canaan to be a servant unto his brethren, how do we know that our colored brethren and sistren *is* the desendants uv Ham and Canaan? It may be *us* for all we know! Is it his color? Is not black jest ez convenient a color ez white?"

"More so," murmured Mrs. Pogram, half asleep, "more so— it don't show dirt."

"Is it his shape? O, my brethren, I ain't a handsome man, nor wood I exactly anser for a model for Apoller. Ef beauty, or comeliness, or shape, is to decide the pint, the Lord help us! Is it his smell? The New York World asserts that the nigger hain't no smell, and ef he hez, why shoodent he hev? Standin under the common flag uv our country, with his hand upon that magna charta, the Deklarashen, and his beamin eye turned exultinly toward our nashnel emblem, the eagle, shall not our Afrikin brother be allowed to smell jist ez he chooses? Ef smell must be uniform, then let our Government establish a Burow uv Perfoomery to-wunst. I take high religious grounds in this matter. Ef he hez a natural odor, the Lord give it to him. Let us not fly in the face uv the Lord by condemin it. Judge not, lest we be judged. The odor uv the colored gentleman or lady is the work uv the Lord—the odor uv yoor unwashed feet is yoor own— wich shood stand the highest?

"I acknowledge that I hev not long held these views. I hev

shared the common prejudis, and hev contemned our friends uv color; I hev despitefully used 'em; I hev gone for 'em, and banged 'em like old boots. But it wuz becoz I didn't know 'em. I didn't see the kernel of meat under the rough shell: I didn't recognize the glitrin diamond in the ebony coal. My eyes hev bin opened. Like Saul of Tarsus, I see a lite. Sence the passage uv the Military Bill I hev diskivered many things. I hev mostly found out all these things sence that occurrence. Let us accept the situashen, and bless the Lord that it hez resultid in developin excellences where we didn't expect to find 'em."

There wuz an affectin scene after service wuz over. Deekin Pogram, Captain McPelter, and Elder Gavitt shook hands with em with a degree uv corjality I didn't expect. They develop a degree uv adaptability to circumstances wich I didn't look for. I really bleeve if I'd a told em that it wood hev a good effeck to kiss the nigger babies all round, that they'd a done it. But I spared em this. There is such a thing ez laying it on too thick.

But all this wuz spiled the next day. There wuz a heavy mail that day. In addition to the paper wich Pollock, the Illinois store-keeper, takes, ther wuz eight others; and to my surprise they wuz all directed to niggers. "Wat is this?" thot I to myself. "Hev the Ablishnists uv the North determined upon proselytin these men, and are they goin to flood this country with their incendiary readin? Ez a Federal officer it's my dooty to look into the matter!" Imagine my delirious joy at findin that they wuz Democratic papers from Noo York and Ohio! "Thank Heaven!" sed I, "our people hev awakened to a sense uv the necessity uv doin suthin;" and I handed the papers out to em, exhortin uv em to read em, ez they wuz trooth, and nothin but the trooth.

I ruther think they read em, for from that time out they avoided me ez though I hed the plague. Ef I wuz a goin down the street, and one uv em wuz a comin up, he'd cross the street; and the pecoolyer expression uv his countenance indicatid that it wuzn't my majestick presence wich awd him. They hed loathin depicted on their classick feechers. Unable to endoor this, I seezed one uv em, and asked why I wuz treated thus?

Delibritly he pulled out uv his pockit one uv them cussid Northern papers, and pintid indignantly to a editorial article. It was perfoosely headed in this wise:—

Shel niggers vote?—Shel the prowd Caucashen be redoost to a ekality with the disgustin Afrikin?—Is this a white man's government or not?—Ameriky for white men!

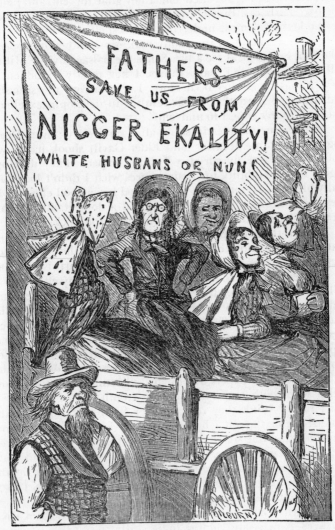

"Ameriky for White Men!"

Sed this Ethiopian, with his fingers on this headin, " 'Pears like ez ef dah wuzn't jist dat good feelin towards us colored men on de part ob de Dimoc'sy ob the Norf dat dah ought to be. 'Pears like as dough up dah wha de niggah ain't got no vote, dat dey don't intend he shel hab it. 'Pears like, ef Dimoc'sy's one ting all ober de country, dar's a cussid site ob humbug a goin on down heah!"

Wat cood I say? Wat cood I do? There it wuz in black and white; and from papers whose Dimocrisy cood not be questioned. I wuz dumbfounded. The nigger stalked hawtily and proudly away in one direckshen, while I sneaked off ruther sneakinly in another.

I hev one word to say to our brethren in the North. Yoo'r doublin our troubles, and makin our burdens harder to bear. Why havn't yoo common sense? Wat hurt wood nigger suffrage do yoo up there wher ther ain't no niggers, and how much wood it benefit us down here wher ther's millions uv em? Can't yoo see it? On all questions heretofore the Dimocrisy hez allowed a liberal license. We hev bin Free Trade in Noo York and Tariff in Pennsylvany the same year, and we cood do it. Then Dimocrats didn't git ther asshoorences from papers, owin to their inability to perooze em rapidly, it being so long afore they got a word spelled out that they forgot the one precedin it, wich destroyed the continuity uv the narrative, ef I may so speak, and wat we told em really wuz gospel. That won't do with the niggers down here. He reads, he does; and ef he don't, ther's alluz everywhere some sich sneakin cuss ez Pollock, who reads for him, and they know wat they know jist ez well ez anybody. Let em stop hammerin the nigger. It won't do. Ef he's to be a man and a brother here, he must be a man and a brother there. Ef the Dimocrisy must hev a race to look down on, let em turn their attenshun to the Chinese or the Injuns, but from this time out the nigger is sacred.

PETROLEUM V. NASBY, P. M.
(wich is Postmaster), and Professor in the
Ham and Japheth Free Academy for the
Development uv the Intelleck uv all
Races, irrespectiv of Color.

9. Ethnology at Confedrit ✕ Roads: "Possibly the Seat uv the Intelleck Is in the Heel"

POST OFFIS, CONFEDRIT ✕ ROADS
(wich is in the Stait uv Kentucky),
July 19, 1867.

The Radikel party hed bin forst into takin nigger suffrage into their embrace, and methinks we hev em now. To aid our friends in the North, we hev taken the step backward, and are now where we started from. The directers uv the college met and changed the name uv the Institooshn back to the "Southern Military and Classikle Institoot," and the Corners wuz itself agin. Deekin Pogram lookt ez tho ten years hed bin lifted off him. "How pleasant 'tis," sed he, "to walk erect agin in front uv a nigger, and to pass em ez tho they wuz niggers! O, ef I cood only wallop one wunst more, methinks I cood die happy!"

The trouble is, we oppose nigger suffrage from too many stand-pints. Some oppose it on the skore uv the inferiority of the Afrikin; but our people may hev assented to it outwardly, but in ther own minds they objected. "Ef," sed a reliable Dimokrat to hisself, "ef that's the rool, WAT IN THUNDER IS TO BECOME UV ME!"

Likewise the idea uv onfitness. "They can't read nor rite!" shreeks a injoodishus cuss, speekin to a audience, two thirds uv wich go to him reglerly to reed their ballots to em, and who, when they sign promissory notes, put an ✕ atween their first and last names.

Anuther speeker quotes Noah to em, and boldly asserts that the nigger is the descendant uv Ham, and that he is the identikle indivijjle wich wuz cust by Noah; but he runs agin the fact that the rest uv em, wich is in Afrika yet, hev managed to dodge the cuss, ez they ain't servin ther white brethren, and them wich wuz brot here to be Chrischinized hev busted ther bonds, and are jest about ez free ez anybody.

I want a Convenshun uv the lights uv the party to set forth authoritively WHY we oppose nigger suffrage—to give a reason for it, that all our people may act together, ez do other well-regulated machines.

I hev made up my mind wot platform to lay down. I shel go back on Ham, Hager, and Onesimus. I shel turn from the inferiority idea, and take the broad ground that *the nigger is a beast; that he ain't a man at all;* and consekently he hez no more rites than any other animal. I put my foot onto him by authority of the decree that unto man wuz given dominion over the beasts; that we are men, and they are beasts. Ef they admit the first propo-sishen, they will the last. I shel assert boldly and brodly his onfit-nis to mingle with us, becoz his fizzikle structure bein different, goes to show that he wuz uv a different origin, and uv a lower origin. I shel plant myself on the stoopenjus, yet simple propo-sishen, that the Almity made him at a different time and for a different purpus, wich I shel show by citin the color uv his skin, the length uv his foot, the shape uv his head, and sich other mat-ters as I kin git together in time for the Convenshen.

Uv course this doctrine will meet with objectors. We hev a few thin-skinned perfessers uv religion, whose piety service in our ranks hezn't quite obliterated, who will say that these dog-mas undermines the Christian religion. To this I shel answer, Uv wot comparison is any religion a Orthodox Dimocrat hez to a triumph uv the party? Wot hez Dimocrisy to do with religion anyhow? It hez never permitted it to mix in its pollytix. Dimocrisy bleeves in keepin Church and State ez far apart ez possible.

Shood the Ablishnists pint to niggers wich reed and write, I say to-wunst that there is different degrees uv instink,—that ez one dorg hez more instink than another, that so one nigger hez more than another; and then I shood wind this answer up by askin him, "Sir, wood you force yoor dawter to marry a nigger, even ef he cood reed and write?" This hez alluz done good serv-ice, partikelerly ef yoo walk hurridly away before there is time for an answer.

Ther is one pint wich is a stumper—but only one. One man to whom I unfolded this theory, asked me, sneeringly, wat I wuz a goin to do with a mulatter who wuz half white and half black —half man and half beast—half instink, wich dies with him, and half sole, wich wuz to be saved and fitted for the skies, or lost? When a mulatter dies, wat then? Does the half sole uv the half man drag the instink uv the beast behind it in a limpin, lop-sided fashion, into heaven? or does the instink drag the sole into the limbo for animals? "Ef this latter idea be correct," sed he, "in that limbo how much Southern sole is floatin about, held in solooshen in animal instink!"

We hed a meetin last nite to consider this nigger question, wich wood hev resultid in great good, and hed a powerful in-

flooence towards strengthenin the hands uv our brethren in the
North, who are fightin the heresy uv nigger suffrage, hed it not
bin for that irritashen, Pollock, and that pest, Joe Bigler. I hed
made my regler speech on the nigger, and with much effect. I hed
quoted from sumboddy's quotashen from Agassiz, which demonstrated the radicle difference there is atween the Afrikin and the
proud Caucashen, arguin from the length uv his heel and arm,
the thickness uv his skull, and so forth, that the nigger wuz totally
unfit to exercise the rites uv free men. I wuz applauded vociferously, and by none more than Pollock and Joe Bigler. Ez I took
my seat, and wuz a wipin the perspirashen from my classikle
brow, feelin that I hed settled that question, Pollock riz, and desired to say a few words.

"I hev listened with interest to the elokent speaker, and am
happy to say I hev learned fax wich is new to me. Ef I hev ever
doubted the inferiority uv the nigger, them doubts are removed,
pervidin alluz, that the statements uv the speaker is troo, uv
wich I hev no doubt, ez the caracter uv the speaker is a suffishent
guarantee for the trooth uv wichever he sez."

I bowed, stately-like, with the air uv one to whom sich com-
pliments wuz a every-day affair, wich they ain't, by no means; on
the contrary, quite the reverse.

"But I want it demonstrated to the satisfackshen uv the most
obtoose. I want rite here a measurement uv the average Afrikin
and the average white man, that all the world may know the difference. I move that it be did."

I acceded. "Let it be done," sed I, "that the vexed question
may be settled forever."

Joe Bigler sed he saw Napoleon Johnson—a nigger wich
wunst belonged to Deekin Pogram—in the audience. "Napoleon," sed he, "will yoo contribbit yoorself to the great science uv
ethnology? Ain't yoo willin' to let us yoose yoo a while to demonstrate the grate and growin trooth, that yoor grandfather wuz a
monkey? Step up, Napoleon."

Napoleon stept up, and Pollock and I measured him, with
this result:—

Height	5 feet 8 inches.
Weight	150 lbs. averdupoise.
Length uv foot	12 inches.
Breadth uv foot	5 inches.
Length uv hand	8½ inches.

Breadth uv hand	4 inches.
Length uv forearm	11 inches.
Length uv bone from ankle to knee	16 inches.
Projeckshun uv heel	4 inches.
Capassity uv skull, wich, bein the top or cap uv the vertebral column, so to speek, is, accordin to Hippocratees, a trooly scientific Greek, a very important bone for pretty much all uv the races	66 cubic inches.

"Now," sed Pollock, "let us examine in the same way a aver-age specimen uv the Caucashen race, ez he is found in this delect-able spot. Will Issaker Gavitt be good enuff to step forrerd? I per-pose to demonstrate the sooperiority uv the Caucashen with a two foot rool. Figgers won't lie."

Issaker stept up and wuz measured:—

Height	5 feet 8 inches.
Weight	150 lbs.
Length uv hand	7½ inches.
Breadth uv hand	3½ inches.
Length uv foot	11 inches.
Breadth uv foot	4½ inches.
Projeckshen uv heel	1½ inches.
Length uv forearm	10 inches.
Length uv bone from ankle to knee	15 inches.
Capassity uv skull	97 cubic inches.

Pollock wuz delited! "Here," sed he, "it is in a nut-shell. Issaker hez a shorter hand, a more narrer hand, a shorter and narrerer foot, and his heel projecks less than the nigger's by 2½ inches! Good Lord, how I hev bin deseeved! Wat errors I hev bin nussin! How kin a human bein hev intelleck whose heel projecks four inches? How rejoict am I that I am at last set rite on these important pints!"

I smiled beninantly onto him.

Bigler riz. "I, too," sed he, "am satisfied that the nigger is not wat we, who wuz disposed to consider him fit to exercise rites, supposed him to be. I held firm when the measurement uv his hands and arms wuz being made, but the heel staggered me. It's clear that no one kin hev intelleck whose leg isn't set in his foot better than that. I shel persoo this investigashen. Hevin now a startin-pint,—a heel, ez I may say, to stand on,—I shel go on to prove the inferiority uv the nigger. With that heel for a fulcrum, I shel, with the lever uv trooth, proceed to upset the fabric uv nigger ekality, and carry confooshen into Boston. I shel assoom that Napoleon is a average specimen uv the lower, or unintellectooal Afriken type. Is it so?"

"It is! It is!" yelled we all, delited at the happy turn the thing wuz takin.

"I shell also assoom that Issaker Gavitt is a avrage uv the higher or intellectooal Caucashen type. Is it so?"

"Certinly! Certinly!"

"Very well. Now quake, Massachoosets! Napoleon, *kin yoo read?*"

I saw the trap into wich we hed fallen, and risin hastily, protestid that the examinashen hed bin carried far enuff, but Bigler swore he wuz a goin to kiver Massachoosets with shame.

"Kin yoo read, Napoleon?"

"Yes, sah!"

"Read this, then," sed Bigler, handin him a noosepaper.

The nigger read it ez peert ez a Noo England skool marm, wich well he mite, ez he learned it from one uv em.

"Kin yoo write?"

"Certinly;" and taking a pencil he writ half uv the Declarashen uv Independence.

"Set down, Napoleon. It's a devilish pity yoor heels is so long; otherwise yood be credited with hevin intellek. Now Issaker, my bold Caucashen, *kin yoo read?*"

"I protest!" shreeked I, in agony. "Issaker, don't answer the skoffer at ethnology!"

But Issaker, white ez a sheet, and tremblin under the eye uv Bigler, stuttered "No!"

"Kin yoo rite, my gay desendant uv the sooperior race?"

"No!"

"Kin yoo cipher?"

"What in thunder's the yoose uv cipherin, when the old man alluz kep a nigger to do his figgerin?"

"Set down, Issaker. We're done with you. There's an error sumwher. The nigger's capassity uv skull is less by sevral cubic inches, but he seems to hev made a lively yoose uv wat he hez. But it's all rite, Parson. Issaker shel vote, and the nigger shan't. Reedin and writin never wuz a qualificashen for votin down here, any way. Possibly the seat uv the intellek is in the heel instead uv the brain, wich accounts for the nigger's hevin the most uv it."

And Pollock and Bigler, and the niggers present, left the meetin-house, laffin uproarously.

I doubt whether the result uv the investigashen will help our friends North. The fact is, it wuz overdone. It wuz carried too fur. There is a pint at wich facts ought to stop—Dimekratic facts in partikeler. In this instance, the investigashen shood never hev bin carried beyond the heel. Hed it stopt there, we wood hev hed em. But carryin it to the radical pint to wich Bigler and Pollock took it, the foundashen we built wuz upset, and we are all at sea agin.

Petroleum V. Nasby, P. M.

(wich is Postmaster).

VIII. "Cussid Be Canaan!"

(1867)

NOTE TO THE CHAPTER

The existence of slavery on Southern soil challenged the dedication of Americans to the idea of human equality. When the Civil War resolved the issue, force of arms superseded all arguments attempting to rationalize the dilemma. A few years earlier, Charle's Darwin's theory had demolished the scientific hypothesis of plural creations of man and made "the Negro and the Hottentot," in the words of Asa Gray, "our blood-relations." However, Negrophobes kept the differences between freedmen and white men before the nation to justify the enforced inferiority in which they held the colored man. And even if the distinctions did emerge as the scientist suggested and were not marks of human and animal life, they nevertheless existed.

Nasby devoted his lecture, "delivered at Music Hall, Boston, Dec. 22, 1867," to meeting this problem. "Let us raise ourselves from the low, dead, and flat plane of self-interest," he entreated, "and demonstrate our strength, not by trampling upon the defenseless heads of those weaker and lower than ourselves, but by lifting them up to us." Resting his eloquence squarely on Jefferson's Declaration, the pastor, politician and professor once more paraded the variety of views which agitated his contemporaries and then mustered all arguments in support of the basic tenet of American life "that all men are created equal."

In a colorful pageant the "Nasbyan theory" displayed persons and images purified by the reasoning of the devil's advocate. Noah dominated the array of Biblical figures, seconded by his children Shem, Japheth and Ham, and Ham's son, Canaan. Hagar, the servant of Sarah who gave her as a wife to Abraham, and Paul, who sent Onesimus back to his master Philemon rounded out the tableau.

In the arena of politics Nasby presented Franklin Pierce, James Buchanan, Clement L. Vallandigham, Fernando and Benjamin Wood, Horatio Seymour, John Morrissey and others as Democratic politicians who exploited the enforced inferiority of the Negro. Some of them struck him as a compound of the Mormon Brigham Young and the pirate Captain William Kidd. The way of life built on slavery, Nasby found, was defended by Jefferson Davis, James Mason, Robert E. Lee, Nathan B. Forrest, Wade Hampton and P. T. G. Beauregard.

As spearheads of the attack on slavery Nasby singled out three groups: Abolitionists, Union soldiers and Negroes. William Lloyd Garrison, Elijah Parish and Owen Lovejoy, Wendell Phillips, Frederick Douglass, Josiah Giddings and other Abolitionists pointed the way for men who fought slavery on battlefields, in hospitals and in prison camps at Andersonville, Georgia, on Belle Isle in the James River at Richmond, and at Salisbury, North Carolina. Slaves guided escaped soldiers to safety and strove for their own freedom. Some of them died as heroes or martyrs in the attack on Port Hudson, in the massacre of the Union garrison at Fort Pillow, and in the crater during the Petersburg Mine Assault. Two colored brigades fought at Nashville, Tennessee, where one Negro unit lost 221 soldiers, the greatest regimental loss of the battle.

Appomattox stopped the carnage, Nasby realized, but not the fight. Andrew Johnson's impetuous utterances on Washington's Birthday, 1866, hastened the clash between President and Radical Republicans, long foreseen by Secretary of the Navy Gideon Welles. The triumph of the Radicals imposed the agonies of Reconstruction on the nation, but opened also the final struggle for the equality of men. At the end of that long road, Nasby believed, "when the flag has under its shadow only free men . . . we can look the world in the face, and repeat without a blush that grand old Declaration . . . that all men are created equal."

"Cussid Be Canaan!"

We are all descended from grandfathers. Nearly a century ago the grandfathers of some of us, in convention assembled, uttered as doctrine, which they believed could not be gainsayed, these words: "We hold these truths to be self-evident, that all men are created equal; that they are endowed by their Creator with certain inalienable rights; that among these are life, liberty, and the pursuit of happiness."

Thomas Jefferson was the particular grandfather who wrote these high-sounding words, and, as a consequence, he has been ever since hailed as the father of the only political party which never believed in them. My particular mission is to show that Jefferson was a most shallow person, which opinion of Jefferson is very general in the South. True, the Democracy claim him as its father; but when we remember that the same party claim Jackson, the strangler of secession, as another father, we can easily see how that can be. We have claimed these men as ancestors only since they departed this life. Should they rise from the dead, and be blessed with a view of their reputed sons, particularly the branch of the family that has taken up its residence in the city of New York, they would, I doubt not, hold up their hands in horror, and exclaim, "It's a wise father who knows his own child."

It was well enough for Jefferson to assert the equality of men before there was profit in inequality; but had he been really a prophet, he would have done no such thing. In his day Slavery was unprofitable, and, consequently, not the holy thing it has been since. The slaves were burdens instead of aids, for the planters were compelled to provide for them. The hogs ate the corn, and the negroes ate the hogs, leaving the poor owners only what they left. But happily there came a change. An ingenious Yankee invented the cotton gin, slave labor became valuable, and, presto! the doctrine of the equality of men was consigned to the limbo for worn-out and useless rubbish, and Jefferson went out of fashion. Had he been really desirous of being held up as the prophet of the people who afterwards claimed him as such, we should not have had the forcible sentences I have read. He would have diluted them into something like this: "We hold these *supposed* truths to be *tolerably* self-evident, that, as a rule, all *white* men are created equal; that *they* are endowed by their Creator with divers and sundry rights, which may be considered inalienable; that among these are life, liberty, and the pursuit of——niggers!"

It will be observed that the two Declarations differ somewhat. One is as Jefferson wrote it, and the other is the version we use at Confedrit × Roads.

Jefferson was in fault in his lack of appreciation, and strange omission of the word "white." The same omission is painfully observable in all the literature of the world. I have searched faithfully the realms of poetry and history, and am compelled to acknowledge that nowhere outside of the Constitutions of certain States is the word "white" made a necessary prefix to the word "man." And against this I protest. Literature should conform to law, and to the great Caucasian idea. The term employed to designate responsible beings in the Constitutions of our States being "white male," I insist that we go through all our books, and substitute "white male" for "man" wherever the word occurs. Thus we shall make Sir Walter Scott say,—

"Breathes there a white male, with soul so dead."

Addison shall say, in Cato,—

> "When vice prevails, and impious white males bear sway,
> The post of honor is the private station."

In Macbeth, the murderers shall say,—

> "We are white males, my liege."

And Macbeth shall answer,—

> "Aye, in the catalogue ye go for white males."

And Othello, before the senators,—

> "She swore, i' faith, 'twas strange—'twas passing strange;—
> 'Twas pitiful; 'twas wondrous pitiful.
> She wished she had not heard it, yet she wished
> That Heaven had made her such a white male."

But in the Bible the improvement would shine out in a clearer and stronger light. In our Caucasian—our white men's Bibles—we shall have such words as these:—
1 Samuel 13:14,—

> "A white male after his own heart."

2 Samuel 12:7,—

> "And Nathan said unto David, Thou art the white male."

Psalms 37:37,—

> "Mark the perfect white male, and behold the upright; for the end of that white male is peace."

> "Thou shalt love the Lord thy God, and thy white male fellow-citizen as thyself."

And in the mouth of our Saviour we shall put these words:—

> "Suffer little *white* children to come unto me, and forbid them not, for of such is the kingdom of heaven."

This passage would be especially grateful to us of Kentucky, showing as it would that the distinction between the races would be kept up through all eternity. But, unfortunately, the Books do not so read. The American people, when slave labor became of value, forsook Jefferson, put the word "white" into their laws, and painted the word "nigger" on their banners, which word has been a political Shibboleth ever since. It is this Nigger which we shall investigate to-night. I am the more anxious that the people shall understand the nature of this being, and the absurdity of the attempt to elevate him into manhood, for the reason that an effort to that end is now being made. The insane agitators, who deny the truth of Kentucky theology, are resisting us in our efforts to put him in his old place. In the face of our desires, they insist upon deluging the country with Massachusetts, and making of the South a second New England,—factories, farms, churches, school-houses and all.

Upon the 957th page of the Dictionary you will find the word "negro" defined as follows: "One of the black, woolly-headed, thick-lipped, flat-nosed race of men inhabiting Africa." The Negro of the Dictionary is not the individual of whom I shall speak. The Negro I know nothing about; the Nigger I have spent much time in investigating, and flatter myself I understand it thoroughly. I say *it* of the Nigger, and *him* of the Negro, for there is a wide difference between them. The Negro is a *man,* born in Africa, or descended from natives of that country; the Nigger is an idea, which exists only in the imagination of persons of the haughty Caucasian race resident in the United States. It is an idea which sways men, and influences their action, without having being; a myth, which influences the world, without possessing form or shape. It is possessed of many attributes, is many-sided, many-shaped, vastly endowed, and fearfully and wonderfully made. To clear up as I go, I may as well specify some of the peculiarities of the Nigger. For instance, it is firmly believed that he could never provide for himself; but those so contending, also declare that the wealth of the country is dependent upon him, and that without him weeds would grow in the streets of our cities. It was asserted that he would not labor; yet the same men undertook the large job of conquering the North, that they might continue to enjoy the fruits of his labor. He was said to be so stupid as to be incapable of receiving even the rudiments of an education, and yet we found it necessary, in our States, to pass stringent laws, with fearful penalties attached, to prevent him from doing it! It was held by eloquent speakers that he would invade the North, and, as he was too indolent to work, he would fill our almshouses and jails; and the same speakers would assert a moment later, with equal eloquence, that, accustomed as he always had been to labor, he would work for less pay than white men, and throw them all out of employment. This last assertion, I have noticed, was always made by gentlemen in the vicinity of bar-rooms, whose noses were solferino-hued, whose hats were crownless, and whose wives, for amusement probably, took in washing to feed the children. It is an unfortunate fact for us, that men who labor in earnest have never been afraid of the competition of the Nigger. Lower down in the scale of creation than the baboon, they were fearful he would, if not restrained by law, teach their schools, sit as judges, and be elected to Congress; so repulsive in appearance had they painted him, with his thick lips, black face, and kinky hair, that the very thought of one would make a white damsel shudder; nevertheless they demanded the enactment of laws in States where women may choose their husbands unrestrained, to prevent these same white damsels from marrying them. Immeasurably beneath them in every particular, they felt called upon to perpetually cry, "Protect us from nigger equality!"—and so on.

Jefferson's fault was the result of a lack of knowledge. He knew all about the Negro, but nothing about the Nigger, and it was well for him, therefore, that he lived in the year of our Lord 1776. Had he lived ninety years later, and enunciated the same doctrine, we should have shot him, as we did Lovejoy. Were he alive now, he could not have been elected to Congress in the district represented by the Hon. John Morrisey! No, indeed! The gentlemen who left their native soil because of the scarcity of this equality (and of potatoes), the men who would have been carpet-baggers but for the lack of carpet-bags,—those who have kindly taken charge of the politics of several of the Atlantic cities,— these men are the sharp sticklers that the distinctions between man and man which drove them from the land of their birth be kept up here. Their motto is, "One man is as good as another;" but when their eyes rest upon a black man, they very properly add, "and better too!" This class have cultivated such a delightful hatred of the Nigger that they won't even drink with one, unless, indeed, the Nigger pays for the fluids. This makes some difference. And that this distinction may be kept up, we have interpolated into Jefferson's Declaration the word "white," and assert, vehemently, that both Scripture and science, of which we know much, justify the interpolation. In Kentucky, we don't take the Declaration of Independence as we do our whiskey, straight, but we sweeten it to our taste. We have all the passages of Scripture relating to it at our tongues' end. At the Corners, you can hear at any time those whose appearance hardly denotes erudition, whose noses blossom as the lobster, whose hair asserts

The Curse of Canaan from Josiah Priest, Slavery . . . (1843).
Noah and his descendants: left, Ham; center, Japheth; right, Noah.

impatience of restraint by obtruding itself through the corners of their hats, whose toes manifest themselves through their ventilated shoes, and to whose perpendicularity posts are necessary, exclaim, unctuously, "And Noer planted a vineyard, and drank of the wine, and was drunken. Cussid be Canaan."

Having dwelt as long as is profitable upon the attributes of this interesting being, I pass to an examination of his origin. It is found in the 9th chapter of Genesis. The world, sunk in wickedness, was destroyed by a flood. But it was not the design of the Almighty to exterminate the race. I will not stop here to argue whether it would have been better to have made clean work of it or not. I was in New York a few weeks ago, and thought, perhaps, it would. Be that as it may, one family he preserved in an ark, and when the tempests that had wrought His judgments had subsided, and the purified earth was again fit for the occupancy of man, this family left their floating home, and went out upon its face. The Book gives a short, though satisfactory account of what followed. Noah, six hundred years old at the time, having seen nothing but water for nearly twelve months, wanted a change. He planted a vineyard, pressed the grapes, drank the wine therefrom, and was drunken; which was a very indiscreet performance for one at his age. Had he been a mere infant of one or two hundred years, it wouldn't have been so singular, but a mature man of six hundred ought to have known better. It has always been a mystery at the Corners how Noah could become inebriated on so thin a drink as new wine. Deacon Pogram remarked that Noah wuzn't a seasoned vessel. In that condition he lay down within his tent with insufficient clothing upon him. As it was in the beginning, so it is now, and ever shall be. To this day the man who drinks will sooner or later get down with too little clothing upon him. Ham, his youngest son, saw him, and laughingly told his brethren. Shem and Japheth reproved Ham for his levity, and took their garments upon their shoulders, and going backward, laid them upon him. When Noah awoke, he knew what Ham had done, and he cursed him in these words: "Cursed be Canaan; a servant of servants shall he be unto his brethren."

Upon this one act of our common father hung momentous results. That one draught of wine set in motion a succession of events that affected the fate of the greatest nation of the world, in all conceivable ways, from the election of constables to the fighting of great battles. For in that cup of wine was Democracy,—

then and there it was born, and that cup of wine gave that party its Nigger—all the capital it ever had. The temperance people tell us that in every cup of wine there is a devil; in this cup you will acknowledge there was a large and particularly lively one.

The drinking of this wine, and the drunkenness that it produced upon the inexperienced Noah, was the cause of a division of the human race into two classes,—white men and niggers. Under the head of white men, we class the red man of America, with his aquiline nose, coppery complexion, and straight hair; the Mongolian, with his olive-colored skin, black hair, and flat nose; the Caucasian, with his fair complexion, hair of all colors, and features of all shapes; the Celt, with his variable features; and—Democrats. A Democrat is counted a white man, no matter what his complexion may be; no matter what the color of his hair—or nose. All the rest of the human family—and Radicals—we set down as Niggers. To the white race we ascribe all the glory of the South—to the others nothing.

This elevation of the white race, and consequent degradation of the black, is justified by the few of us who read the Bible, by the sin of Ham; though, by the way, we have nothing to say in particular of the sin of Noah, which preceded and led to it, Noah's sin being one that we are compelled, for obvious reasons, to look upon with much leniency.

To be frank, I have never believed that poor Ham was fairly dealt with. I have always pitied Ham. He was, doubtless, a great, good-natured fellow, with a keen appreciation of the ludicrous, and was vastly amused at the condition of his sire. Drunkenness was not so common in that day as to excite disgust; and as he saw the old navigator on his back, his face twisted with inebriety, his snores waking the echoes, and the walls of his tent swaying from his hard breathing, he doubtless thought he had, as the slang-users of this day would say, "a good thing on the old man."

But if it was a laughing matter with the foolish Ham, it was not so with the shrewd Shem and Japheth. They pierced the future. To get into the good graces of their father, they turned their backs upon his sin and folly (as we do nowadays upon the sin and folly of those from whom we want favors), and, precisely as we do, cast over his sin their garments. The only parallel to this we have in modern times occurred in Washington a few years ago. Andrew Johnson was very much in the condition of Noah upon one memorable 22d of February, and a small army of patriots, who had assessorships, post offices, and collectorships in their eyes, made haste to cast their garments over him. But they did not succeed in covering him. Noah awoke, and in the ill-humor which always follows excess, cursed poor Ham, and condemned his son Canaan to be the servants of his uncles forever. This was the beginning of Democracy. Drunkenness brought exposure, exposure shame, shame a curse, and thus cursed, Ham went out a Nigger. Drunkenness made Nigger, Nigger made Democracy, and the two have been running the machine ever since.

We have now plainly before us the origin of the Nigger, and have, therefore, a starting point for our investigations. Here were three brothers, Shem, Ham, and Japheth, with a curse upon Ham, condemning his children to serve the others. We, the whites, claim to be the descendants of the other two, and consequently assert the right to own and work the children of our unfortunate uncle. The claim is a comfortable one. Labor is something all men dread; and if it can be positively fixed that Noah did curse Ham, and that he spoke by authority, and that the negro is really the descendant of Ham, and we are the descendants of Japheth, we have really a good thing of it. We of Kentucky have always desired to fulfil the great law of labor, as our particular friends at the North served in the army—by substitute.

One cup of wine, and a curse after it, made a difference in the history of the world.

How differently history would have been written had Noah started a temperance society at the beginning, or had the Maine liquor law been in operation in that country. Or had he taken up any other branch of agriculture! Had he planted corn instead of grapes, or gone into sheep or poultry; had a frost blighted his grapes, or a mildew struck them, or had the screw of his press broken; had any one of these things happened, he would not have become inebriated; Ham would not have seen him; there would have been no curse, no Nigger, no Democracy. For who can imagine a Democracy without a Nigger to be kept in subjection! Or, suppose that all of Ham's children had died of diphtheria! Had any one of these things happened, the whole course of political events would have been changed. We never should have seen at political meetings in the West, wagon-loads of ancient females, with banners over their venerable heads, and inscribed thereon this agonizingly touching appeal: "Fathers, protect us from negro equality!" as though they were not old enough, as a rule, to protect themselves. Or, this heroic declaration: "White husbands or none!" which, taken in connection with their age and single condition, would indicate that if they had ever had offers they must have come from black men. In the East, the gentlemen who sent the Hon. John Morrisey to Congress from New York, would have been spared the crimes of arson and murder, for there would have been no nigger orphan asylums to awaken their righteous indignation; no adult male niggers to hang to lamp posts. But as any one of these things would have changed the complexion of affairs, and prevented the unfortunate change in Ham's complexion, and as they did not happen, we are bound to admit that Providence intended the negro to be kept down, and in the eternal fitness of things, arranged for an organization to keep him down.

This curse is the great pivotal fact upon which American politics has turned for years. But we found many difficulties in it. The first difficulty which occurred to me, is the fact that all of Ham's children did not suffer in consequence of their father's little indiscretion. It ought to have fallen upon all alike, but it did not. Nimrod was a descendant of Ham, but he was not the servant of anybody, very much. On the contrary, quite the reverse. He was a mighty hunter before the Lord; and mighty hunters have never been servants. The man strong enough to struggle with the lion and to overcome the tiger, and brave enough to dare the dangers of the chase for the fierce delight it affords, is not the man to humbly hump his shoulders, and to a mere man say that most hateful of all words, "Master." Besides, Nimrod built cities and established kingdoms, which is not the work of servants. We were forced to the conclusion, therefore, that the curse held to Canaan only; that Nimrod's children mingled with the sons of Shem and Japheth, and that their descendants are to-day white men. This troubles us; for, counting it a truth, we were associating with those having the blood of the cursed Ham in their veins; and besides, if one of the descendants of Ham escaped the curse, may not others get out from under it at the same place? Again; if the negroes of Africa, from which country we procured the stock we are blessed with, are really the descendants of Canaan, the son of Ham, the curse which Noah imposed upon them lost its adhesive power for many centuries. The brethren separated, and each went about his business. I have spent sleepless nights upon this question, but I must confess that I can find no proof that Canaan, or any of his descendants, were, until a

comparatively recent date, the servants of anybody! Can it be
that the curse was as temporary in its effects as the wine that produced it? Did it evaporate with the fumes thereof? Did it pass
away with Noah's headache the next morning? Did Noah make
over to Shem and Japheth property for which *he* had no title?

Unfortunately Shem's descendants are said to have stayed in
Asia, Ham's went to Africa, and Japheth's peopled Europe. Here
is the difficulty that besets me. How could Ham's descendants
serve their brethren, they staying in Africa, while the brethren
were comfortably established in Europe and Asia? It may be answered that they went after them; but, alas! they had no need of
that. The strong Shemites found enough weak Shemites to enslave without going after their cousins, and the same is true of
the Japhethites. The Tartars made servants of the Chinese, the
Normans of the Saxons, and the Romans had a cheerful habit of
gobbling up all the weaker people within their reach. Among
these, I regret to say, were the ancestors of those before me—your
fathers and mine. The curse was in existence, and had power, but
somehow it was demoralized. When Noah fired it off, it missed
its aim. It scattered like a poor shot-gun, and hit where he did
not intend it. For in all ages of the world slavery has existed.
There never has been a time when strong men were not too lazy
to work; never a time when there were not brutes and imbeciles
—the two classes necessary to the system. The strong enslaved the
weak without regard to Noah. They did it in a manly way, too.
The enslavers did not ask the person they wished to enslave for
their family record; they did not attempt to ascertain whether or
not he was descended from Canaan. Not they. If they wanted a
servant, they sought out a man weaker than they; they knocked
him down, in the old-fashioned way, with a club; they beat him
till the original man was pretty much pummelled out of him, and
then, reduced to the condition of a beast, he was the individual
they desired. History is full of these instances, and Jefferson had
this kind of history in his mind when he wrote the Declaration;
which would have been well enough had he put the word "white"
in its proper place, that there might be no doubt as to his mean-
ing.

As he left it, it applies to black as well as white, and strictly
construed robs us of our Nigger.

We could never find any testimony in the Scriptures that
the dusky sons of Africa were the descendants of Canaan; and
this is another difficulty. To be a servant, as our people under-

stand it, one ought to be an inferior; and we held that the negro was our inferior, and ought to be our servant, because of the curse. Behold the snag upon which our boat runs. Our conservative brethren oppose the conferring of any rights upon these people, because we dread the *supremacy* of the negro! That sweet boon to an oppressed people, Andrew Johnson, in his annual messages, always devoted a chapter to the danger of this race taking possession of the government, and conducting it themselves; and I am not certain but that I have seen the same fear expressed in the reports of Secretary Welles, as he said regularly whatever the President has said. Seward once dwelt upon it at length, but I do not like to quote him. The distance from Abraham Lincoln to Andrew Johnson was so great, that the leap from the one to the other broke his moral back. He has never stood upright since. The friends of the race jeeringly say that if the negroes should take the government in their own hands, they hope they will conduct it to better advantage than the late President has, for if they do not, it would prove to the satisfaction of everybody that the curse was a reality, and that they are not fit, as yet, to be intrusted with political rights.

Now we have in the United States four millions of these people, all told, and thirty millions of whites. It is as certain as the multiplication table that if laws are necessary to prevent them from governing us, they must be the superior and we the inferior race. If, in a clear field, the four millions can control the thirty millions, it must certainly be because of the superiority of the four millions. It troubles us to reconcile this pet fear of ours with our claims of superiority.

I have never been able, from the Book, to determine just how far that curse extended. Noah's words were, "Cursed be Canaan; a servant of servants shall he be unto his brethren." I ask especial attention to the wording of this text, as it affords a complete justification of the practice of amalgamation, so common in the South under the old system. The Canaanites were condemned to be servants unto their *brethren*. Not unto the stranger, but their brethren. How, except through this, let me ask, could the slaves of the South be brethren unto their masters? But we have full faith that the curse was intended to include not only Canaan, but his descendants. If it was only to cover Canaan, and was to die with him, of what use would it have been to us? Had it died with Canaan, we of Kentucky would have been

doing our own work to-day, and we might have put on its tomb-
stone the epitaph written for the kitten which died too young:

> "If I was so soon to be done for,
> What was I begun for?"

It may be well here to consider briefly the question of color,
which has worried and perplexed all of us. We are white, or
copper-colored, and the negroes, such of them as stayed at the
North, are black. The question is, "Why black?" One theory is,
that color is the result of climate, diet, habits of life, and other
conditions, which, persevered in for many generations, will
change the appearance of families of men. The people of my
State know better. They ascribe it to the curse of Noah; that
Ham, being the brother of Shem and Japheth, was originally
white, even as they were, but that he went out from the presence
of his father with this mark of his displeasure, not only upon his
face, but spread all over his body. The very name to us is sig-
nificant of color. The curse changed at once his physical nature,
and the change took place suddenly. When Ham got to his room
that morning, and gazed at himself in his mirror, he called, in
astonishment, for Shem and Japheth, that he might be introduced to himself.

Noah, when he changed Ham's style and shape, had doubtless a glimpse of the future, and he made of him precisely the
kind of man that the future required. As he was to be the menial
of his brethren for all time, he considerately gave him a complexion suited to his condition; one that would not show dirt.
To further fit him for the discharge of the duties that were to be
his, his nose was flattened, that it could never be turned up in
scorn at anything; his arms were elongated, his shoulders were
broadened, his forehead was driven backward, and his hair, long
and straight like ours, was converted into wool, that he should
waste no time in dressing it, and also that we, his masters, might
have a better hold for our fingers. These are the physical char-
acteristics of the race in America, and we affirm that the negro
must and ought to be a slave, because the Almighty, working
through Noah, made him exactly of the shape and style necessary
to that condition.

There may be a mistake here. It is possible, as I once heard
a philosophical son of Ham say, that those who hold these views
have been all along mistaking their own work for the Almighty's.

He had the impudence to say that it was possible that when the first negro was landed upon our shores he was neither flat-nosed, long-heeled, or large-handed. He was, however, forthwith set at work grubbing land in Virginia; his nose was being continually flattened by the fist of his chivalrous master; his shoulders were broadened by the burdens piled upon them; his hands were widened by constant holding of the hoe, and his heel was providentially lengthened to enable him to maintain his equilibrium under the loads he was compelled to carry. Had they been shorter, he would, when overloaded, have fallen backward. His receding forehead he accounted for in this way: "Of what use," said he, "would a head shaped to hold brains be to one who had no brains to hold? and why should he have brains who has no occasion to use them?" But I noticed that this particular nigger, who had learned to read and write, had a head shaped very much like those of ordinary people of intelligence, and that his children, who could not only read and write, but cipher, were still more so. He had put out his one talent to usury, and it had become ten in his descendants. We of the South feared this. We would not fly in the face of the Lord on any account. Zealous to fulfil his word, and determined that for his glory Canaan should forever be a servant unto his brethren; and fearful that if they should gain knowledge they might give the Lord the slip, and be their own men, we withheld knowledge from them. Piously, therefore, we enacted laws making the teaching of these foreordained slaves to read the sacred word of God a penitentiary offence. And in our determination that they should not be unfitted for their destiny, we did hang very many meddlesome Yankees who doubted it all, and proposed to do something towards elevating them above the condition of beasts. In those happy days, south of the Ohio River, it only required twenty minutes of time to arrest, try, hang, and divide the clothes of a Northern school teacher. And when one of these Noah cursed men demonstrated, by opposing the will of his master, that he had brains, the matter was pleasantly and peremptorily settled by knocking them out. A great deal of brain has been thus disposed of in the Southern States.

Another trouble that besets us, is the fact that the curse remained inoperative and in abeyance for centuries after it was pronounced. The children of Ham, it is supposed, occupied Africa all by themselves. They fell, as did their cousins in Europe and Asia, into vice; their vices being just as much more detestable than those cultivated by their cousins as the climate of their country is hotter. Vice, like vegetation, attains its greatest perfection in hot climates. The farther south you go, the less orthodox you find mankind. Vermont, where man wrestles with Nature, and wrests a subsistence from an unwilling soil by main strength, has never faltered in her devotion to humanity. Louisiana, on the other hand, where Nature yields her treasures at the asking, is as true to the Democracy as the needle to the pole, or the Kentuckian to his whiskey: two examples of fidelity equalled by nothing else in this world. Where men find a living ready made, they have too much time upon their hands to be good. The Ten Commandments have but little chance where labor is unnecessary. Had South Carolina been blessed with a month of sleighing each year, she never would have passed an ordinance of secession. No climate less hot than that of Mississippi could develop such a man as Jeff Davis; and Salisbury, Andersonville, Belle Isle, and General Forrest were only possible where the thermometer stands at one hundred for months together. It may be, indeed, it has been said by a few soldiers who survived Andersonville, that the heat in which the men I have mentioned, exist, was not meant to affect the moral natures, but was intended by a kind Provience, who foreknew their destination, to prepare them, in some slight measure, for the still greater heat to which they are certain to be subjected in the future.

The Japhethites harried, murdered, and plundered each other in Europe, and the Shemites fell to a still deeper depth of barbarism, as did our African brother.

In Europe the Japhethites built large castles, and rode about upon horses, clad absurdly in cast iron, with inverted pots upon their heads, killing each other with iron spears, and the Africans were doing the same things, on a smaller scale, with spears pointed with fish-bones.

But the sons of Canaan had not been as yet introduced to the curse, unfortunately. There were slaves in Africa, but they were slaves not unto Japheth's children, but unto themselves, precisely as the children of Shem and Japheth enslaved men of their own race. When Cæsar conquered a nation at war with Rome, he made slaves of his captives; and when Gumbo Quashee, prince of Borriaboola Gha, led his hosts of warriors against a neighboring king, he dragged back captives in his train, who were at once enslaved. If Gumbo met defeat, the only difference was, he took his turn at the mill. The enslaved have always been the victims of a curse, not of the drunken Noah, but of that more terrible curse, weakness.

There is another ugly point in this matter of the curse that is hardly worth referring to, but it may be as well. The fact is (and this hurts us), the Africans, the woolly-headed, thick-lipped, dark-skinned, Africans, of whom we have made slaves under the curse, are not the descendants of Canaan, upon whom the curse fell, at all.

Unfortunately for us, who have risked our all upon this, the Scriptures are explicit upon this point.

Canaan begat Sidon and Heth, and their descendants were the Jebusites, the Amorites, the Girgashites, and—sights of other tribes. The Book tells us precisely where they are located.

Too lazy and shiftless to move any distance, they pre-empted the ground upon which Jerusalem stands, their territory including those New Yorks of the old world, Sodom and Gomorrah. They were not a nice people to have for next door neighbors. They had many disagreeable habits. They were a compound of Brigham Young and Kidd the Pirate, and it is supposed that Salt Lake City and New York were modelled after their principal towns as near as may be. It will be remembered that these two cities, Sodom and Gomorrah, came to a sudden end.

Notwithstanding the love I bear the metropolis, because of its politics, the reading of the account of the destruction of these cities, and knowing that what has been may, for the same cause, occur again, has deterred me from investing very largely in real estate in New York. But these Canaanites did not go to Africa; they stayed in Asia; and as we have been enslaving only Africans, it is clear that there has been a mistake somewhere, and that we have been innocently enslaving the wrong race all this time. You all remember the venerable story of the tub. An old woman brought suit once upon a time for the value of a tub which she had loaned, and which had been returned to her piece by piece, the hoops having all dropped off. The defence set up by the borrower was comprehensive. First, and to begin with, the defendant never borrowed the tub. Secondly, she returned it with the hoops all on, and, thirdly, the plaintiff never had a tub.

It is about so with this pet curse of ours. It wasn't good for much at best, it didn't stick to the people at whom it was levelled, and the Africans, upon whose shoulders we have piled it, are not Canaanites. Our ancestors did not believe this, however. They believed in this curse, with the childlike simplicity of a pawnbroker. It is very easy for us to believe in anything that holds out promise of personal benefit. Men whose love for gain cannot be satisfied with six days of labor, very generally question the sanctity of the Sabbath; and we all insist that laws shall be made to fit our desires, rather than to bring our desires to fit laws. These ancestors of ours were a greedy set. They hungered after a life of no labor, and they believed, therefore, that the Lord directed Columbus across the untried waste of waters that rolled between Spain and America solely that this long retired and almost forgotten curse might be revived and put in force. It had been a failure thus far; but as they looked out upon the new world, and saw how magnificently they could live, if they could only get their labor for nothing, their faith in it revived. They found here field and forest, gold and water, everything but labor.

The emigrant might, it is true, have done the labor himself, but then this cherished curse of ours would have been still floating around the world, like the dove of the eminent navigator who uttered it, with no place to rest the sole of its foot. Besides, they did not want to do the labor. The first settlers of Virginia, from whom the chivalry of that State claim descent, never labored at home, and why should they here? The settlers of Carolina were men to whom labor was as distasteful as it has ever been to their descendants. The negro was precisely what they wanted. The original decree was, "In the sweat of thy brow shalt thou eat bread." They were determined that the decree should be fulfilled, but they wanted the dividing of it.

They were perfectly willing to do the eating, but they wanted the negro to do the sweating; and had he been content with this division of the decree, all would have been smooth to-day.

They prayed, "Give us this day our daily bread;" but they added to the petition, "and furnish us a nigger to feed it to us."

Of course they believe in the curse. The planter on the banks of the James felt the convenience of an arrangement which would obviate the first curse of labor, by a second curse; of having the sin brought into the world through the agency of the apple, done away with by another sin which had its origin in the grape.

They found it a blessed thing to have a being rich in muscle to perform their share of the penalty of the first curse, giving them wasteful summers at Saratoga, and ample time and means for the cultivation of the Southern Christian graces—gambling, horse-racing, pistol-shooting, and the like. It was a glorious life they led! Did the proud Caucasian master have an ill run of luck at cards? a nigger on the block made it all right the next morning. Did madam, his wife, mourn, and refuse to be comforted, because a thousand dollar shawl was not? the matter was easily arranged. The tearing apart of a husband and wife, and the sale of one; the condemning of a quadroon of her own sex to a life of shame, was all that was necessary. Did they desire to entertain their friends sumptuously? Why should they not? There was no sordid counting of cost, as it was farther North; for were there not niggers to sweat? Virginia hospitality was celebrated. Vermont hospitality might have been, had Vermont fostered this curse, and partaken of its benefits. It's easy enough to be hospitable with a hundred negroes, more or less, sweating for you gratis. We did not invent reapers or sewing machines, for we didn't need them. Flesh and blood was to be bought in any market, and it was cheaper than iron and steel. We down South were happily circumstanced. We had black slaves at home to do our labor, and white serfs up North, just as humble, to do our voting. Nature kindly furnished us a race white enough to vote, and low enough to be owned.

Interpreting the curse to include all Africa, our pious fathers set about bringing as many of its inhabitants as possible under its operations. They sent out missionaries, whom a censorious world was wicked enough to stigmatize as pirates and slavers, clad in red shirts, with pistol at belt and cutlass by side, bearded like pards, and full of strong oaths. These evangelizers, full of zeal and rum, sailed up the rivers of Africa, and surprised villages of these accursed people, killing the accursed men and women too old to work, and the accursed children too young to work, but selecting out carefully the able-bodied ones of both sexes. Packing these in the holds of their vessels like herrings, they turned their prows homeward, throwing overboard, from day to day, the bodies of those who had so little regard for the curse of Noah as to die on the way to the fulfilment thereof. And so at last the curse was fulfilled. On the cotton plantations, in the rice swamps, in the cane and tobacco fields, the supposed sons of Ham toiled on, expiating the stupidity of their supposed father, who, a great many centuries before, hadn't any more sense than to look in upon his father when he was drunk.

But just as this convenient and comfortable curse got into good working order it was killed.

Abraham Lincoln smote it under the fifth rib, and it died the death.

The nation, in deadly peril, called upon our black cousins to aid in its deliverance, and it gave up the ghost. The sons of Ham, inferior as they were in all other respects, were discovered to be able to pull a trigger or push a bayonet with anybody, and to the astonishment of those who stood before them, they had the will to do it. They dared to stand in battle array before the chivalry of the South. We very soon accounted for the daring.

When Lincoln put the musket in the hands of the Southern negroes, it was Greek against Greek, brother against brother. The blood of the old cavaliers, which gave courage and daring to the Beauregards, Lees, Masons, and Hamptons, made cavaliers also of Scipio, Pompey, and Cæsar, their half-brothers; and why not. The Federals turned against the Confederates twenty thousand men having the best blood of the South coursing through their veins, and inspiring them to high chivalrous deeds.

Then the struggle became literally fratricidal. Another thing made these fellows fight. They had treasured up that old saying of Jefferson, and they rejoiced when the firing upon Sumter gave them promise of the glad day when it should be a reality. When they were satisfied that the nation was really divorced from slavery, they flew to arms to prove themselves worthy of the future they hoped for. We must confess that they fought bravely and died grandly.

The swart hero in the death-trap at Petersburg, on the plain at Port Hudson, and in the enclosure at Fort Pillow, showed an example of heroism that any people might be proud of.

The slave who remained on the plantation, who risked life to feed, nurse, and guide the flying fugitive from Andersonville, showed a devotion the like of which the world never witnessed before. We of the South were whipped, and by their aid.

I do not say that we would not have been beaten had they not thrown themselves into the breach, but it was done the easier because of them. They stopped bullets at least. The bullet that let out the life of the negro soldier at Nashville, might, had he not stood in its way, made life-long sadness in your home; and many a son of a Northern mother who came home laurel crowned, owes his life to the unknown black man who lies in an unhonored grave upon the fields from which he plucked honor.

These poor deluded Canaanites, as we shall term them, believed that they had earned their promotion to a higher rank, and really expected it.

But we knew better. Down in Kentucky we held a consultation on this very question. That blessed saint and keen observer of men, Deacon Pogram, remarked sagely, "that men and women was the most ungrateful members of the human family." Said he further on this head, "The sense of gratitood the Fedrals feel will die out with the peals of the bells which celebrate the victrys the nigger allies helped to win. They endured the nigger because they needed him; but now, thank the Lord, they don't need him no more, and, halleloogy, he'll be the same cussed nigger he alluz wuz." I use the Deacon's exact words.

He was right. The wholesome prejudice against color swallowed up gratitude, and the pride of race swallowed justice. The negro stepped one foot upon the threshold of the Temple of Liberty, but we rudely pushed him back. They wanted not only freedom, but the elective franchise, the ungrateful wretches not being satisfied with what we had given them.

They had been provided for generously. We of the South accepted the situation, and acknowledged their freedom, but we felt that it was necessary that they be regulated. And so we decreed that they should not leave the plantations on which they were employed without passes from their employers, under penalty of being shot at sight.

They should have the right of suing any one—of their own color—if they could give white bail for costs; and here was a privilege—they were to have the unrestricted right of being sued the same as white men. They should not purchase or lease real estate outside of any incorporated city or village; and as large bodies of them were considered dangerous, they should not purchase or lease real estate within any incorporated city or village. As we fixed their wages at four dollars per month, they boarding themselves, these laws relating to the purchase of real estate might seem unnecessary. But we wanted to be on the safe side. And we proposed to give them the ballot, in time. Of other men we required no preparation, but we felt it necessary of these. We only required them to pass a creditable examination in Greek, Latin, embroidery, French, German, and double-entry book-keeping, and to facilitate their acquiring these branches we burned all their school-houses.

These regulations were made in Mississippi. In my State of Kentucky it was not necessary to do anything in the matter, for

Kentucky did not rebel. We preserved a strict neutrality. That estimable pillar in the Church at the Corners, Elder Gavitt, who has since gone to his reward, remarked that "no one cood be more nootraller than he was." He loyally stayed at home all day, and bushwhacked Federal pickets all night, and after battles he robbed the dead and wounded of both sides impartially. For thus remaining neutral we have been permitted to manage our niggers in our own way.

The curse was by this time abandoned, but the hankering after cheap labor remained. We found at once a new reason for degrading this race—a new theory for keeping them down. We discovered, just in the nick of time, that they were not men at all. And this suited our friends of the North. They had always objected to the theory that the negro was a man, and that he was enslaved because of his inferiority. They murmured to themselves, "If the stronger shall own the weaker, if the intellectually superior shall hold in slavery the intellectually inferior, God help us! We might as well select our masters at once."

When Lee surrendered at Appomattox Court House, we felt that all was gone. We felt as grateful, as men of our stamp could feel, that our lives were not forfeit, that we had yet our property, save and except our niggers. But this feeling wore off. Andrew Johnson became suddenly tired of the rôle of Moses, or rather he changed his Israelites. He led the astonished Africans into the Red Sea, and left them there; and putting himself at the head of their Egyptian pursuers, he pulled *them* out of the troubled waters they had fallen into. We were not slow to take advantage of this changed condition of affairs. There is a modesty in the Southern character, but it does not crop out very much. We began to talk of *our* rights; *our* niggers, and *our* system. We felt that all was not lost so much as it had been. True, they were free, but had we not legislatures? Congress, in its wisdom, left them in our hands after all. They could vote by law, and by law some of us could not; but what of law, so long as we had the executing of it? We were admitted to the Georgia legislature, and we at once expelled enough of our black enemies to give us the control of that body. Elsewhere force—the rifle, the pistol, the knife—gave us the control we wanted, and by a liberal use of these peculiarly Southern agencies, the doomed sons of Canaan were practically as far from freedom as ever. They were by law competent to vote in Louisiana, but of what avail to them was that privilege so long as the power was in the hands of our people, who by force controlled one election, that they might use the power thus gained to disfranchise them forever, and reduce them to the old status?

It was necessary to satisfy our friends of the North that we were right in this matter. We had no trouble to do it. Our learned men measured their arms, legs, hands, and skulls, and finding a difference, held it was right and proper that all political rights be denied them. Smelling committees were appointed, who discovered that the nigger was possessed of an odor not perceptible in the white, and forthwith that odor took the entire conservative part of the people by the nose, and led them at its own sweet will. It was not as agreeable as Night-blooming Cereus, and it was decided that therefore he ought not to vote. His color was next critically considered, and in a new light. It was not like ours; and should a man presume to exercise the rights of freemen whose complexion rivalled charcoal? Their heels protruded more than ours, and therefore they must be deprived of all privileges save that of living, and that only by sufferance. This rule we find to be weak in some respects.

The first objection that occurs to me to this method of determining a man's qualifications for the exercise of the great privilege of a freeman is the uncertainty of its application. We will suppose a white man to have arms, legs, and skull, of the average negro shape and measurement; does that unfit him for the ballot? We must admit this, if these measurements are to be the test. Or, suppose, from inattention to personal cleanliness, he should carry with him an odor unpleasant to persons of refined sensibilities, would that unfit him? The adoption of this rule would require boards of election to smell of each elector who offered a ballot; and that there might be uniformity in the matter, which is necessary in a republic, the government would be forced to establish a bureau of perfumery.

Ignorance we would urge as a disqualification; but alas, we have a most excellent reason for sailing clear of that. A very large per cent. of those who oppose giving the ballot to the negroes, because of their ignorance, put a cross to their names when they sign a promissory note, and accomplish that simple feat with much difficulty and running out of tongue.

Fielding, the great English novelist, gave us a most amusing picture of a terror occasioned in a small English village on the coast, by a rumor that the French had landed at a time when the pugnacious Gauls were threatening an invasion of that coun-

try. At the grated window of a debtor's prison appears the face
of a person who had been incarcerated for many years for a debt
which he could never hope to pay, and whose imprisonment was
therefore like to be perpetual. With an expression of the most
earnest indignation upon his faded face, he exclaims, from behind the bars, "Zounds! are the French coming to deprive us of
our liberties?"

Even so. I must admit that the men who tremble the most
for their country, when they contemplate the ignorant negro
possessing the ballot, are those who cannot read, and the patriot who sells his vote for a drink of rum, is the identical fellow
who talks the loudest of the danger of giving the ballot to a mass
of people whose votes can be so easily influenced.

Several other reasons prevented us from making all that we
hoped for out of the ignorance of the negroes, particularly of
the South. Did we point to the ignorant field hand, and ask
triumphantly if such as he was fit to vote? Forthwith our opponents held up, as an offset, the degraded brutes of our Northern
cities. Did we point to the vicious negroes? They could and did
point to the roughs of New York, Philadelphia, and Baltimore.
And they rather troubled us when they asserted that the ballot
in the hands of ignorant white men was just as dangerous as in
the hands of ignorant black men; that the ballot, ignorantly or
viciously cast, is what hurts us, not the color of the man who
casts it. They asserted that he who says "Stand off" to the colored
man because he cannot read his ballot, ought to say "Stand off"
to the white man equally ignorant. There is no denying this.
Were intelligence made the test, it would scarcely be worth while
to open polls in half the districts of New York City, and one
fourth of our entire strength would fade out like frost under a
May sun. Finally we adopted as ground upon which we could
stand, the theory that there were many creations instead of one;
that Adam was not the Simon pure, original man; that the nigger is a different being altogether from us—a beast, a sort of superior baboon; and being a beast, that we have the right to own
and work him, as we have the horse or ox.

This position seemed to many of us impregnable; but it
didn't stand a minute. Miscegenation or amalgamation knocked
the support out from under us. Up stepped a pert abolitionist,
and asked, "What will you do with the mulatto—he who is half
man and half beast?

And here is a difficulty. If we count them as beasts, we do

the man that is in them injustice. If we count them as men, we profane manhood, by elevating with it the lower creation.

And when such a one dies, what then? Does the man half, for which Christ died, claiming its inheritance in his blood, go into the next world on an equality with us, dragging with it the half that is beast? Or should there be ever so slight a preponderance of beast, does the hybrid topple over in a lopsided way into the limbo for departed animals, dragging with it the half that is man? If so, O, my Kentucky friends, how much of Kentucky soul and Kentucky spirit is there in that limbo, held in solution by the animal surroundings into which your gross sensuality has condemned it?

That unmitigated wretch, Joe Bigler, it will be remembered, reproached that old saint, Deacon Pogram, for walloping one of these nearly white negroes who had the Pogram nose. "Deacon," said he, "how kin yoo bear to thrash so much Pogram for the sake of walloping so little nigger?" Another objection to this theory is the fact, that while treating them as beasts in the matter of voting, we treat them very much like men in the matter of tax-paying. I have known men who grew furious at the idea of being jostled at the polls by a negro, do violence to the theory by standing side by side, quietly and without a murmur, with a very black one in the rush to pay taxes at the treasurer's office! And during the late unpleasantness, what man of all our people objected to having the name of the blackest and most offensive negro in his township or ward written just before his own on the draft enrolment? That was what hurt us, for during its continuance we heard nothing of this hatred of race. The nigger of 1861, when we didn't want him, softened down wondrously into the "colored man" in 1863, when we did want him. The negro's face, black as it was, looked well to our friends of the North under a blue cap, and he was a very Apollo in their eyes when they wanted their quotas filled. Ours was a white man's government; but we were all wondrous willing that black men should die for it in our stead.

If I remember aright, I have, in the course of these remarks, referred to the Democracy once or twice. I cannot avoid making mention of their competitors, the Republican party, and here acknowledging the assistance it has been to us. In 1856 that party got hold of an idea that for many years was too large for it. They grasped it by the tail, and they have been trying to manage it from that end ever since until this minute. They never dared to look it in the face. The crusade upon slavery, squarely made years ago by Wendell Phillips, Lovejoy, Garrison, Giddings, and the few terrible agitators who were bent upon turning the world upside down, which they did, was entered into by those who followed them afar off, only when they were compelled to. And how feeble their assent! They endeavored not to pierce its centre, its weakest point, but to flank it. They commenced the movement against it by declaring their willingness that it should continue to exist in the States—that the slave-pens, under the shadow of the Capitol at Washington, should continue to show forth the beauties of a republican form of government, and that they themselves, free men, should continue to be used as bloodhounds, with United States marshals to set them on, to hunt down the fugitives from bondage. They made haste to announce in advance their determination not to interfere with it where it existed, and they never did till they were compelled to. They frittered away the first two years of the war before they were manly enough to tie themselves to what they believed to be a truth, and permit it to drag them to victory. Forced by circumstances they could not control, they mustered up courage at last to declare the only friends they had in the South free: but what followed? They started in affright at the spectre they had raised. The Republican party was brave enough to face the armies of the rebellion, but it was not brave enough to face a prejudice. From the close of the war up to this winter, in the very flush of the victories they had won by the aid of the strong hands of their black allies, they coolly betrayed them. So magnanimous were they, so generous were they to their enemies, that they forgot their friends. They gave us, their late masters, the right to disfranchise them at any time. They gave Southern legislatures the power to reduce them again to serfdom, and even those in the Northern States were denied their rights. How much these foolish people have made by their motion, how much they have of safety, how much of the rights they have earned, how much they have of citizenship, let Memphis, New Orleans, and the Georgia legislature answer. The Republican party lacked the courage, and we knew it would, to follow to its logical conclusion the idea upon which it was based. Too many of its members shuddered at the Nigger as soon as the Nigger was of no use to them. And there is a reason for this. It is a soothing thought to too many men that there is somebody lower down in the scale of humanity than themselves. Such men have an uncontrollable desire to look down upon somebody, and hence their desire to keep the negro down, as that is the only portion of the race they can, with any show of truth, claim to be above. And feeling the danger of his rising above them if let alone, they seek to keep him down by piling upon his head the dead weight of unfriendly legislation. It is a philosophical truth this. The more despicable the man, the more anxious he is to have it understood that somebody is lower still. The most ardent defenders of slavery eight years ago were those who hadn't a particle of interest in it,—those who, if negroes had been selling at five cents apiece, could not have raised money enough to have purchased the paring of one's finger nail; and to-day those most bitterly opposed to Nigger suffrage are those whose stolid ignorance and inwrought brutality makes any attempt at further degradation a hopeless task. They can be got lower—by digging a hole.

How shall we dispose of the negro? He was ever a disturbing element in American politics, and ever will be so long as left in the position he has occupied. The curse theory is worthless, and the beast theory leaks like a sieve. If there ever was anything in the curse it has all faded out, and if he is not a man, he is a most excellent imitation. We have abandoned the Nasbyan theory, and have fallen back upon Jefferson. Now that the government is in a transition state, now that we can make of it what we will, suppose that we rebuild upon a safe and sure foundation. Suppose we overhaul the laws of the country, and strike out the word "white," leaving standing alone the all-sufficient word man. We are trying now the experiment of being a genuine republic. Suppose that there may be no longer a dispute upon this head, that we insist upon incorporating into the Constitution—the supreme law of the land—the Jeffersonian Declaration, that all men are equal. I want, and insist upon it, that the Declaration of Independence shall be no longer a "glittering generality," as that meanest of all mean things God ever created, a Massachusetts pro-slavery man, once said, but a living, robust truth, possessed of as much vitality as any other truth which has blessed the world.

What stands in the way? Prejudice! Only this, and nothing more, and that may be overcome. New England did it, and New York, years ago, took one step in that direction. In New York, the negro who owns a mule worth two hundred and fifty dollars, votes, no matter what his other qualifications may be, while he who lacks that, does not, no matter how well he is fitted for the exercise of the right in other respects. This is not well, but it is something. By this rule the mule votes, not the man; and the late election in that State shows the mules to have been largely in the majority.

Until this principle is adopted our republic is no republic, and our boasted freedom is a hollow sham. We must have no more of this inequality. We must make all men before the law equal. We must not leave the rights of a single citizen in the hands of timid legislatures, interested oligarchies, and ex-slaveholders. The rights of the negro must be secured by law, above the reach of ex-slaveholders; men who, to live a life of luxurious idleness, would garrote the Goddess of Liberty for the white robes she wears. We must make him not only free in name, but in reality, and must give him that potent weapon, the ballot, that he may maintain and defend his freedom. I want all distinctions based upon color wiped out in all the States. I want all the roots of this bitterness eradicated. I want the great principle upon which a republic should be founded incorporated into the Constitution. If, now that it can be done, we do less than this, we are cowards and faithless men.

I want them to have all privileges enjoyed by other classes. "Do you want niggers in office?" shudderingly asks the member of Congress, who sees in his mind's eye one sitting beside him. I answer, "Certainly, if the people desire it, not otherwise"; and they are a part of the people. I have no particular care in the matter; I only insist that they shall be eligible. Whether they are elected to official position or not, is something that is entirely within your control. If you return a man a horse that is his, it does not follow that you must give him also silver-plated harness and a carriage. If you pay a debt, it does not follow that you must likewise marry into the family of your creditor. You have in this city an overwhelming majority of whites—it is for you to choose. Where they have a majority, I presume they will do as we have done—elect men of their own race; and I should advise them to. But there is no law to compel you to elect black men, or men of any other color, to official position. You have a right to vote for whom you please. I am not certain but that the good of the public would be subserved by substituting some negroes I know of for some white officials. For instance, were I a citizen of New York, I would most gladly exchange John Morrisey for Frederick Douglass, and rather than spoil the trade, I would throw in Fernando Wood and his brother Ben, and esteem the bargain a most excellent one at that. But our conservative friends do not so see it. "My God!" said one of them, with horror in his countenance, "think of my being tried afore a nigger jury for hoss-stealin!"

The people elect, or ought to elect, men to office to serve them. If you desire whitewashing done, do you look at the *color* of the artist to whom you intrust the purifying of your walls and ceilings? No; you select the *man* who has the most skill. Why not so in official positions? If you have among you negroes who have ability superior to the whites, if you have those who can better fill the offices, you as tax-payers, do yourselves gross injustice by not electing them. It does not follow that you must therefore take them to your bosoms as social equals. You have, under the Constitution of the United States, the blessed privilege of choosing your own associations. We do not care to associate with all white men, but all white men vote nevertheless.

I would not make them superior to the white. I would do nothing more for them than I would for other men. But I would not prevent them from doing for themselves. I would tear down all bars to their advancement. I would let them make of themselves all that they may. In a republic there should be no avenue to honor or well-doing closed to any man. If they outstrip me in the race, it proves them to be more worthy, and they are clearly entitled to the advantages resulting. There is no reason for this inequality. Knowing how deep the prejudice is against the race, knowing how low down in our very natures its roots have struck, I demand, in our renewed and purified republic, the abrogation of all laws discriminating against them. I demand for them full equality with us before the law. Come what may, let it lead to what it will, this demand I make. I make it as a worshipper of true Democracy; as one who believes in the divine right of man —not white man, red man, or black man, but MAN, to self-government. I make it as one who will be free himself; and that he may be free himself, would have all others free. I demand it, not as a gracious gift to the colored man of something we might, if expedient, withhold, not as a right he has earned by service done, but humbly, and with shame in my face at the wrong we have done, I would give it him as returning a right that was always his; a right to which he has a patent from God Almighty; a right that we had taken from him by brute force, and the taking of which by us was almost the unpardonable sin. I demand it, for until it is done our boasted freedom is a sham, and our pretence of republicanism a miserable lie. I demand it, for I would have no privileged classes in this government, for fear that some day my children may by force be deprived of the rights I enjoy by a class arrogating to themselves superiority. I demand it, because I believe governments were instituted on earth for the protection of the weak against the strong, and that in a republic the ballot is the weak man's only protection. I demand it, because we cannot afford to give the lie to our professions; because we cannot afford to say to the world one thing and do another.

What shall we do with the negro? Do by him what enlightened Christianity commands us to do to all. Let us square our action in this, as in all other matters, by that sublime precept, "Do unto others as ye would have others do unto you."

Casting behind us, as unworthy of a moment's serious consideration, the miserable sophistries of the false teachers who have well nigh ruined the republic, let us dare to do right. Let us declare and crystallize our Declaration into unchangeable laws, that under the flag all men shall be men. Let us build an altar, the foundation of which shall be Reason, the topstone Justice, and laying thereon our prejudices, let them be consumed in the steady, pure flame of Humanity. The smell of that sacrifice will be a sweeter savor to the Father of all races than any since Abel's. Let us raise ourselves from the low, dead, flat plane of self-interest, and demonstrate our strength, not by trampling upon the defenceless heads of those weaker and lower than ourselves, but by lifting them up to us. And then, when the flag has under its shadow only free men, when all men are recognized as men, we can look the world in the face, and repeat without a blush that grand old Declaration, that Magna Charta of human rights, that Evangel of Humanity: "We hold these truths to be self-evident, that all men are created equal; that they are endowed by their Creator with certain inalienable rights; that among these are life, liberty, and the pursuit of happiness."

Chronology: David Ross Locke

1833 Born September 20 at Vestal, Broome County, New York (of American Revolutionary stock; parents strongly anti-slavery).

1843 Leaves school; apprenticed to Cortland, N.Y., *Democrat.*

1850 Finishes apprenticeship; works as itinerant printer both South and North; reaches Ohio by way of Pittsburgh, early 1850s.

1852 Founds Plymouth, Ohio, *Advertiser;* marries Martha Bodine (their children: three sons).

1856 Founds Bucyrus, Ohio, *Journal,* for which he writes weekly short fiction. Other brief journalistic ventures with the Mansfield *Herald* and Bellefontaine *Republican*, both Ohio, in late 1850s.

1858 Meets Abraham Lincoln at Quincy, Illinois.

1859 Meets Lincoln again at Columbus, Ohio.

1860 Lincoln elected president; secession movement begins.

1861 Assumes editorship of Findlay, Ohio, *Jeffersonian.* Fort Sumter attacked April 12; further secessions by border states; battle of Bull Run, July 21. First Nasby letter, "The Secession at Wingert's Corners," in Findlay *Jeffersonian*, dated March 21.

1862 Battles of Shiloh, *Merrimac-Monitor*, Seven Pines, Antietam, Fredericksburg; December cabinet crisis.

1863 Visits Lincoln in Washington. Emancipation Proclamation; siege of Vicksburg; Gettysburg Campaign; battle of Chattanooga.

1864 Battles of Wilderness, Cold Harbor, Petersburg; Sherman's march through Georgia; Lincoln defeats McClellan for second term. Publication of *The Nasby Papers* (Indianapolis: C.O. Perrine & Co.— the edition owned by Lincoln).

1865 Visits Lincoln in Washington second time; moves to editorship of Toledo *Blade*. Fall of Richmond and surrender of Lee; assassination of Lincoln, April 14; final capitulation of Confederacy. *The Nasby Papers* published in London by S. O. Beeton.

1866 Beginning operations of Freedmen's Bureau; Ku Klux Klan founded; Civil Rights bill passed over Johnson's veto; Radical-Republican election gains. Publication of *Andy's Trip to the West* (New York), a pamphlet; issued also as *Androo Johnson, His Life*; *Divers Views, Opinions and Prophecies of Yoors Trooly, Petroleum V. Nasby* (Cincinnati: R. W. Carroll & Co., illus. by Thee Jones); *Swingin Round the Cirkle* (Boston: Lee & Shepard, illus. by Thomas Nast); *The Nasby Papers* republished in London as part of *Yankee Drolleries* (Ward, Lock, Tyler).

1867 Meets Thomas Nast; reads "Cussid Be Canaan!" in Boston, December 22.

1868 Impeachment of Johnson fails; Fourteenth Amendment ratified; U. S. Grant elected president. Publication of *The Impendin Crisis uv the Democracy* (Toledo), a pamphlet; *Ekkoes from Kentucky* (Boston: Lee & Shepard, illus. by Nast).

1869 Assists Francis Ellingwood Abbot in establishing the "Free Religion" Index Association, Toledo, and underwrites publication of radical church paper *The Index*. Gould and Fisk financial manipulations; speculations of Tweed Ring.

1870 Fifteenth Amendment ratified.

1871 Moves to New York as editor of *Evening Mail*; contributes to *Nast Almanac*. Civil Service reform; Tweed Ring broken.

1872 Amnesty Act; Crédit Mobilier scandals; Grant defeats Greeley for second term. Publication of *The Struggles of Petroleum V. Nasby* (Boston: I. N. Richardson & Co., illus. by Nast).

1873 Money panic and subsequent depression.

1875 Helps found and foster Draconian Club (art and discussion group, Toledo). Publication of *Inflation at the Cross Roads* (New York), a pamphlet; reprinted in Philadelphia, 1876; *The Morals of Abou Ben Adhem* (Boston: Lee & Shepard), essay-dialogues.

1876–7 Hayes-Tilden disputed election.

1877 End of Radical Reconstruction. Publication of *The President's Policy* (Toledo), a pamphlet.

1879 Dramatizes F. M. Whitcher's *Widow Bedott Papers* (1855) as *Widow Bedott*, played through 1880s; retires from editorship of *Evening Mail*. Publication of *A Paper City* (Boston: Lee & Shepard), novel on real estate speculation.

1880 James A. Garfield elected president (assassinated 1881). Publication of *The Democratic John Bunyan* (Toledo), a pamphlet.

1880–1 Tours Europe.

1881 *The Diary of an Office Seeker* (Toledo), a pamphlet.

1882 *Hannah Jane* (Boston: Lee & Shepard), narrative poem on the devotion of a long-suffering wife. *Nasby in Exile* (Toledo & Boston: Locke Publishing Co.), European travel letters originally published in Toledo *Blade*.

1884 Incorporates Jewel Manufacturing Company (to make sewing machines).

1885 Contracts tuberculosis.

1886 Elected alderman of Third Ward, Toledo; forms natural gas drilling company.

1886–7 Visits various health resorts.

1888 Dies after four months' final illness, February 15, at Toledo, Ohio.

1891 *The Demagogue, A Political Novel* (Boston: Lee & Shepard).

1893 *The Nasby Letters* (Toledo: Toledo Blade Co.).

Selected References

(*Note:* The definitive biography of Locke remains to be written. Information about him currently in print is fragmentary and inconclusive.)

Blair, Walter. *Native American Humor.* New York: American Book Co., 1937.

Clemens, Cyril. *Petroleum V. Nasby.* Webster Groves, Missouri: International Mark Twain Society, 1936.

Clemens, Samuel L. *Mark Twain's Autobiography*, 2 vols. New York: Harper, 1924.

Estes, Joseph A. "Locke, David Ross." *Dictionary of American Biography* XI: 336.

Jones, Joseph. "Petroleum V. Nasby Tries the Novel: David Ross Locke's Excursions into Political and Social Fiction." University of Texas *Studies in English* 30 (1951), pp. 202-218.

Paine, Albert Bigelow. *Th. Nast, His Period and His Pictures.* New York: Macmillan, 1904.

Pond, J. B. *Eccentricities of Genius.* New York: Dillingham, 1900.

Ransome, Jack Clifford. "David Ross Locke: Civil War Propagandist." *Northwest Ohio Quarterly* 20: 5-19. January 1948.

———. "David Ross Locke: The Post-War Years." *Northwest Ohio Quarterly* 20: 144-158. Summer 1948.

Sandburg, Carl. *Abraham Lincoln, the Prairie Years and the War Years,* one-vol. ed. New York: Harcourt, Brace, 1954.